Volume III

MATHEMATICS

People · Problems · Results

Edited by Douglas M. Campbell
and John C. Higgins

Brigham Young University

Wadsworth International
Belmont, California
A Division of Wadsworth, Inc.

Acquisitions Editor: John Kimmel
Production Editor: Andrea Cava
Copy Editor: Ann Draus
Cover Designer: Catherine Flanders
Interior Designer: Leigh McLellan

Printed in the United States of America

1 2 3 4 5 6 7 8 9 10—88 87 86 85 84

ISBN 0-534-03201-X (hardback)

ISBN 0-534-03204-4 (paperback)

Library of Congress Cataloging in Publication Data
(Revised for Vol. 3)
Main entry under title:

Mathematics : people, problems, results.

1. Mathematics—Addresses, essays, lectures.
I. Campbell, Douglas M. II. Higgins, John C., 1935–
QA7.M34466 1984   510   82-17039
ISBN 0-534-03201-x
ISBN 0-534-03204-4 (pbk.)

Contents

part one

Computers

SUPPOSE THAT DURING one of the countless and often unremembered battles on the eastern front in World War II, a certain Russian soldier received a serious head injury. A field ambulance carried him from the front to an aid station. There his wounds, which seemed untreatable to the physician, were superficially bandaged and the soldier was left to his fate while those with more hopeful prognoses were awarded such care as was available. Some hours later, to the physician's astonishment, the soldier, although comatose, was still alive. Still insensible, the unfortunate victim was evacuated to the rear and sequestered in a military hospital, where he remained in a coma for over forty years. Then he woke up.

One might sympathize with the social worker to whom was given the task of introducing the recently awakened soldier to a world four decades removed from his last experience. What should he be told first? Which things are most nearly like the time of his recollections and which most different? Which historical events are the most significant and which technological achievements the most important? Are the developments in atomic science more significant than those in the exploration of space? Are jet-propelled aircraft more incredible than television? And what of computers? One cannot ignore computers—not if one must account for what has occurred in the development of society for the past two or three decades, never mind what will happen in the future.

The Russian soldier, aroused from his decades of slumber, would be lucky indeed if he had an informant who could put the technological developments of the past forty years in their proper perspective. Many people might believe that the computer is a device of very recent invention. Yet almost all major technological achievements since the beginning of World War II have used, in one guise or another, some type of mechanical or electronic computing machine. For example, one can plausibly argue that the "cracking" of the German enigma cypher machine by the British was the single most important breakthrough of the entire World War II period for it most influenced who won and who lost. A significant part of the cracking of the German cypher machine was the construction of some crude electro-mechanical computers without which it would have been impossible for the British to reset their decoder to conform to the German resetting of the code machines.

The development of atomic energy, the design of aircraft, and the exploration of space all would have been impossible without a variety of computing devices. Technological development and the development of computing devices have histories that are surprisingly parallel. Until the general-purpose programmable digital computer was developed, there could be no "explosion" in the growth of technology such as we are witnessing in the second half of this century. It is not an overstatement to suggest that without a knowledge of computing machines and their history, one cannot obtain a proper perspective on the history of technology in this century.

The Language of Computers

Lord Bowden

Lord Bowden is principal of the University of Manchester Institute of Science and Technology in England. He was chairman of the Electronics Research Council of the British Ministry of Aviation from 1960 to 1964 and was Minister of State in the Department of Education and Science from 1964 to 1965.

In 1951 the leading expert on computing devices in England assured the author of this article that it was inconceivable that more than three general-purpose digital computers would ever be needed in all of Great Britain (one assumes he also included Northern Ireland). This conservative estimate was in part due to the fact that programming the computers of 1951 was so difficult and time consuming that the array of problems to which they could be applied was very narrow indeed. What was required to increase the range of applications was an elementary method of using the computer itself to form the incredibly long strings of specific instructions used in information processing. In 1951 no one in the world had the key to this process. But a lady of noble birth and amazing mathematical gifts had obtained a solution to this problem in 1846, in England!

Thus does Lord Bowden unfold the remarkable history of the development of computer languages. To those unfamiliar with computers, it would seem that the development of the electro-mechanical devices that form the machines is the entire history of computers. Nothing, in fact, could be further from the truth. Until elementary and easily grasped methods were developed for forcing the machine to behave as the users wished, the hardware was essentially useless. The first electronic computers were large and hideously expensive devices that could rapidly solve one and essentially only one problem. To solve a different problem it was necessary to rebuild the machine. The modern computer did not exist until the device was made to instruct itself. The history of this effort is contained in this amusing and insightful essay.

MOST PEOPLE NOWADAYS realize that computers are mysterious and important devices. It does not surprise the average man to learn that they are as complicated as supersonic aircraft or space vehicles. But few people realize that the work of the mathematicians who prepare the programs for these machines has been as taxing, as difficult, and as complicated as the design and creation of the machines themselves. Today machines have become faster and more reliable, and more and more complicated, but computer manufacturers still need programmers, just as much as gramophone manufacturers need musicians.

Twenty years ago, there were only a few dozen programmers in the world. They were all very competent professional mathematicians, and I think I knew most of them myself. Today there are hundreds of thousands of them, but most of

Source: Lord Bowden, "The Language of Computers," *American Scientist* 58 (1970): 43–53. "The Language of Computers" was the first Richard Goodman Memorial Lecture, delivered in Brighton, England, in May 1969.

them are not even graduates. A few inspired mathematicians have invented some astonishing techniques which make it possible for ordinary men to communicate with computers and exploit them. Today a schoolboy can use a computer to solve problems that would have baffled experienced mathematicians only fifteen years ago.

Perhaps I may be forgiven a few personal reminiscences. I joined Ferranti in 1950. They had nearly finished building the first digital computer ever to be made by a commercial firm in England and they asked me to see if it would be possible to manufacture such machines and sell them at a profit. Our machine could do simple arithmetic a thousand times as fast as a man with an adding machine, but it was not at all obvious that anyone would be prepared to pay a hundred thousand pounds or so for it. It wasn't as reliable as we would have liked it to be; it absorbed information slowly by reading teleprinter ticker tape, and it could only print out its answers digit by digit. The census had disclosed the astonishing fact that the clerical labor force was growing faster than any other category known to the authorities. We decided to try to automate clerical work somehow; we were absurdly optimistic although we realized that our machine was ill-adapted for the large-scale commercial work out of which we hoped to make our fortunes.

I must remind you that this was in the days before IBM. I went to see Professor Douglas Hartree, who had built the first differential analyzers in England and had more experience in using these very specialized computers than anyone else. He told me that, in his opinion, all the calculations that would ever be needed in this country could be done on the three digital computers which were then being built—one in Cambridge, one in Teddington, and one in Manchester. No one else, he said, would ever need machines of their own, or would be able to afford to buy them. He added that the machines were exceedingly difficult to use, and could not be trusted to anyone who was not a professional mathematician, and he advised Ferranti to get out of the business and abandon the idea of selling any more of them.

It is amazing how completely wrong a great man can be. The computer business has since become one of the biggest in the world. Hartree used to tell this story against himself as long as he lived, but I want to emphasize the fact that in 1951 it was much harder to see into the crystal ball than you might think. Ferranti needed a new product, and they were more hopeful than Professor Hartree, so I canvassed the optical industry, the aircraft industry, the civil engineering industry, and our newly established Atomic Energy Authority, and I found that they all faced the same problems.

If the calculations were short, they were done on desk calculating machines operated by clerks. During World War II, Professor Sydney Chapman asked the Home Office to teach long-term convicts to use adding machines for the war effort, but this admirable suggestion was rejected on the grounds that it was unfair to punish a man twice for the same offense and that it was bad enough to be in jail. Nevertheless, there were large numbers of professional calculating-machine operators, and Dr. Comrie had worked out complicated ballistic tables and flight paths for the RAF on the National Cash Register machines which he had used to calculate the *Nautical Almanac.*

If the calculations were long and complicated, there were three overwhelming objections to the use of a computer. The machine usually broke down before it finished the calculation, its memory was too small to hold all the data it needed, and, worst of all, it took so long for the mathematicians to get the program right that it was usually quicker (and cheaper) to get the calculation done by clerks, or to build the device the computer was trying to design, whatever it might be, and try it out. This was quite good enough for opticians who designed new lenses. But experimental aircraft are very expensive to build, and the test pilot takes his life in his hands when he goes up for the first time. It would obviously be cheaper and safer to calculate as much as possible about new machines before they were built, and try to make sure that they would not kill anyone.

I came to the conclusion that there *were* a few calculations that would be worth doing on a computer. They were neither too big nor too small—

the biggest was not more than a hundred times as big as the smallest. A few firms needed the results and were willing to pay for them, so we decided that there might be a future for the computer business, although it would be hard to find enough customers and much harder to find enough mathematicians. It did not seem a very promising enterprise. No one in the world foresaw the boom which has made the industry grow so explosively since about 1960.

We were more worried by the shortage of mathematicians and programmers than by anything else, so I must try to explain why programming was so difficult in those days. A computer can do only and exactly what it has been instructed to do. The first machines were programmed in the very greatest detail by the mathematicians who used them. Every single instruction had to be identified and all its implications had to be considered before it was put into the machine. It is astonishing, and rather amusing in retrospect, to realize how difficult it used to be to get *any* programs right—and to persuade the machine to work for long enough to use them. It was no small job to work out such a simple sum as the sine of an angle. I recall my struggles with a few simple routines only too well. Strong, patient men were reduced to frenzy, and many a competent, diligent programmer began to doubt his own sanity when an apparently perfect routine failed to produce the answers he expected.

I think that part of our trouble was caused by our upbringing. We believed subconsciously that a mathematician ought to be able to solve a problem and get the right answer sooner or later, even if he were wrong the first time he tried it. We were sure that if we took enough trouble, we should get our programs right before we ever put them on the machine. But they were wrong time after time. It was humiliating. It was infuriating. Lots of people gave up altogether. I did, for one.

Our task was complicated by the fact that we fed information and numbers into the machine through a teleprinter, and instructions such as "add," "subtract," "clear the accumulator," and so on, had symbols such as @, quotation marks, and the ordinary alphabet all mixed up. Programs which had taken hours to prepare looked like gibberish to people who had never seen a program

before and behaved as if they were gibberish when they went into the machine.

It was obvious that if programming was going to be like this, our expensive computers would only be used by a few very remarkable people. I remember deducing that, if the speed of our machine had been increased a thousandfold, we should not have increased its output by as much as a factor of two, because we spent so long in getting our trivial routines to work. And I had to sell the wretched things, if I was to earn my living and keep my firm in business. I thought I had the most peculiar job in the world until I met a man on the *Queen Mary* who sold lighthouses on commission and I heard about some of *his* problems.

We decided to recruit some good chess players who could do crossword puzzles in their heads, but someone in the personnel department must have slipped up. We actually recruited some of the prettiest, most delightful young women I have ever had the good fortune to know. Women mathematicians in the mass can be astonishingly nice. They tackled our programs with skill, determination, and enthusiasm. We began to get results more and more often. We were in business at last. We never looked back! It was not until years later (when she was married and had several children) that I discovered that one of the girls could in fact do crossword puzzles at extraordinary speed—sometimes in her head—and that she was very fond of chess!

We persevered because we knew how much arithmetic had to be done in a design office or a bank and we felt certain that someone needed a machine which could add up a thousand numbers in a second. Sooner or later we were sure we should learn how to write those programs more easily. We were relying on the fact that most calculations are repetitive, so that the machine can use the same routine thousands and thousands of times; for example, it could work out the logarithm of any number we chose. All we had to do was to get the routine right once. We knew that a machine can steer its own way through a program and adapt its own procedure as it goes. It uses what is called a "conditional transfer of control," and I shall explain how it does that later. The applications of these two ideas have created a giant modern industry. The first seems obvious and had been used for many years; the second is much more sophisticated and it was unfamiliar to all of us when we began.

The First Programmer

You can imagine our astonishment when we realized that both ideas had been described in detail more than a hundred years before us, in 1846, by Lady Lovelace, who was the daughter of Lord Byron and one of the most beautiful programmers who ever lived. She was the confidante of Charles Babbage, that eccentric Cambridge professor who devoted his life to an unsuccessful attempt to make a computer out of cogwheels and levers and fonts of type. We should all be thankful—and amazed—that Babbage's work and Lady Lovelace's book invalidated a whole series of master patents which were being filed in America after the war.

But for nearly ninety years after she died, Lady Lovelace's ideas were completely forgotten. Professor Aiken did not use them when he built the first mechanical digital machines at Harvard during the war with the help of IBM. Engineers in the Moore School in Pennsylvania built the first electronic computer (ENIAC) to work out the trajectories of shells for the American Army during the war. This was probably the bulkiest machine that has ever been made, but it was very inflexible and it could only keep on doing the same sum, over and over again, because it could not use a conditional transfer. Lady Lovelace's principles were rediscovered by von Neumann in Princeton, by Turing in England, and by Wilkes, Williams, and Kilburn, who built the first machines in England about 1950.

I was fascinated by Lady Lovelace. I met her granddaughter, Lady Wentworth, who was a magnificent old lady. She showed me her grandmother's papers and her portrait, which I used as the frontispiece of my book *Faster than Thought.**

*Bowden, Vivian. 1953. *Faster than Thought*. London: Pitman. Lady Lovelace's fundamental paper is reprinted as an appendix, and some of Charles Babbage's more important passages are included also.

Then she took me to see some of the finest Arab horses in the world. But that is another story.

Lady Lovelace explained how easy and how important it would be to use the same routine again and again. Her programs were to be punched on cards, much as they are today, and Babbage devised techniques to send the same deck through the machine time after time. She went much further than that. She said, "The machine is capable under certain circumstances of feeling about to see which of a certain set of eventualities has occurred and of shaping its future course of action accordingly." She knew how to make it steer itself through a complicated calculation by deciding what to do next after studying for itself what it had done so far. She knew, as Babbage put it, how to "make the machine drive itself forward by biting its own tail."

What happens is this. The machine is made to examine the contents of a particular store which contains a number it has computed. If the number is positive, it then follows one set of instructions, if it is negative, it does something else. The programmer does not know which course of action the machine will actually take because he has not done the sum himself, but he has had to specify in detail what the alternatives are. If, for example, a client is in credit, a firm can let him have more goods, otherwise not. If the tension in a girder is less than the breaking strain, the bridge may be safe, otherwise not—and so on. Any calculation depends on decisions like these. This "conditional transfer of control," as it is called, is simple but all-important. We based our plans upon the fact that our machines could do it. They could, as it were, play a mathematical version of Twenty Questions. They could steer their way and chart a course for themselves. Their power seemed to be limitless.

I believe that I was the first person who ever sold an electronic digital computer on the commercial market. It went to Toronto in 1951, and the first job it tackled was to study the flow of the St. Lawrence River through the fragmented channel past the Thousand Islands. These calculations had to be done before the seaway could be built. It had been estimated that clerks using desk machines would take twenty years to finish them. Our machine did the work in three months. The

Canadians told us that the machine had paid for itself several times over by doing this one calculation so quickly.

The Rapid Education of Computers

Within four years of the installation of the first machine in Manchester, Gordon Black had made it design a photographic lens all by itself. He instructed it to trace a series of rays through the system to find where they intersected the focal plane of the lens. The machine deduced the imperfections of the image; it then changed one of the parameters of the lens system, such as the curvature of one face of one component, and tried again. If the change had improved the lens, the machine went a bit further until it had optimized the first parameter, and then it started on the second. It went on and on until any change of any parameter degraded the lens, and then the machine printed out the specifications of the best lens it could make. The machine was instructed to make a three-component lens out of Chance's best optical glass. Half an hour later it produced a first-class Cooke lens. This was the design that had revolutionized the whole optical industry when it was invented by Dennis Taylor in 1893. It made the fortune of Taylor, Taylor, and Hobson in Leicester; and Zeiss based their Tessar on it. Not bad for half an hour on a computer!

But, of course, the computer had done nothing really new. Optical designers had done as well fifty years ago. The point was that calculations done by hand were slow and time-consuming; a complicated lens would occupy a designer for half a lifetime. The machine was much faster than a man and much better able to tackle a dull, repetitive calculation. Dr. Wynne, in Imperial College, London, has used a machine to optimize a system with seven or eight components, and produced a lens incomparably better than anything that any man had ever designed by hand; this lens is in use today.

By 1960 a similar technique was optimizing the design of nuclear power stations, and at one time a bell rang in the design office in Risley every time the machine had reduced the price of electricity from the proposed new station by one thousandth of a penny per kilowatt hour. People came for miles to listen.

All these calculations depended on the repetition of scores of similar computations and a series of very simple choices that were well within the power of the machine. They would have appealed enormously to Lady Lovelace; to a remarkable degree they are implicit in her work.

But these programs were written by a few very able men at a time when computers were an esoteric mystery, and very few people understood them, or could use them. Today a computer is an essential tool for a mathematician, and the art of programming has been so much simplified that big modern machines can be used by competent undergraduates, precocious schoolboy mathematicians, and by professional accountants and bankers and insurance clerks who have never been educated as mathematicians in their lives. I believe that the development of the techniques of programming that make it possible for ordinary men to use these most complicated machines is one of the most remarkable of all the intellectual achievements of mankind. Very few people appreciate it. The work was done by a handful of men in fifteen years. Few of the men concerned are known to the public.

It is notorious that it usually takes an enormous amount of hard work to develop any new technique so that ordinary people can use it. Just think, for example, how long it took to produce motor cars that ordinary people could drive. It is just as hard to popularize new mathematical ideas as it is to get new machines into mass production. The computer revolution depended on the simultaneous development of completely new electronics and completely new mathematics. I shall speak first, and very briefly, about the machines.

Since I first knew them, computers have become thousands of times faster, much cheaper, much more complex, but much smaller in size and very much more reliable. No one could possibly have foreseen the rate at which they have improved. Our first machine had about 10,000 digits in its fast store. Each digit cost about £2 in circuitry, and it took a quarter of a millisecond to get at it.

A modern machine may have a million or more

digits in its fast store, each of which costs about six pence in circuitry and each of which can be read in a little more than half a microsecond. The backing store in my old machine was a drum that held about six hundred thousand digits which cost about one penny each. A modern machine may have a hundred million bits which cost 1/100 of a penny each in a disk file. It may have another thousand million bits on magnetic tape. This is equivalent to all the information in all the volumes of the *Encyclopaedia Britannica!* Table 1 summarizes the achievements of fifteen years.

Transistors have replaced valves, and sandwiches of printed circuits, made automatically from strips of copper, have replaced the old-fashioned wires which had to be individually soldered. The printed circuits are far too complicated for engineers to understand. They have to be designed by another computer—a fact which must astonish the layman but which, so far as I know, has no theological significance at all and throws no light on the origin of life!

The price of all components has come down dramatically. Today a single solid state package about an inch long which has four norgates in it costs 13 shillings to make. It replaces four circuits each of which had two valves and two diodes in it. In my time, the manufacturing costs of such a package would have been £20 a valve and £10 a diode. A single package would have cost £200 and occupied a chassis 12 inches square. Machines have become much more reliable as they have become faster. We were once very pleased if our slow old machine ran for an hour without a mistake. Today a machine a thousand times as fast

need not make a mistake more often than once a week. These changes are among the most dramatic in the whole of modern industry.

The smallest computer now being made in the ICL factory in Manchester has two-thirds the power of the Atlas computer, which was the biggest machine in the world five years ago. The firm has sold more than a thousand of its latest series, any one of which can do much more work than all the machines in the world could have done in 1953.

But I want to explain this all-important revolution in the art of programming. There have been intellectual revolutions before, and some of them have made it possible for unfamiliar techniques and ideas to spread among the ordinary people. For example, Mr. Pepys was Clerk of the Acts and the Administrative Head of Charles the Second's Navy. He never learned his multiplication tables until he was grown up and wanted to check some of the bills that he paid for timber in the King's ships. He described in his diary how he rose before daylight to learn the simple arithmetic which we expect our own children to learn in primary school. He was so pleased with himself that he taught his wife to add, subtract, and multiply, but she found division too hard, and Sam taught her the "use of globes" instead. Mr. Pepys became President of the Royal Society, and his name appears on the flyleaf of Newton's *Principia*, in which the laws of gravity were first expounded to the world.

Sir Isaac Newton had invented the calculus and he used it to investigate the dynamics of the solar system, but, before he wrote the *Principia*, he

Table 1   Changes in Backing and Fast Stores of Computers since 1952

| Computer | Date | Backing Stores | Fast Stores | | Remarks |
			Price per Bit	Access Time (microseconds)	
Mark 1	1952	600,000 bits @ 1 penny	50 shillings	240	10,000 bits filled a room
Mercury	1955		2 shillings	10	
Atlas	1960		4 shillings	2	
1900	1968	100,000,000 bits @ 1/100 penny	6 pennies	6.6	1 million bits take about half a filing cabinet

had to spend an enormous amount of time and effort to prove his theorems again by classical Euclidian geometry. He was one of the most inventive geometers who ever lived and some of his proofs are incredibly ingenious, but he had to be ingenious because his contemporaries could not understand his calculus.

Today a schoolboy mathematician who knows the calculus can prove that a uniform sphere behaves as if all its mass were concentrated at a point, but it takes a very good man to prove the same theorem by Euclidian geometry as Newton did in the *Principia*. Newton's mathematics was beyond most of his contemporaries, and the calculus was not used very much in England for nearly a hundred years after he discovered it. For one thing, Englishmen got carried away by absurd arguments about the rival claims of Newton and Leibnitz. They felt it was unpatriotic to use Leibnitz's notation of dx/dt for differentiation instead of Newton's less convenient $\dot{x}$. Babbage's first recorded ambition was to recommend the principles of *d-ism* instead of the *dot*-age of the University! A couple of generations passed before professional mathematicians used the calculus freely as a conventional technique.

Euler, who was one of the greatest and most creative mathematicians of all time, devoted many years to the task of simplifying Newton's mathematics. He made the calculus useful to ordinary people, and in the process he formulated most of the mathematics that is studied today by sixth-form schoolboys and undergraduates.

I believe that the achievement of the mathematicians who have converted programming from a mystery to a discipline in the last decade ranks in significance with a century's work by Euler, his contemporaries, and his successors. There were giants in those days; I believe that we have giants among us today, but I am afraid that we do not always recognize them for what they are.

The Invention of Computer Languages

And now I can turn at last to the development of those wonderful and most sophisticated inventions which are usually called "languages" and upon which all modern programs depend. I am not going to talk about the details of individual languages. I don't understand them. There are scores of them. They are all very complicated and most of them have dialects which come and go as years go by. Men argue bitterly about them and their merits, but languages are here to stay and without them ordinary mortals couldn't hope to use modern machines at all. Fortunately people do not need to understand the logical structure and nature of the language they speak every day. Programmers can use machine languages with confidence, however little they know about the real nature of their syntax and organization.

They began very modestly. I have explained how some routines, such as those which work out the tangents of angles and the logarithms or square roots of numbers, can be prepared once and for all and kept permanently in the backing store of the machine. It was fairly easy, therefore, to arrange that they could be called out and used if the programmer punched up the English words *sine* or *log*. This phrase identified the appropriate routine, much as the first three letters of the name RINgway identify the number 746 and connect a caller to my local telephone exchange. That was an easy and very important first step to help the programmer. Then there was the problem of computing a number, storing it somewhere, and retrieving it when it was needed. It was a nuisance if the programmer had to do such a trivial task for himself every time and keep track of all his intermediate results. It was not hard to make the machine choose a pigeonhole for the number and record where it was without bothering the programmer. Methods such as these were used fifteen years ago—they helped a lot, but they could not be called a language.

Soon afterwards people began to write detailed instructions, such as V1 = V2 + V3, in which the sign = had a meaning—that V1 is to be computed by adding V2 to V3.

And then came V3 = V4/V5, which meant that the machine had to work out the ratio of V4 to V5, and thereby compute V3, which was stored somewhere in a location the programmer never knew, but which the machine recorded as V3. This rather rudimentary language was used in

Manchester fourteen or fifteen years ago. It meant that the ordinary programmer had much less to do, because part of his job was being done for him by the machine, which computed the details of its own operations from the relatively brief outline which the programmer wrote.

This scheme may appear to be quite simple, but the master program in the computer that interpreted these instructions was very complicated. The order code in the machine was still much as it always had been. It defined the successive operations the machine actually performed and it was restricted to simple instructions, such as "add," "subtract," "transfer the number to the accumulator," and so on. This was the fundamental order code which the pioneers had used, but now the machine itself translated from one system of instructions to the other.

As time went on, people became more and more ambitious, the shorthand the machine could interpret became more complex, the interpretive routine in the machine itself became even more sophisticated, more detailed, and much longer.

Despite all the care which was lavished on subroutines, on interpretive routines, and on symbols, progress was slow. Ordinary men found it easier to use the computers, but easy programming was bought at a price. A program that had been interpreted by the machine was less efficient and much slower than one that had been written out in detail by a man. The system was very helpful to programmers. So many people used it that the few key men in England who were writing the interpretive routines were under great pressure to develop the system even further.

At about the same time, and for much the same reason, the Americans began to develop a similar system, which turned into Fortran—the first computer language to be accepted internationally and the one used for three-quarters of all the programs in the world today.

One thing led to another. Now we have Fortran and Cobol and Algol and scores of other languages. Each of them has a grammar and a syntax of its own, to say nothing of a vocabulary and its subject matter. They were developed and used in America before we could use them in Europe, because at the time our machines lacked the enor-

mous memories that are needed to hold all the complex routines which convert programs written in the languages into the detailed sequence of operations the machine must follow.

Cobol, which looks more like English prose than the other languages do and is much used in business and commerce, can interpret such instructions as "subtract deductions from gross giving net," which will be needed by anyone who draws up a balance sheet. It involves several subtractions and a comprehensive search for "deductions," and I must emphasize once again that the task of the man who writes out this simple and unambiguous instruction is easy and straightforward, whereas the man who devised a routine to make the computer obey it did something very remarkable indeed. Many phrases in Cobol involve thousands of operations which are quite unknown to the man—an accountant perhaps—who is using the machine. Some of the "interpretive routines" that are needed to exploit a programming language have become so complicated that many people have begun to wonder if they can ever be worked out in detail and be free from ambiguity.

For example, a Cobol program can accept such instructions as "perform tax calculation." But in real life *that* operation requires the collaboration of a very good lawyer and an experienced accountant. To make matters worse, it is essential that the same Cobol program must extract the same answer from any machine which uses it, although the machines may be big or small, fast or slow, and although the individual operations they can perform may be quite different in detail. Is it possible that anyone can produce the complete routine for a machine?

Lawyers use incomprehensible jargon—or so many of us think—in their attempts to make the meaning of new legislation completely unambiguous. Some of the ablest men of every generation have devoted themselves to this task for hundreds of years, and yet the ambiguities of the law are obvious in nearly every case which comes to trial. Pure mathematicians are often vexed and astonished to discover that it is very much harder to program the accounts of quite a small company than it is to work out the solutions to a dozen complex partial differential equations. Anything that involves people seems to be complicated and potentially ambiguous. Can a computer language be infallible?

English is a language full of redundancies. It seldom happens that a single mistake is of itself enough to make a sentence totally incomprehensible if one reads it in context—that is why crossword puzzles are possible. But the instructions a machine must follow are usually such that a single error, however trivial, produces total chaos. It is as if a single spelling error in a text destroyed its meaning completely and turned a whole book into gibberish. For this reason, a good interpretive routine makes the machine investigate the programs it accepts. It will reject them if they disobey the simple rules of grammar which the machine has learned. The master instructions inside the machine which must be prepared by its makers are becoming unbelievably complicated.

The Exponential Growth Rate of Programmers

In 1955 IBM used to supply 5,000 lines of code with their 650 sets; in 1957, about 40,000 lines with their 704s; in 1964 they provided 600,000 lines with their 7090; in 1966 they provided a million lines for the 360 series, and in 1968 they provided eight million lines for the same machines—and these enormous programs were intended to make it possible for other men to write their own programs as easily as possible. They will take at least 5,000 good mathematician-years to prepare, and they will cost about 50 million dollars a year while they are being written. Fifteen years ago, the software cost at least half the price of the machine on which it was used. Five years ago, people complained that their software cost as much as their machine. Today the software is often more expensive than its machine, and it is at least as important.

The *total* number of programmers in the USA (the men who use machines for their own problems) has grown exponentially and increased tenfold every five years ever since the business began nearly twenty years ago. If the number goes on growing in the same way until 1975 (which will

soon be with us), there will be half a million programmers in America. This will be 10 percent of the number of Americans in the age group 25–45 who are clever enough to learn to program. If present trends continue until the mid-1980s every intelligent, able-bodied American might be programming!

The same sort of thing is happening in Europe. In 1958 ICT had about fifty programmers. Ten years later they had 2,500. This corresponds to a fifty-fold increase in ten years, which is nearly as fast as the growth of IBM. If all the mathematicians who will graduate from all the universities in Europe became programmers, we could not sustain this rate of growth for another decade. I repeat, the profession only began twenty years ago. In another ten years it will dominate the earth, if it goes on growing at the same rate!

The problem of uninterrupted exponential growth afflicts many other industries and it is beginning to cause trouble all over the Western world. I think that this is one of the immediate causes of the brain drain, because so many professions which have always been independent have suddenly begun to compete with each other for the same very able men. For example, the number of men in the electrical engineering industry in England has doubled every eight years or so since 1850. If the process continues until the end of this century, every employed Englishman will be an electrical engineer. One can deduce with equal confidence that he will be a chemist too—and permanently stuck in a traffic jam!

All of these exponential growths will have to stop before long and I think that the computer business, which has grown faster than any other, must reach its limit quite soon. In particular, it is obvious that the master programs (the computer software as it is called), which are going to take thousands of man-years to write, will need large well-organized groups of mathematicians to make them. But all the best programs there are today have been produced by small groups of very able people who were left to get on with it for a year or so in peace. Every man understood everything in the program. A group might grow to a dozen before it lost its coherence. Some big groups have written some very bad programs in the last year or two, and I am afraid that ten thousand men would spend a long time doing an estimated 5,000 man-years of programming, even if there are ten thousand men to be found who are good enough to do the work. It seems to be impossible for a very large group to work really efficiently. Everyone must know what his colleagues have done, if he is to do his own work. It is not possible to trample these big programs to death. No executive can shorten the nine months it takes to produce a child however many men he puts on the job. These are enormous programs—the gestation period of an elephant is very long.

An observer must ask quite seriously if the enterprise has already reached the limits of human endurance—or exceeded them. Is it going to be possible to write all these complicated programs? Is the present crisis—for it is little less—really due to a valiant attempt to exceed the bounds of the possible? It is even more difficult, more expensive, and more time-consuming to test these elaborate programs than it is to write them in the first place. How can anyone check every possible case a machine may have to deal with in the next few years?

It is notorious that bureaucracies become inflexible as soon as they apply their rules rigidly in circumstances which were not foreseen by the men who framed the regulations in the first place, and probably did not begin to imagine all their implications. How much worse—how very much worse—it must be for men who are trying to program a machine which has no sense of the realities of ordinary life! You will recall the story of the computer that was owned by the Gas Board. One of the customers was away for several months and he duly received a bill for £0.00. He ignored it, but the machine expected a reply. It sent another bill and, when that was ignored, it sent a final demand note which included a threat to cut off supplies from the customer's house. He thereupon sent his check—which pacified the computer. After a few days his bank manager asked to see him urgently. Why had he written such a peculiar check? "To pacify the Gas Board's computer." "Damn the Gas Board's computer. Do you realize that you have sent the bank's computer crazy?"

How does one expect a machine to know that, if a young man of twenty can gather five pounds of blackberries in a day and a girl of eighteen can gather three, one cannot assume that they will gather eight pounds a day between them? I once threw the whole of the American Census Department into hopeless confusion all by myself. I had filled in a form which required me to state which languages I could (a) speak; (b) read; and (c) understand. I replied that I could read Latin, but I couldn't understand it. A little man came all the way especially to see me. It turned out that they could not code "read without understanding" on the census cards, and if I insisted that this is what I did, they would have to alter and repunch the cards for 150 million American citizens! How *can* one make any system idiot-proof? Even in principle?

A new American installation has been specified to have no more than two hours of "down time" for all causes, including the failure of the hardware and of the software, for forty years. Is this possible? Does it really mean anything? Can such a specification be satisfied by any technique that has yet been devised or can be imagined? How on earth could anyone be sure that he had met the specifications? I can only hope that this installation is not going to be used by Dr. Strangelove.

Perhaps a new and more manageable system will be devised some day. Perhaps someone will drastically simplify the task of the relatively few courageous men who created the languages we have in use today. It will take a genius to do it, and I can only hope that the hour will bring forth the man—and before too long, otherwise the whole system may collapse under the weight of its own complications and complexity. Computers have produced their miracles quite often in the last twenty years; new miracles may not be beyond the bounds of the possible. Perhaps the Chinese may do better than we have done so far. Their ideograms are comprehensible to men who cannot talk to each other. I wonder what will happen.

Problems for the Future

In spite of what we have all lived through in the last twenty years, lots of men who have designed new machines and installed them have assumed that Providence is with them, that the miracle has just happened and that this time a new program would be easy and cheap to prepare. Scores of people who should have known better have grossly underestimated the amount of work needed to produce their software. There are far too many examples of machines which did not work or earn a penny for their owners until they had done four times as much programming as they allowed for when they bought the machine and costed the installation. Large-scale programming is so expensive that a firm which makes such a bad forecast can bankrupt itself, and many firms have discovered the hard way that software always costs more than you expect.

But in spite of all its troubles and setbacks, the computer business keeps on growing. ICL is the biggest computer manufacturer in Europe. They have sold more than a thousand big machines in the last three years. Their engineers are talking of the two billion pounds worth of business they would like to do in the next decade. And IBM grows beyond all imagination. Four years ago, it was the sixteenth biggest firm in the world. In the following year its sales were as big as those of the Imperial Chemical Industries and the British Motor Corporation put together. Its profits were as big as those of the Imperial Chemical Industries and the British Motor Corporation put together twice over, and it climbed to be seventh in the league table. It has done very much better since then, and it is beginning to challenge Standard Oil. If it goes on growing in the same way, it will dwarf General Motors and take over most of American industry by the early 1980s. No great industry has ever grown so fast in the history of the world. What would poor Lady Lovelace think about it all? When will it ever stop?

Every time one is reduced to despondency by the difficulties of programming and by fear of future catastrophe, one finds that the engineers have saved the situation once again. Cheerfulness keeps breaking in. They may not have solved the problems of the software manufacturers, but they have just done something which will help the multitude of ordinary programmers very much indeed.

Ten years ago a programmer could go into the operations room and put his own tapes on the ma-

chine during the gaps between other people's programs. Today hundreds of men use the same machine and the old informal system has broken down. A man prepares his tape, punches it up, sends it in to the machine operators, waits for a day, and finds that something is wrong. He may discover his mistake in ten minutes, but he has to wait for another day before his revised program gets on the machine, and he finds that something else is wrong. He has spent a day doing ten minutes' work.

For this reason the engineers now build a series of quite independent consoles, from each of which a programmer can have direct access to a big machine. The machine itself will be working continuously, solving half a dozen problems at once; it switches itself automatically from one problem to another, so as to make the best possible use of all its resources, but it can spare the time to enter into a dialogue with a man at a desk a mile away. He types something on his teleprinter, and at the next convenient opportunity (which may be after a second or so in which it has processed a few million digits) the machine calls down his program from its store. The solitary mathematician can alter his program and try it again. He will soon know if he is wrong again. The poor man may still be confused, but he has become confused in a more sophisticated way than he was before. He tries again. Slowly but surely he progresses until he gets his program right. At this point someone may come in to tell him that the original equations are wrong, and he must begin again, but in the end all should be well.

The concept is magnificent, and most of the hardware is finished and working. The master program in the main machine has to ensure that all the operators get their turn, that they do not interfere with each other or with the main calculations which are being done half a dozen at a time, that each can get at his own routines in the machine without being confused by a bit of someone else's, and finally that everyone gets the answers to his own problems. Does it alarm you or surprise you to learn that this master program is not yet perfect? Until someone can get it right, everyone is going to have to develop his own programs at the old rate of ten minutes' effective work a day.

The limited success of these independent consoles has already inspired even more ambitious plans. If a machine can be linked to a console some distance away, it ought to be possible for anyone to use a complicated program which has been put into the machine by someone else. If, for example, a man in London wants to design an electric filter, he can be linked by trans-Atlantic cable—or by satellite if he prefers—to a machine in Cambridge, Massachusetts, which contains a program to help him. He can supply the machine with details of band width and cut-off frequencies, and it will work out the number of components and the sizes of the inductances and condensers he needs.

I tried it myself a few years ago, and just to fool it, I asked it to design a filter with impossible parameters. It solemnly printed out a table of enormous inductances and absurdly small condensers. The design could never have worked. The machine should have printed "Ask a silly question and you will get a silly answer," but all it had been programmed to do was a simple routine calculation which an engineer could do for himself.

It is clear that computer-aided design has its limitations. How are we ever to be sure that the general formulae for designing, say, a suspension bridge can be taken over from one calculation to another, or be used safely by a simpleton after a genius has worked them out?

It is only too easy to assume hopefully that a very complicated routine will get sensible results from poor data. This is never true. "Nonsense in, nonsense out" is a good working rule for all computations, and it always has been. About thirty-five years ago one of my seventeen-year-old students built a simple analogue computer out of half a dozen transformers to solve simultaneous equations. I set it to solve the set

$$X + Y + Z = 1$$
$$X + Y + Z = 2$$
$$X + Y + Z = 3$$

The machine reacted sharply. It blew the main fuse and put all the lights out. Digital computers are never so dramatic, but they can and do print out yards and yards of rubbish unless absolutely everything is right!

The bright promise of centralized computation, which, so it was thought, would allow anyone to use his console to solve almost any problem, has not been fulfilled. I think the idea has been a mirage which has misled many a weary traveler. I shall be fascinated to see what happens in the next decade.

But even if this type of dialogue between mathematicians and computers is less attractive than it might have been, the business of transmitting data in bulk for processing all over the world has grown explosively fast. Telephone engineers have used conventional cables to link computers to each other and to places where information is collected. The system did not exist ten years ago. Today as much information is transmitted over telephone lines in digital form as is transmitted by all the voice channels put together. The Americans say that, if they were to start designing their main telephone system again, they would begin with digital transmission and add the telephones as a simple afterthought. Western Union was once the biggest telegraph system in the world, but it has been bought by a computer firm, and that is indeed a sign of the times.

The millions of digits which flow every second all over North America and Western Europe carry information about inventories for the armed services, about stocks and supplies for shops and warehouses, about the accounts of the main banks, about the income tax returns of millions of citizens, about reservations on air lines, and about commercial transactions of all kinds in infinite variety. At this moment the American armed services are much the biggest users. They have adopted a very elaborate system to describe everything from a bobbin of cotton to a bazooka. They never seem to use 10 digits if 100 will do. But the fact remains that an entirely new industry has emerged in the last few years. An astonishingly large fraction of all the information which is created and used in the world is intended for the use of computers. Before long, whether we like it or not, we shall all be talking to computers, and their languages will form part of every undergraduate course.

I wonder how Babbage and Lady Lovelace would have reacted to all this. The most rapidly growing industry in the world still depends on their ideas. Their own contemporaries were baffled and so, I think, are many of us. Babbage once remarked that most people reacted to his machine in the same way as a naked savage reacted to the sound of a musket shot. What would he say today? There are not many naked savages left, and most of them have heard the sound of gunfire. What are we going to do about computers? They are going to influence all our lives. Can we ever learn to communicate with them?

Infinite Loops in Computer Programs

Arthur Charlesworth

Arthur Charlesworth received his doctorate at Duke University in 1974 for research on infinite cardinal functions that are minimal on metrizable spaces. He is a member of the faculty of the department of mathematics at the University of Richmond, Virginia.

In the story of the sorcerer's apprentice, the novice magician is undone by his inability to force his magically animated implements to stop. It seemed easy enough to get them started, but then the broom sweeps on relentlessly, unstoppably, mindlessly, piling all in its path into a gigantic heap of rubbish. The bucket fills the basins to overflowing and creates a tidal wave of flotsam that the unstoppable broom stirs into a frothing surf.

To the novice computer programmer the palpable panic of the sorcerer's apprentice is an all-too-familiar sensation. The broom and bucket of the alchemist's closet are replaced by a digital computer gone amok, an electronic maniac endlessly churning out gibberish, squandering precious minutes of computer access while a wizard is sought to incant the monster back into tractability.

Such is the impact of the infinite loop in computer programming. Anyone who has even a nodding acquaintance with computer programming has often wondered why such abominations have not been totally excised from the computer's repertoire of behavior.

Charlesworth's article responds to this question in unarguable terms that have the finality of death. Perhaps humanity may permanently cure halitosis and perhaps we may exterminate the man-eating shark, but the infinite loop will forever be with us. As long as the digital computer is in our midst the infinite loop or its equivalent will be here, a logically unexcisable part of the fundamental process of computation.

Yet Charlesworth's essay is much more than a most readable tour of the infinite loop. Church's thesis, to which the author refers, is one of the most fundamental assumptions of the mathematical foundations of computer science. Church's thesis partakes of the same character as Gödel's theorem so frequently mentioned in Volume II. The statements that Church's thesis describe often have the same self-referential character as those of Gödel. Church's thesis establishes bounds for what may and may not be achieved by computing devices. While results of this type are generally viewed as esoteric, the fact that they impinge on the creation of loop detectors in computers gives them practical significance. This is especially true as computer programs become longer, more convoluted, more expensive to construct, and concomitantly much more difficult to check for error.

Source: Arthur Charlesworth, "Infinite Loops in Computer Programs," *Mathematics Magazine* 52 (1979): 284–291. (References omitted.)

IT IS NOT unusual for students in an introductory Basic programming course to write programs containing branching errors as in the following examples.

When run, each of these Basic programs goes into what is commonly called an "infinite loop": the procedure described by the program will never terminate and thus the program will continue to execute until a prearranged time limit has been reached or until someone decides to intervene. After finding that printed answers do not appear at their interactive terminal within a reasonable length of time, students would, one hopes, take a closer look and see that line 80 in SUMNUM should be changed to GO TO 50 and the branch in line 60 of PRIMES should be to line 90 instead of line 30. (Notice that if 4 is replaced by 5 in line 30 of PRIMES, the new program goes into a type of infinite loop which executes a print statement over and over, producing a list of 5's.)

Students who look ahead are apt to wonder what to do with longer and more complicated programs. Such programs might take several minutes, perhaps hours, to print out their results; if a long pause occurs at the interactive terminal after the program has begun executing, how can one be sure the program is not in an infinite loop? Computers routinely tell us of many types of errors in programs. (For example, most systems which execute Basic will refuse to run SUMNUM if line 90 is omitted, printing a message such as UNDEFINED STATEMENT REFERENCE IN LINE 60.) It is thus natural to wonder why no one had programmed the computer to check for infinite loops in programs before running them.

Turing's Theorem

In a classic article published over forty years ago, A. M. Turing has argued that *no computer could ever be programmed to solve the problem of detecting infinite loops in computer programs*. In this paper we present a nontechnical proof of Turing's Theorem, accessible to those familiar with the Basic language.

We first prove that no program can be written *in Basic* to detect those Basic programs which would go into infinite loops. We want to make it clear that this is not the case simply because of some unique limitation of the Basic language; thus we shall freely assume an extended version of Basic. In particular, we shall place no upper bound on the number of statements in a program and shall assume that our Basic is being run on a computer having unlimited memory. In addition we shall use the symbol % to enclose data items which are strings and such strings shall be permitted to contain up to 72 characters. (The reason for these last two assumptions will soon be clear.)

It is easy to see that whether or not a program will go into an infinite loop can depend upon

```
          SUMNUM
10  REM: THIS PROGRAM FINDS THE
20  REM: SUM OF THE FIRST 1000
30  REM: NATURAL NUMBERS.
40  LET S = N = 0
50  LET N = N + 1
60  IF N > 1000 THEN 90
70  LET S = S + N
80  GO TO 40
90  PRINT "THE SUM IS"; S
100 END
```

```
          PRIMES
10  REM: THIS PROGRAM FINDS THE
20  REM: PRIMES BETWEEN 4 and 1000.
30  FOR N = 4 TO 1000
40  FOR I = 2 TO N − 1
50  REM: DOES I DIVIDE N?
60  IF N/I = INT(N/I) THEN 30
70  NEXT I
80  PRINT N
90  NEXT N
100 END
```

FERMAT

```
10 REM: THIS PROGRAM PRINTS A COUNTEREXAMPLE TO A CONJECTURE
20 REM: OF FERMAT. (IF THERE IS A COUNTEREXAMPLE.)
30 LET I=3
40 FOR N=3 to I
50 FOR X=1 to I
60 FOR Y=1 TO I
70 FOR Z=1 to I
80 IF X↑N+Y↑N=Z↑N THEN 150
90 NEXT Z
100 NEXT Y
110 NEXT X
120 NEXT N
130 LET I−I+1
140 GO TO 40
150 PRINT "X=";X;"Y=";Y;"Z=";Z;"N=";N
160 END
```

Suppose the above Basic program is run on an ideal computer capable of storing and performing arithmetic on numbers of unlimited size. Will the program go into an infinite loop? The answer, of course, depends upon the unknown resolution of the celebrated conjecture of Fermat: there do not exist positive integers x, y, z, and n (with $n>2$) such that $x^n + y^n = z^n$. Turing's Theorem asserts that no single computer program can be written which could determine, for every Basic program P, whether or not P goes into an infinite loop.

the data, if any, which is to be read by the program. For example, consider the following program.

SAMPLE

```
10 READ N
20 IF N≠1 THEN 50
30 GO TO 40
40 GO TO 30
50 PRINT N
60 STOP
        (data)
100 END
```

This program goes into an infinite loop if and only if the first element of data is the number 1. In Basic, a single letter, such as N, represents a number variable; we assume a computer system such that if the first element of data read by SAMPLE were not a number but a string, such as "SMITH", a fatal error would be printed out and the program would stop. Since we will certainly not want the computer stopping a program just because it has used too much time, we will assume our programs will be executed until a STOP or END statement is reached or until a fatal error occurs.

A few more examples of the effect of data on a program will help prepare us for the proof of Turing's Theorem. First consider

```
                        BRANCH
1000  DIM A$(72)
1010  REM: THIS PROGRAM READS BASIC STATEMENTS AND
1020  REM: PRINTS ALL UNCONDITIONAL BRANCH STATEMENTS.
1030  READ A$
1040  IF A$(6,10) = "GO TO" THEN 1070
1050  IF A$(6,9) = "STOP" THEN 1090
1060  GO TO 1030
1070  PRINT A$
1080  GO TO 1030
1090  STOP
         (data)
2000  END
```

In this program, A$ is a string variable of length at most 72 characters and A$(6,10) denotes the substring of A$ consisting of the characters at positions 6 through 10.

To run properly, the Basic statements which BRANCH reads should have line numbers consisting of four digits and the last item of data should contain a line number and the string "STOP"; one must also be careful to use blanks carefully in the data "statements." To see an example of appropriate data, we need look no further than BRANCH itself! More precisely, we have in mind the following data lines.

```
1100  DATA %1000 DIM A$(72)%
1110  DATA %1010 REM: THIS PROGRAM READS BASIC STATEMENTS AND%
1120  DATA %1020 REM: PRINTS ALL UNCONDITIONAL BRANCH STATEMENTS%
1130  DATA %1030 READ A$%
1140  DATA %1040 IF A$(6,10) = "GO TO" THEN 1070%
1150  DATA %1050 IF A$(6,9) = "STOP" THEN 1090%
1160  DATA %1060 GO TO 1030%
1170  DATA %1070 PRINT A$%
1180  DATA %1080 GO TO 1030%
1190  DATA %1090 STOP%
```

For convenience our extended Basic uses the percentage symbol to enclose data items which are strings. This permits us to use double quotes within the data strings. Since Basic statements can consist of up to 72 characters, our extended Basic also allows data strings to use an extra line, permitting any Basic statement to be considered as a data string.

When the above combination of program and data is executed, we say that "BRANCH is being run with BRANCH as its data." Notice that BRANCH would eventually stop when run with BRANCH as its data, and before stopping it would print

```
1060  GO TO 1030
1080  GO TO 1030.
```

Let us create a program BRMATE from BRANCH by replacing line 1060 in BRANCH by 1060 GO TO 1040. Notice that BRMATE would go into an infinite loop when run with BRMATE as its data since it would examine the string "1000 DIM A$(72)" over and over again.

We could actually consider running SUMNUM with data; since SUMNUM does not contain any read statements, this would not alter the logical flow within the program. Thus SUMNUM would go into an infinite loop when run with SUMNUM as its data. A similar statement could be made about the program PRIMES. Notice, on the other hand, that SAMPLE would stop when run with SAMPLE as its data since a fatal error would immediately occur. (The string "10 READ N" is not a number.)

Proof of Turing's Theorem for Basic Programs

We are now ready for the proof of Turing's Theorem for Basic programs. Let us suppose there did indeed exist a Basic program which checks Basic programs to see whether or not they would go into an infinite loop when run with certain data. (We show that the existence of such a program would lead to an absurdity.)

In particular, then, we may assume a program CHECK, designed so that when it is run with a program P as its data,

1. If P would go into an infinite loop when run with P as its data, CHECK prints the message "INFINITE LOOP" and then stops.
2. If P would eventually stop when run with P as its data, CHECK prints the message "NO INFINITE LOOP" and then stops.

For example, if CHECK is run with BRANCH or SAMPLE as its data, CHECK prints "NO INFINITE LOOP" and stops. On the other hand, if CHECK is run with BRMATE or SUMNUM as its data, CHECK prints "INFINITE LOOP" and stops.

Since we are assuming that CHECK exists, we are free to do anything with CHECK that can be done with any Basic program. In particular, let us modify CHECK somewhat. Wherever the program CHECK contains a statement which causes "NO INFINITE LOOP" to be printed out, say

3000   PRINT "NO INFINITE LOOP",

let us replace it with two statements of the form

3000 GO TO 3005
3005 GO TO 3000.

Call the new program CHMATE and notice that data for which CHECK would print "NO INFINITE LOOP" will cause CHMATE to go into an infinite loop.

Thus when CHMATE is run with a program P as its data,

1. If P would go into an infinite loop when run with P as its data, CHMATE prints the message "INFINITE LOOP" and then stops.
2. If P would eventually stop when run with P as its data, CHMATE goes into an infinite loop.

Of course, the role of P above can be replaced by BRANCH, BRMATE, or any other program. Consider what would happen if P is replaced by CHMATE: we learn that when CHMATE is run with CHMATE as its data,

1. If CHMATE would go into an infinite loop when run with CHMATE as its data, CHMATE prints the message "INFINITE LOOP" and then stops.
2. If CHMATE would eventually stop when run with CHMATE as its data, CHMATE goes into an infinite loop.

In summary, we have learned that when CHMATE is run with CHMATE as its data, it eventually stops if it goes into an infinite loop and it goes into an infinite loop if it eventually stops. This absurdity shows that the program CHMATE, and thus CHECK itself, could never exist. Therefore we have shown that "no program can be written in Basic to detect those Basic programs which would go into infinite loops."

Proof of Turing's Theorem Assuming Church's Thesis

In order to conclude the general version of Turing's Theorem that "no computer could ever be programmed to solve the problem of detecting infinite loops in computer programs," it would clearly be sufficient to show that any algorithm which eventually terminates (and thus any candidate for CHECK) could be programmed in Basic. This follows from a principle known as Church's Thesis which was introduced by Alonzo Church in 1936 and which asserts that every algorithm which eventually terminates corresponds to a recursive function. (The definition of a recursive function is given in Figure 1; it is a mathematically precise concept which is intended to corre-

The mathematical notion of "recursive" function is a precise attempt to single out exactly those functions f whose values can be calculated using an algorithm which terminates after a finite number of steps. There are many equivalent ways to define the recursive functions. One approach is to define a recursive function as any function from a finite Cartesian product $N \times N \times \cdots \times N$ to the set N (of nonnegative integers) which can be constructed from the functions listed in (1) using the operations in (2) finitely often.

(1) (addition) $f(x,y) = x + y$

(multiplication) $f(x,y) = x \cdot y$

(comparison) $f(x,y) = \begin{cases} 0 \text{ if } x < y \\ 1 \text{ if } x \geq y \end{cases}$

(projections) For each n such that $n \geq 1$ and each i such that $i \leq n$, the function $f_{n,i}$ from N^n to N defined by

$$f_{n,i}(x_1, x_2, \ldots, x_n) = x_i.$$

(2) (composition) If f is a function from $N^m (m \geq 1)$ to N and $g_1, g_2, \ldots, g_m$ are functions from $N^n (n \geq 1)$ to N, then the composition of f with $g_1, g_2, \ldots, g_m$ is the function h from N^n to N defined by

$$h(x_1, x_2, \ldots, x_n) = f[g_1(x_1, \ldots, x_n), g_2(x_1, \ldots, x_n), \ldots, g_m(x_1, \ldots, x_n)].$$

(minimization) If g is a function from $N^n (n \geq 2)$ to N such that for every $(x_1, x_2, \ldots, x_{n-1})$ in N^{n-1} there is an x in N for which $g(x_1, x_2, \ldots, x_{n-1}, x) = 0$, then the minimization of g is the function h from N^{n-1} to N defined by

$$h(x_1, x_2, \ldots, x_{n-1}) = \min\{x \mid g(x_1, x_2, \ldots, x_{n-1}, x) = 0\}.$$

It is clear that each function in (1) would be programmable in an ideal version of Basic. (For example, a program could be written to accept the numbers x and y as input and give the number $x + y$ as output.) One can also observe that the composition of programmable functions is programmable and the minimization of a programmable function (which satisfies the required condition) is programmable. Thus it is intuitively clear that every recursive function is programmable.

Figure 1   A Definition of Recursive Functions.

spond to the informal notion of a function which is calculable by an algorithm.) The general version of Turing's Theorem follows from Church's Thesis since it is well known that every recursive function is programmable in languages such as Basic. There is very strong evidence for Church's Thesis and it is widely accepted today, although it has not been proven in a rigorous sense. Indeed it may be inappropriate to expect a rigorous proof that a vague concept such as algorithm actually corresponds to its intended mathematical formulation. For more about Church's Thesis, see Chapter 12 of S. C. Kleene, *Introduction to Metamathematics* (Van Nostrand, New York, 1952).

An Alternative to Church's Thesis

We can thus extend our proof to a proof of the general Turing Theorem by relying upon Church's Thesis. Although it is not unusual to use Church's Thesis in this way, let us see how it may be replaced in this instance by a different assumption. Our wish, of course, is to conclude that if CHECK were written in any given computer programming language and CHECK could correctly process both Basic programs and programs in the given language, the absurdity obtained by constructing CHMATE would still arise. If the given programming language will not permit programs to be read as data (roughly, if the language does not satisfy analogues to the conditions of our extended Basic), then a program like CHECK could not exist, so we may assume that the language permits programs to be data. Notice that we made fundamental use of only one additional property in going from CHECK to CHMATE: that we could replace a print statement in a program by statements which cause an infinite loop to occur. Thus we may conclude that CHECK cannot be written in any programming language if we are willing to assume the following proposition: any programming language which is powerful enough in which to write a program like CHECK must also allow statements which can be combined to form an infinite loop.

The proposition would be false if it is possible to develop a programming language that is powerful and that, in addition, incorporates a clever new kind of loop structure which guarantees that all loops terminate. To demonstrate that such a programming language is very unlikely, we show

the following: if $\mathscr{L}$ is a programming language which is powerful enough to write an $\mathscr{L}$-syntax checking program, an $\mathscr{L}$-interpreter, and a program which has the same effect as the program CREATE in Figure 2, then $\mathscr{L}$ must also allow statements which can be combined to form an infinite loop. (By an $\mathscr{L}$-syntax checking program we mean a program in $\mathscr{L}$ which checks to see whether or not a candidate for a program in $\mathscr{L}$ really has the correct syntax, i.e., the correct

```
10  DIM C[72],C$[72],S$[72]
20  PRINT "WHAT IS THE ORIGINAL STRING OF CHARACTERS";
30  INPUT C$
40  PRINT "WHAT IS THE MAXIMUM LENGTH OF THE STRINGS YOU WANT";
50  INPUT N
60  FOR K=1 TO N
70  REM: THE STRINGS GENERATED AT THIS STAGE HAVE LENGTH K
80  FOR I=1 TO K-1
90  C[I]=1
100 NEXT I
110 C[K]=0
120 I=K
130 C[I]=C[I]+1
140 IF C[I]>LEN(C$) THEN 240
150 REM: WE NOW PUT TOGETHER THE NEXT STRING S$
160 REM: THE I'TH CHARACTER IN S$ IS DENOTED S$(I,I) AND IS ASSIGNED
170 REM: THE C(I)'TH CHARACTER IN THE ORIGINAL STRING C$
180 FOR I=1 TO K
190 S$[I,I]=C$[C[I],C[I]]
200 NEXT I
210 PRINT S$
220 I=K
230 GO TO 130
240 C[I]=1
250 I=I-1
260 IF I>=1 THEN 130
270 NEXT K
280 END
```

Given a string of characters C$, CREATE generates all strings which consist of the characters in C$ and which have length at most N. Thus if C$ is "AB" and N is 3, then CREATE generates the strings A,B,AA,AB,BA,BB,AAA,AAB,ABA,ABB,BAA,BAB,BBA, and BBB.

Figure 2   CREATE

form. An $\mathscr{L}$-**interpreter** is a program in $\mathscr{L}$ which decodes and executes statements in $\mathscr{L}$. Such programs are, of course, routinely included in most computer systems.)

Suppose that $\mathscr{L}$ does not allow statements which can be combined to form an infinite loop; we can reach a contradiction as follows. Consider listing all the symbols used in the language $\mathscr{L}$, then all pairs of such symbols, all triples of such symbols, etc.; that is, list all the finite strings S_1, $S_2, S_3, \ldots$ of symbols used in $\mathscr{L}$. Since each program in $\mathscr{L}$ is such a finite string, this means that we can enumerate all possible programs in $\mathscr{L}$; in particular, we can enumerate those programs which accept a single number as input and have as their only output either "YES" or "NO", terminating immediately after printing one of these words. Let us label these programs P_1, P_2, P_3, $\ldots$. The contradiction arises by using a Cantor diagonal argument to construct a program P in $\mathscr{L}$ which is of this type, yet which is different from each P_i. Given the number n as input, P generates S_1, S_2, S_3, etc., until it has generated the string P_n. [A program like P can be written in $\mathscr{L}$ since we can use an idea similar to that of CREATE to generate the S_i's (with C$ containing all the symbols used in $\mathscr{L}$), we can examine each S_i as it is generated and eliminate those which do not have the correct syntax to be a program in $\mathscr{L}$, and we can check to see if those S_i's which are programs have the form required for being a P_i.] Immediately after discovering P_n, our program P decodes and executes the statements of P_n. When P reaches the step in which P_n asks for its input, P supplies the number n. Since P_n, by assumption, doesn't go into an infinite loop, eventually P_n will be ready to print either "YES" or "NO". Our program P determines what answer P_n would print and then P prints the opposite answer and stops. Clearly P qualifies as one of the P_i's, yet for each n, the programs P and P_n differ in the output they give with n as input. Thus P is not one of the P_i's, a contradiction.

What about Programs Which Don't Have Data?

Since many important programs do not read in any data, you may wonder whether a program

could exist which at least detects which of these "simpler" programs would go into an infinite loop when run. Let us briefly describe how our proof of Turing's Theorem may be modified to show that such a program is impossible. For each Basic program P there is a Basic program P' which has no READ statements and which has the same effect when run as running the program P with P as data. Moreover it is straightforward to construct P', given P. (We sketch such a construction procedure in the next paragraph.) Now assume that there is a program CHECK2 which, given any program Q (having no READ statements) as data, prints exactly one of the messages "INFINITE LOOP" or "NO INFINITE LOOP", depending upon whether or not Q would go into an infinite loop when run. Then we could write the program CHECK as follows: given a program P as data, CHECK would first construct the program P' and then CHECK would apply the steps in the program CHECK2 to P'. Thus the existence of CHECK2 implies the existence of CHECK, so no such program CHECK2 could exist.

To see how P' can be constructed from P, first order all characters used in Basic and put them into a single string C$. Recall that for integers K which are no greater than the length of C$, the notation C$(K,K) denotes the Kth character in C$; we can thus consider that each such K is a numerical code for a character of Basic. Begin writing P' by defining C$ and by assigning values to an array C(I,J) so that C(I,J) is the numerical code for the Jth character in the Ith statement of P. Next place each statement of P (preserving the order of the statements) into P', with the following exceptions. Do not place any READ statements into P'. Wherever P considers the Jth character A$(J,J) in the Ith statement which P has read in, P' should consider instead the character C$(C(I,J),C(I,J)). (If P contains a string variable named C$ or an array named C, other straightforward adjustments would be required.)

What Does Turing's Theorem Really Mean?

You may have noticed that it would be easy to write a program CHECK3 in Basic which, when run with a program P as its data, would satisfy the following: if P would eventually stop when run with P as its data, CHECK3 prints the message "NO INFINITE LOOP" and then stops. Indeed, CHECK3 would need to do little more than perform the statements of P. Of course, if P went into an infinite loop instead, CHECK3 would never report it.

One could also observe that a single program can be written, perhaps based upon the program BRANCH, which would alert us to certain types of infinite loops; for example, the type found in SAMPLE and, perhaps, even those found in SUMNUM and PRIMES. One can, in addition, hope that eventually a program can be written to determine whether or not the program FERMAT (in the box at the beginning of this note) has an infinite loop.

The point of Turing's Theorem seems to be that there is an infinite variety of really different infinite loops. That is, even if for each program P we knew of a program $CHECK_P$ (which would tell us whether or not P goes into an infinite loop when run with P as data), and even if each of the $CHECK_P$'s could accurately process a large collection of programs, there would be no way to combine some of the $CHECK_P$'s into a single program which would accurately process every program.

An important philosophical question is whether computers can think, and closely related to this, to what extent the brain can be viewed as a computer. Turing's Theorem concerning the limitations of computers can stimulate interest in such questions, as one wonders whether Turing's ingenious discovery implies an inherent limitation to human ingenuity itself.

Social Processes and Proofs
of Theorems and Programs

Richard A. De Millo,
Richard J. Lipton,
and Alan J. Perlis

Richard A. De Millo received his Ph.D. in computer science in 1972 from the Georgia Institute of Technology. He has worked at the Los Alamos Scientific Laboratory, the University of Wisconsin, and Georgia Tech. De Millo has served as a consultant for the U.S. Army Electronics Command, the U.S. Army Computer Systems Command, the Math Research Center at the University of Wisconsin, and U.N.E.S.C.O.

Richard J. Lipton is currently at Yale University. He is a prolific writer of papers in many areas of computer science.

Alan J. Perlis received his Ph.D. in mathematics in 1949 from M.I.T. He has worked for Digital Computing Lab and the Aberdeen Proving Grounds. He was chairman of the department of mathematics at Carnegie Mellon from 1960 to 1971. Since 1971 Perlis has been a professor of computer science at Yale. He has been editor in chief of the Communications of the Association of Computing Machinery and president of the Association of Computing Machinery.

It would be unfair and inaccurate to suggest that all mathematicians are intellectually arrogant. But on one occasion or another there exudes from the writings of almost all successful research mathematicians an aroma of superiority that, no matter how innocently or subconsciously concocted, can be most annoying to the educated nonmathematician. Like gentlemen from the England of Victoria and Albert in the land of the Hottentots, they cannot imagine why anyone in the world would not wish to think, feel, act, and perceive the universe in exactly the same way that proper Englishmen do. There is reason to suspect that the authors of this essay are reacting to the unspoken suggestion of some mathematician that computer science ought to conduct its affairs in a way as nearly parallel to the fashion of mathematics as the nature of the subject allows. The authors suggest that the two subjects are different in a number of fundamental ways. Indeed, it is precisely these differences that give computer science its power to attack and solve problems of interest to computer users. It is the authors' position that if the processes of computer science were subjected to the reforms proposed by well-meaning mathematicians, then computer science might wither, dry up, and blow away.

Source: Richard A. De Millo, Richard J. Lipton, and Alan J. Perlis, "Social Processes and Proofs of Theorems and Programs," *Communications of the ACM* 22:5 (1979), 271–280. Copyright 1979, Association for Computing Machinery, Inc., reprinted by permission. (Acknowledgments omitted.)

I should like to ask the same question that Descartes asked. You are proposing to give a precise definition of logical correctness which is to be the same as my vague intuitive feeling for logical correctness. How do you intend to show that they are the same? . . . The average mathematician should not forget that intuition is the final authority.—J. BARKLEY ROSSER

MANY PEOPLE HAVE argued that computer programming should strive to become more like mathematics. Maybe so, but not in the way they seem to think. The aim of program verification, an attempt to make programming more mathematics-like, is to increase dramatically one's confidence in the correct functioning of a piece of software, and the device that verifiers use to achieve this goal is a long chain of formal, deductive logic. In mathematics, the aim is to increase one's confidence in the correctness of a theorem, and it's true that one of the devices mathematicians *could* in theory use to achieve this goal is a long chain of formal logic. But in fact they don't. What they use is a proof, a very different animal. Nor does the proof settle the matter; contrary to what its name suggests, a proof is only one step in the direction of confidence. We believe that, in the end, it is a social process that determines whether mathematicians feel confident about a theorem—and we believe that, because no comparable social process can take place among program verifiers, program verification is bound to fail. We can't see how it's going to be able to affect anyone's confidence about programs.

Outsiders see mathematics as a cold, formal, logical, mechanical, monolithic process of sheer intellection; we argue that insofar as it is successful, mathematics is a social, informal, intuitive, organic, human process, a community project. Within the mathematical community, the view of mathematics as logical and formal was elaborated by Bertrand Russell and David Hilbert in the first years of this century. They saw mathematics as proceeding in principle from axioms or hypotheses to theorems by steps, each step easily justifiable from its predecessors by a strict rule of transformation, the rules of transformation being few and fixed. The *Principia Mathematica* was the crowning achievement of the formalists. It was also the deathblow for the formalist view. There

is no contradiction here: Russell did succeed in showing that ordinary working proofs can be reduced to formal, symbolic deductions. But he failed, in three enormous, taxing volumes, to get beyond the elementary facts of arithmetic. He showed what can be done in principle and what cannot be done in practice. If the mathematical process were really one of strict, logical progression, we would still be counting on our fingers.

Believing Theorems and Proofs

Indeed every mathematician knows that a proof has not been "understood" if one has done nothing more than verify step by step the correctness of the deductions of which it is composed and has not tried to gain a clear insight into the ideas which have led to the construction of this particular chain of deductions in preference to every other one.—N. BOURBAKI

Agree with me if I seem to speak the truth.—SOCRATES

Stanislaw Ulam estimates that mathematicians publish 200,000 theorems every year.[20] A number of these are subsequently contradicted or otherwise disallowed, others are thrown into doubt, and most are ignored. Only a tiny fraction come to be understood and believed by any sizable group of mathematicians.

The theorems that get ignored or discredited are seldom the work of crackpots or incompetents. In 1879, Kempe[11] published a proof of the four-color conjecture that stood for eleven years before Heawood[8] uncovered a fatal flaw in the reasoning. The first collaboration between Hardy and Littlewood resulted in a paper they delivered at the June 1911 meeting of the London Mathematical Society; the paper was never published because they subsequently discovered that their proof was wrong.[4] Cauchy, Lamé, and Kummer all thought at one time or another that they had proved Fermat's Last Theorem.[3] In 1945, Rademacher thought he had solved the Riemann Hypothesis; his results not only circulated in the mathematical world but were announced in *Time* magazine.[3]

Recently we found the following group of footnotes appended to a brief historical sketch of some independence results in set theory[10]:

1. The result of Problem 11 contradicts the results announced by Levy (1963). Unfortunately, the construction presented there cannot be completed.
2. The transfer to *ZF* was also claimed by Marek (1966) but the outlined method appears to be unsatisfactory and has not been published.
3. A contradicting result was announced and later withdrawn by Truss (1970).
4. The example in Problem 22 is a counterexample to another condition of Mostowski, who conjectured its sufficiency and singled out this example as a test case.
5. The independence result contradicts the claim of Felgner (1969) that the Cofinality Principle implies the Axiom of Choice. An error has been found by Morris [see Felgner's corrections to (1969)].

The author has no axe to grind; he has probably never even heard of the current controversy in programming; and it is clearly no part of his concern to hold his friends and colleagues up to scorn. There is simply no way to describe the history of mathematical ideas without describing the successive social processes at work in proofs. The point is not that mathematicians make mistakes; that goes without saying. The point is that mathematicians' errors are corrected, not by formal symbolic logic, but by other mathematicians.

Just increasing the number of mathematicians working on a given problem does not necessarily insure believable proofs. Recently, two independent groups of topologists, one American, the other Japanese, independently announced results concerning the same kind of topological object, a thing called a homotopy group. The results turned out to be contradictory, and since both proofs involved complex symbolic and numerical calculation, it was not at all evident who had goofed. But the stakes were sufficiently high to justify pressing the issue, so the Japanese and American proofs were exchanged. Obviously, each group was highly motivated to discover an error in the other's proof; obviously, one proof or the other was incorrect. But neither the Japanese nor the American proof could be discredited.

Subsequently, a third group of researchers obtained yet another proof, this time supporting the American result. The weight of the evidence now being against their proof, the Japanese have retired to consider the matter further.

There are actually two morals to this story. First, a proof does not in itself significantly raise our confidence in the probable truth of the theorem it purports to prove. Indeed, for the theorem about the homotopy group, the horribleness of all the proffered proofs suggests that the theorem itself requires rethinking. A second point to be made is that proofs consisting entirely of calculations are not necessarily correct.

Even simplicity, clarity, and ease provide no guarantee that a proof is correct. The history of attempts to prove the Parallel Postulate is a particularly rich source of lovely, trim proofs that turned out to be false. From Ptolemy to Legendre (who tried time and time again), the greatest geometricians of every age kept ramming their heads against Euclid's fifth postulate. What's worse, even though we now know that the postulate is indemonstrable, many of the faulty proofs are still so beguiling that in Heath's definitive commentary on Euclid[7] they are not allowed to stand alone; Heath marks them up with italics, footnotes, and explanatory marginalia, lest some young mathematician, thumbing through the volume, be misled.

The idea that a proof can, at best, only probably express truth makes an interesting connection with a recent mathematical controversy. In a recent issue of *Science*,[12] Gina Bari Kolata suggested that the apparently secure notion of mathematical proof may be due for revision. Here the central question is not "How do theorems get believed?" but "What is it that we believe when we believe a theorem?" There are two relevant views, which can be roughly labeled classical and probabilistic.

The classicists say that when one believes mathematical statement *A*, one believes that in *principle* there is a correct, formal, valid, step by step, syntactically checkable deduction leading to *A* in a suitable logical calculus such as Zermelo-Fraenkel set theory or Peano arithmetic, a deduction of *A* à la the *Principia*, a deduction that completely formalizes the truth of *A* in the binary,

Aristotelian notion of truth: "A proposition is true if it says of what is, that it is, and if it says of what is not, that it is not." This formal chain of reasoning is by no means the same thing as an everyday, ordinary mathematical proof. The classical view does not require that an ordinary proof be accompanied by its formal counterpart; on the contrary, there are mathematically sound reasons for allowing the gods to formalize most of our arguments. One theoretician estimates, for instance, that a formal demonstration of one of Ramanujan's conjectures assuming set theory and elementary analysis would take about two thousand pages; the length of a deduction from first principles is nearly inconceivable.[14] But the classicist believes that the formalization is in principle a possibility and that the truth it expresses is binary, either so or not so.

The probabilists argue that since any very long proof can at best be viewed as only probably correct, why not state theorems probabilistically and give probabilistic proofs? The probabilistic proof may have the dual advantage of being technically easier than the classical, bivalent one, and may allow mathematicians to isolate the critical ideas that give rise to uncertainty in traditional, binary proofs. This process may even lead to a more plausible classical proof. An illustration of the probabilist approach is Michael Rabin's algorithm for testing probable primality.[17] For very large integers N, all of the classical techniques for determining whether N is composite become unworkable. Using even the most clever programming, the calculations required to determine whether numbers larger than 10^{104} are prime require staggering amounts of computing time. Rabin's insight was that if you are willing to settle for a very good probability that N is prime (or not prime), then you can get it within a reasonable amount of time—and with vanishingly small probability of error.

In view of these uncertainties over what constitutes an acceptable proof, which is after all a fairly basic element of the mathematical process, how is it that mathematics has survived and been so successful? If proofs bear little resemblance to formal deductive reasoning, if they can stand for generations and then fall, if they can contain flaws that defy detection, if they can express only the probability of truth within certain error bounds—if they are, in fact, not able to *prove* theorems in the sense of guaranteeing them beyond probability and, if necessary, beyond insight, well, then, how does mathematics work? How does it succeed in developing theorems that are significant and that compel belief?

First of all, the proof of a theorem is a message. A proof is not a beautiful abstract object with an independent existence. No mathematician grasps a proof, sits back, and sighs happily at the knowledge that he can now be certain of the truth of his theorem. He runs out into the hall and looks for someone to listen to it. He bursts into a colleague's office and commandeers the blackboard. He throws aside his scheduled topic and regales a seminar with his new idea. He drags his graduate students away from their dissertations to listen. He gets onto the phone and tells his colleagues in Texas and Toronto. In its first incarnation, a proof is a spoken message, or at most a sketch on a chalkboard or a paper napkin.

That spoken stage is the first filter for a proof. If it generates no excitement or belief among his friends, the wise mathematician reconsiders it. But if they find it tolerably interesting and believable, he writes it up. After it has circulated in draft for a while, if it still seems plausible, he does a polished version and submits it for publication. If the referees also find it attractive and convincing, it gets published so that it can be read by a wider audience. If enough members of that larger audience believe it and like it, then after a suitable cooling-off period the reviewing publications take a more leisurely look, to see whether the proof is really as pleasing as it first appeared and whether, on calm consideration, they really believe it.

And what happens to a proof when it is believed? The most immediate process is probably an internalization of the result. That is, the mathematician who reads and believes a proof will attempt to paraphrase it, to put it in his own terms, to fit it into his own personal view of mathematical knowledge. No two mathematicians are likely to internalize a mathematical concept in exactly the same way, so this process leads usually to multiple versions of the same theorem, each reinforcing belief, each adding to the feeling of the mathematical community that the original statement is likely to be true. Gauss, for example, obtained at least half a dozen independent proofs of his "law of quadratic reciprocity"; to date over fifty proofs of this law are known. Imre Lakatos gives, in his *Proofs and Refutations*,[13] historically accurate discussions of the transformations that several famous theorems underwent from initial conception to general acceptance. Lakatos demonstrates that Euler's formula $V - E + F = 2$ was reformulated again and again for almost two hundred years after its first statement, until it finally reached its current stable form. The most compelling transformation that can take place is generalization. If, by the same social process that works on the original theorem, the generalized theorem comes to be believed, then the original statement gains greatly in plausibility.

A believable theorem gets used. It may appear as a lemma in larger proofs; if it does not lead to contradictions, then we are all the more inclined to believe it. Or engineers may use it by plugging physical values into it. We have fairly high confidence in classical stress equations because we see bridges that stand; we have some confidence in the basic theorems of fluid mechanics because we see airplanes that fly.

Believable results sometimes make contact with other areas of mathematics—important ones invariably do. The successful transfer of a theorem or a proof technique from one branch of mathematics to another increases our feeling of confidence in it. In 1964, for example, Paul Cohen used a technique called forcing to prove a theorem in set theory[2]; at that time, his notions were so radical that the proof was hardly understood. But subsequently other investigators interpreted the notion of forcing in an algebraic context, connected it with more familiar ideas in logic, generalized the concepts, and found the generalizations useful. All of these connections (along with the other normal social processes that lead to acceptance) made the idea of forcing a good deal more compelling, and today forcing is routinely studied by graduate students in set theory.

After enough internalization, enough transformation, enough generalization, enough use, and enough connection, the mathematical community eventually decides that the central concepts in the original theorem, now perhaps greatly changed, have an ultimate stability. If the various proofs feel right and the results are examined from enough angles, then the truth of the theorem is eventually considered to be established. The theorem is thought to be true in the classical sense—that is, in the sense that it *could* be demonstrated by formal, deductive logic, although for almost all theorems no such deduction ever took place or ever will.

The Role of Simplicity

For what is clear and easily comprehended attracts; the complicated repels.—DAVID HILBERT

Sometimes one has to say difficult things, but one ought to say them as simply as one knows how.—G. H. HARDY

As a rule, the most important mathematical problems are clean and easy to state. An important theorem is much more likely to take form A than form B.

A: Every ——— is a ———.
B. If ——— and ——— and ——— and ——— and ——— except for special cases
    a) ———
    b) ———
    c) ———,
then unless
    i) ——— or
    ii) ——— or
    iii) ———,
every ——— that satisfies ——— is a ———.

The problems that have most fascinated and tormented and delighted mathematicians over the centuries have been the simplest ones to state. Einstein held that the maturity of a scientific theory could be judged by how well it could be explained to the man on the street. The four-color theorem rests on such slender foundations that it can be stated with complete precision to a child. If the child has learned his multiplication tables, he can understand the problem of the location and distribution of the prime numbers. And the deep fascination of the problem of defining the concept of "number" might turn him into a mathematician.

The correlation between importance and simplicity is no accident. Simple, attractive theorems are the ones most likely to be heard, read, internalized, and used. Mathematicians use simplicity as the first test for a proof. Only if it looks interesting at first glance will they consider it in detail. Mathematicians are not altruistic masochists. On the contrary, the history of mathematics is one long search for ease and pleasure and elegance—in the realm of symbols, of course.

Even if they didn't want to, mathematicians would have to use the criterion of simplicity; it is a psychological impossibility to choose any but the simplest and most attractive of 200,000 candidates for one's attention. If there are important, fundamental concepts in mathematics that are not simple, mathematicians will probably never discover them.

Messy, ugly mathematical propositions that apply only to paltry classes of structures, idiosyncratic propositions, propositions that rely on inordinately expensive mathematical machinery, propositions that require five blackboards or a roll of paper towels to sketch—these are unlikely ever to be assimilated into the body of mathematics. And yet it is only by such assimilation that proofs gain believability. The proof by itself is nothing; only when it has been subjected to the social processes of the mathematical community does it become believable.

In this paper, we have tended to stress simplicity above all else because that is the first filter for any proof. But we do not wish to paint ourselves and our fellow mathematicians as philistines or brutes. Once an idea has met the criterion of simplicity, other standards help determine its place among the ideas that make mathematicians gaze off abstractedly into the distance. Yuri Manin[14] has put it best: A good proof is one that makes us wiser.

Disbelieving Verifications

On the contrary, I find nothing in logistic for the discoverer but shackles. It does not help us at all in the direction of conciseness, far from it; and if it re-

quires twenty-seven equations to establish that 1 is a number, how many will it require to demonstrate a real theorem?—HENRI POINCARÉ

One of the chief duties of the mathematician in acting as an advisor to scientists . . . is to discourage them from expecting too much from mathematics.—NORBERT WEINER

Mathematical proofs increase our confidence in the truth of mathematical statements only after they have been subjected to the social mechanisms of the mathematical community. These same mechanisms doom the so-called proofs of software, the long formal verifications that correspond, not to the working mathematical proof, but to the imaginary logical structure that the mathematician conjures up to describe his feeling of belief. Verifications are not messages; a person who ran out into the hall to communicate his latest verification would rapidly find himself a social pariah. Verifications cannot really be read; a reader can flay himself through one of the shorter ones by dint of heroic effort, but that's not reading. Being unreadable and—literally—unspeakable, verifications cannot be internalized, transformed, generalized, used, connected to other disciplines, and eventually incorporated into a community consciousness. They cannot acquire credibility gradually, as a mathematical theorem does; one either believes them blindly, as a pure act of faith, or not at all.

At this point, some adherents of verification admit that the analogy to mathematics fails. Having argued that A, programming, resembles B, mathematics, and having subsequently learned that B is nothing like what they imagined, they wish to argue instead that A is like B', their mythical version of B. We then find ourselves in the peculiar position of putting across the argument that was originally theirs, asserting that yes, indeed, A does resemble B; our argument, however, matches the terms up differently from theirs. (See Figures 1 and 2.) Verifiers who wish to abandon the simile and substitute B' should as an aid to understanding abandon the language of B as well—in particular, it would help if they did not call their verifications "proofs." As for ourselves, we will continue to argue that programming is like mathematics, and that the same social pro-

Mathematics	*Programming*
theorem . . .	program
proof . . .	verification

Figure 1 The verifiers' original analogy.

Mathematics	*Programming*
theorem . . .	specification
proof . . .	program
imaginary	
formal	
demonstration . . .	verification

Figure 2 Our analogy.

cesses that work in mathematical proofs doom verifications.

There is a fundamental logical objection to verification, an objection on its own ground of formalistic rigor. Since the requirement for a program is informal and the program is formal, there must be a transition, and the transition itself must necessarily be informal. We have been distressed to learn that this proposition, which seems self-evident to us, is controversial. So we should emphasize that as antiformalists, we would not object to verification on these grounds; we only wonder how this inherently informal step fits into the formalist view. Have the adherents of verification lost sight of the informal origins of the formal objects they deal with? Is it their assertion that their formalizations are somehow incontrovertible? We must confess our confusion and dismay.

Then there is another logical difficulty, nearly as basic, and by no means so hair-splitting as the one above: The formal demonstration that a program is consistent with its specifications has value only if the specifications and the program are independently derived. In the toy-program atmosphere of experimental verification, this criterion is easily met. But in real life, if during the design process a program fails, it is changed, and the changes are based on knowledge of its specifications; or the specifications are changed, and those changes are based on knowledge of the program gained through the failure. In either case, the requirement of having independent criteria to check

against each other is no longer met. Again, we hope that no one would suggest that programs and specifications should not be repeatedly modified during the design process. That would be a position of incredible poverty—the sort of poverty that does, we fear, result from infatuation with formal logic.

Back in the real world, the kinds of input/output specifications that accompany production software are seldom simple. They tend to be long and complex and peculiar. To cite an extreme case, computing the payroll for the French National Railroad requires more than 3,000 pay rates (one uphill, one downhill, and so on). The specifications for any reasonable compiler or operating system fill volumes—and no one believes that they are complete. There are even some cases of black-box code, numerical algorithms that can be shown to work in the sense that they are used to build real airplanes or drill real oil wells, but work for no reason that anyone knows; the input assertions for these algorithms are not even formulable, let alone formalizable. To take just one example, an important algorithm with the rather jaunty name of Reverse Cuthill-McKee was known for years to be far better than plain Cuthill-McKee, known empirically, in laboratory tests and field trials and in production. Only recently, however, has its superiority been theoretically demonstrable,[6] and even then only with the usual informal mathematical proof, not with a formal deduction. During all of the years when Reverse Cuthill-McKee was unproved, even though it automatically made any program in which it appeared unverifiable, programmers perversely went on using it.

It might be countered that while real-life specifications are lengthy and complicated, they are not deep. Their verifications are, in fact, nothing more than extremely long chains of substitutions to be checked with the aid of simple algebraic identities.

All we can say in response to this is: Precisely. Verifications are long and involved but shallow; that's what's wrong with them. The verification of even a puny program can run into dozens of pages, and there's not a light moment or a spark of wit on any of those pages. Nobody is going to run into a friend's office with a program verification. Nobody is going to sketch a verification out on a paper napkin. Nobody is going to buttonhole a colleague into listening to a verification. Nobody is ever going to read it. One can feel one's eyes glaze over at the very thought.

It has been suggested that very high level languages, which can deal directly with a broad range of mathematical objects or functional languages, which it is said can be concisely axiomatized, might be used to insure that a verification would be interesting and therefore responsive to a social process like the social process of mathematics.

In theory this idea sounds hopeful; in practice, it doesn't work out. For example, the following verification condition arises in the proof of a fast Fourier transform written in MADCAP, a very high level language[18]:

If $S \in \{1, -1\}$, $b = \exp(2\pi i S/N)$, r is an integer, $N = 2^r$,

1. $C = \{2j: 0 \leq j < N/4\}$ and
2. $a = <a_r: a_r = b^{r \bmod(N/2)}, 0 \leq r < N/2>$ and
3. $A = \{j: j \bmod N < N/2, 0 \leq j < N\}$ and
4. $A^\star = \{j: 0 \leq j < N\} - A$ and
5. $F = <f_r: f_r = \sum_{k_1 \in R_n} k_1(b^{k_1 \lfloor r/2^{r-1} \rfloor j \bmod N}), R_r = \{j: (j - r)$

$\bmod(N/2) = 0\} >$ and $k \leq r$

then

1. $A \cap (A + 2^{r-k-1}) = \{x: x \bmod 2^{r-k} < 2^{r-k-1}, 0 \leq x < N\}$
2. $<\triangleright a_c \triangleright a_c> = <a_r: a_r = b^{r 2^k \bmod(N/2)}, 0 \leq r < N/2>$
3. $<\triangleright(F_{A \cap (A+2^{r-k-1})} + F_{(j: 0 \leq j < N)} - A \cap (A+2^{r-k-1})}$
$\triangleright (<\triangleright a_c \triangleright a_c>$
$\star (F_{A \cap (A+2^{r-k-1})} + F_{(j: 0 \leq j < N)} - A \cap (A+2^{r-k-1})}))$
$> = <f_r: f_r = \sum_{k_1 \in R_r} k_1(b^{\lfloor r/2^{r-k-1} \rfloor j \bmod N}),$
$R_r = \{j: (j - r) \bmod 2^{r-k-1} = 0\}>$
4. $<\triangleright(F_A + F_{A^\star}) \triangleright a^\star (F_A - F_{A^\star})> = <f_r: f_r = \sum_{k_1 \in R_r}$
$k_1(b^{k_1 \lfloor r/2^{r-1} \rfloor j \bmod N}), R_r = \{j: (j - r) \bmod(N/2) = 0\}>$

This is not what we would call pleasant reading.

Some verifiers will concede that verification is simply unworkable for the vast majority of programs but argue that for a few crucial applications the agony is worthwhile. They point to air-traffic control, missile systems, and the exploration of space as areas in which the risks are so high that any expenditure of time and effort can be justified.

Even if this were so, we would still insist that verification renounce its claim on all other areas of programming; to teach students in introductory programming courses how to do verification, for instance, ought to be as farfetched as teaching students in introductory biology how to do open-heart surgery. But the stakes do not affect our belief in the basic impossibility of verifying any system large enough and flexible enough to do any real-world task. No matter how high the pay-off, no one will ever be able to force himself to read the incredibly long, tedious verifications of real-life systems, and unless they can be read, understood, and refined, the verifications are worthless.

Now, it might be argued that all these references to readability and internalization are irrelevant, that the aim of verification is eventually to construct an automatic verifying system.

Unfortunately, there is a wealth of evidence that fully automated verifying systems are out of the question. The lower bounds on the length of formal demonstrations for mathematical theorems are immense,[19] and there is no reason to believe that such demonstrations for programs would be any shorter or cleaner—quite the contrary. In fact, even the strong adherents of program verification do not take seriously the possibility of totally automated verifiers. Ralph London, a proponent of verification, speaks of an out-to-lunch system, one that could be left unsupervised to grind out verifications; but he doubts that such a system can be built to work with reasonable reliability. One group, despairing of automation in the foreseeable future, has proposed that verifications should be performed by teams of "grunt mathematicians," low level mathematical teams who will check verification conditions. The sensibilities of people who could make such a proposal seem odd, but they do serve to indicate how remote the possibility of automated verification must be.

Suppose, however, that an automatic verifier could somehow be built. Suppose further that programmers did somehow come to have faith in its verifications. In the absence of any real-world basis for such belief, it would have to be blind faith, but no matter. Suppose that the philosopher's stone had been found, that lead could be changed to gold, and that programmers were convinced of the merits of feeding their programs into the gaping jaws of a verifier. It seems to us that the scenario envisioned by the proponents of verification goes something like this: The programmer inserts his 300-line input/output package into the verifier. Several hours later, he returns. There is his 20,000-line verification and the message "VERIFIED."

There is a tendency, as we begin to feel that a structure is logically, provably right, to remove from it whatever redundancies we originally built in because of lack of understanding. Taken to its extreme, this tendency brings on the so-called Titanic effect; when failure does occur, it is massive and uncontrolled. To put it another way, the severity with which a system fails is directly proportional to the intensity of the designer's belief that it cannot fail. Programs designed to be clean and tidy merely so that they can be verified will be particularly susceptible to the Titanic effect. Already we see signs of this phenomenon. In their notes on Euclid,[16] a language designed for program verification, several of the foremost verification adherents say, "Because we expect all Euclid programs to be verified, we have not made special provisions for exception handling. . . . Runtime software errors should not occur in verified programs." Errors should not occur? Shades of the ship that shouldn't be sunk.

So, having for the moment suspended all rational disbelief, let us suppose that the programmer gets the message "VERIFIED." And let us suppose further that the message does not result from a failure on the part of the verifying system. What does the programmer know? He knows that his program is formally, logically, provably, certifiably correct. He does not know, however, to what extent it is reliable, dependable, trustworthy, safe; he does not know within what limits it will work; he does not know what happens when it exceeds those limits. And yet he has that mystical stamp of approval: "VERIFIED." We can almost see the iceberg looming in the background over the unsinkable ship.

Luckily, there is little reason to fear such a future. Picture the same programmer returning to find the same 20,000 lines. What message would he really find, supposing that an automatic verifier could really be built? Of course, the message would be "NOT VERIFIED." The programmer would make a change, feed the program in again, return again. "NOT VERIFIED." Again he would make a change, again he would feed the program to the verifier, again "NOT VERIFIED." A program is a human artifact; a real-life program is a complex human artifact; and any human artifact of sufficient size and complexity is imperfect. The message will never read "VERIFIED."

The Role of Continuity

We may say, roughly, that a mathematical idea is "significant" if it can be connected, in a natural and illuminating way, with a large complex of other mathematical ideas.—G. H. HARDY

The only really fetching defense ever offered for verification is the scaling-up argument. As best we can reproduce it, here is how it goes:

1. Verification is now in its infancy. At the moment, the largest tasks it can handle are verifications of algorithms like FIND and model programs like GCD. It will in time be able to tackle more and more complicated algorithms and trickier and trickier model programs. These verifications are comparable to mathematical proofs. They are read. They generate the same kinds of interest and excitement that theorems do. They are subject to the ordinary social processes that work on mathematical reasoning, or on reasoning in any other discipline, for that matter.

2. Big production systems are made up of nothing more than algorithms and model programs. Once verified, algorithms and model programs can make up large, workaday production systems, and the (admittedly unreadable) verification of a big system will be the sum of the many small, attractive, interesting verifications of its components.

With (1) we have no quarrel. Actually, algorithms were proved and the proofs read and discussed and assimilated long before the invention of computers—and with a striking lack of formal machinery. Our guess is that the study of algorithms and model programs will develop like any other mathematical activity, chiefly by informal, social mechanisms, very little if at all by formal mechanisms.

It is with (2) that we have our fundamental disagreement. We argue that there is no continuity between the world of FIND or GCD and the world of production software, billing systems that write real bills, scheduling systems that schedule real events, ticketing systems that issue real tickets. And we argue that the world of production software is itself discontinuous.

No programmer would agree that large production systems are composed of nothing more than algorithms and small programs. Patches, ad hoc constructions, bandaids and tourniquets, bells and whistles, glue, spit and polish, signature code, blood-sweat-and-tears, and, of course, the kitchen sink—the colorful jargon of the practicing programmer seems to be saying something about the nature of the structures he works with; maybe theoreticians ought to be listening to him. It has been estimated that more than half the code in any real production system consists of user interfaces and error messages—ad hoc, informal structures that are by definition unverifiable. Even the verifiers themselves sometimes seem to realize the unverifiable nature of most real software. C.A.R. Hoare has been quoted[9] as saying, "In many applications, algorithm plays almost no role, and certainly presents almost no problem." (We wish we could report that he thereupon threw up his hands and abandoned verification, but no such luck.)

Or look at the difference between the world of GCD and the world of production software in another way: The specifications for algorithms are concise and tidy, while the specifications for real-world systems are immense, frequently of the same order of magnitude as the systems themselves. The specifications for algorithms are highly stable, stable over decades or even centuries; the specifications for real systems vary daily or hourly (as any programmer can testify). The specifications for algorithms are exportable, general; the specifications for real systems are idiosyncratic and ad hoc. These are not differences in degree. They are differences in kind. Babysitting for a sleeping child for one hour does not scale up to raising a family of ten—the problems are essentially, fundamentally different.

And within the world of real production software there is no continuity either. The scaling-up argument seems to be based on the fuzzy notion that the world of programming is like the world of Newtonian physics—made up of smooth, continuous functions. But, in fact, programs are jagged and full of holes and caverns. Every programmer knows that altering a line or sometimes even a bit can utterly destroy a program or mutilate it in ways that we do not understand and cannot predict. And yet at other times fairly substantial changes seem to alter nothing; the folklore is filled with stories of pranks and acts of vandalism that frustrated the perpetrators by remaining forever undetected.

There is a classic science-fiction story about a time traveler who goes back to the primeval jungles to watch dinosaurs and then returns to find his own time altered almost beyond recognition. Politics, architecture, language—even the plants and animals seem wrong, distorted. Only when he removes his time-travel suit does he understand what has happened. On the heel of his boot, carried away from the past and therefore unable to perform its function in the evolution of the world, is crushed the wing of a butterfly. Every programmer knows the sensation: A trivial, minute change wreaks havoc in a massive system. Until we know more about programming, we had better for all practical purposes think of systems as composed, not of sturdy structures like algorithms and smaller programs, but of butterflies' wings.

The discontinuous nature of programming sounds the death knell for verification. A sufficiently fanatical researcher might be willing to devote two or three years to verifying a significant piece of software if he could be assured that the software would remain stable. But real-life programs need to be maintained and modified. There is no reason to believe that verifying a modified program is any easier than verifying the original the first time around. There is no reason to believe that a big verification can be the sum of many small verifications. There is no reason to believe that a verification can transfer to any other program—not even to a program only one single line different from the original.

And it is this discontinuity that obviates the possibility of refining verifications by the sorts of social processes that refine mathematical proofs. The lone fanatic might construct his own verification, but he would never have any reason to read anyone else's, nor would anyone else ever be willing to read his. No community could develop. Even the most zealous verifier could be induced to read a verification only if he thought he might be able to use or borrow or swipe something from it. Nothing could force him to read someone else's verification once he had grasped the point that no verification bears any necessary connection to any other verification.

Believing Software

The program itself is the only complete description of what the program will do.—P. J. Davis

Since computers can write symbols and move them about with negligible expenditure of energy, it is tempting to leap to the conclusion that anything is possible in the symbolic realm. But reality does not yield so easily; physics does not suddenly break down. It is no more possible to construct symbolic structures without using resources than it is to construct material structures without using them. For even the most trivial mathematical theories, there are simple statements whose formal demonstrations would be impossibly long. Albert Meyer's outstanding lecture on the history of such research[15] concludes with a striking interpretation of how hard it may be to deduce even fairly simple mathematical statements. Suppose that we encode logical formulas as binary strings and set out to build a computer that will decide the truth of a simple set of formulas of length, say, at most a thousand bits. Suppose that we even allow ourselves the luxury of a technology that will produce proton-size electronic components connected by infinitely thin wires. Even so, the computer we design must densely fill the entire observable universe. This precise observation about the length of formal deductions agrees with our intuition about the amount of detail embedded in ordinary, workaday mathematical proofs. We often use "Let us assume, without loss of generality . . ." or "Therefore, by renumbering, if necessary . . ." to replace enormous amounts of formal detail. To insist on the formal detail would be a silly waste of resources. Both symbolic and material structures must be engineered with a very cautious eye. Resources are limited; time is limited; energy is limited. Not even the computer can change the finite nature of the universe.

We assume that these constraints have prevented the adherents of verification from offering what might be fairly convincing evidence in support of their methods. The lack at this late date of even a single verification of a working system has sometimes been attributed to the youth of the field. The verifiers argue, for instance, that they are only now beginning to understand loop invariants. At first blush, this sounds like another variant of the scaling-up argument. But in fact there are large classes of real-life systems with virtually no loops—they scarcely ever occur in commercial programming applications. And yet there has never been a verification of, say, a Cobol system that prints real checks; lacking even one makes it seem doubtful that there could at some time in the future be many. Resources, and time, and energy are just as limited for verifiers as they are for all the rest of us.

We must therefore come to grips with two problems that have occupied engineers for many generations: First, people must plunge into activities that they do not understand. Second, people cannot create perfect mechanisms.

How then do engineers manage to create reliable structures? First, they use social processes very like the social processes of mathematics to achieve successive approximations at understanding. Second, they have a mature and realistic view of what "reliable" means; in particular, the one thing it never means is "perfect." There is no way to deduce logically that bridges stand, or that airplanes fly, or that power stations deliver electricity. True, no bridges would fall, no airplanes would crash, no electrical systems would black out if engineers would first demonstrate their perfection before building them—true because they would never be built at all.

The analogy in programming is any functioning, useful, real-world system. Take for instance an organic-chemical synthesizer called SYN-CHEM.[5] For this program, the criterion of reliability is particularly straightforward—if it synthesizes a chemical, it works; if it doesn't, it doesn't work. No amount of correctness could ever hope to improve on this standard; indeed, it is not at all clear how one could even begin to formalize such a standard in a way that would lend itself to verification. But it is a useful and continuing enterprise to try to increase the number of chemicals the program can synthesize.

It is nothing but symbol chauvinism that makes computer scientists think that our structures are so much more important than material structures that (a) they should be perfect, and (b) the energy necessary to make them perfect should be expended. We argue rather that (a) they cannot be perfect and (b) energy should not be wasted in the futile attempt to make them perfect. It is no accident that the probabilistic view of mathematical truth is closely allied to the engineering notion of reliability. Perhaps we should make a sharp distinction between program reliability and program perfection—and concentrate our efforts on reliability.

The desire to make programs correct is constructive and valuable. But the monolithic view of verification is blind to the benefits that could result from accepting a standard of correctness like the standard of correctness for real mathematical proofs, or a standard of reliability like the standard for real engineering structures. The quest for workability within economic limits, the willingness to channel innovation by recycling successful design, the trust in the functioning of a community of peers—all the mechanisms that make engineering and mathematics really work are obscured in the fruitless search for perfect verifiability.

What elements could contribute to making programming more like engineering and mathematics? One mechanism that can be exploited is the creation of general structures whose specific instances become more reliable as the reliability of the general structure increases.* This notion has appeared in several incarnations, of which Knuth's insistence on creating and understanding generally useful algorithms is one of the most important and encouraging. Baker's team-programming methodology[1] is an explicit attempt to expose software to social processes. If reusability becomes a criterion for effective design, a wider and wider community will examine the most common programming tools.

The concept of verifiable software has been with us too long to be easily displaced. For the practice of programming, however, verifiability must not be allowed to overshadow reliability. Scientists should not confuse mathematical models with reality—and verification is nothing but a model of believability. Verifiability is not and cannot be a dominating concern in software design. Economics, deadlines, cost-benefit ratios, personal and group style, the limits of acceptable error—all these carry immensely much more weight in design than verifiability or nonverifiability.

So far, there has been little philosophical discussion of making software reliable rather than verifiable. If verification adherents could redefine their efforts and reorient themselves to this goal, or if another view of software could arise that would draw on the social processes of mathematics and the modest expectations of engineering, the interests of real-life programming and theoretical computer science might both be better served.

Even if, for some reason that we are not now able to understand, we should be proved wholly wrong and the verifiers wholly right, this is not the moment to restrict research on programming. We know too little now to sense what directions will be most fruitful. If our reasoning convinces no one, if verification still seems an avenue worth

*This process has recently come to be called "abstraction," but we feel that for a variety of reasons "abstraction" is a bad term. It is easily confused with the totally different notion of abstraction in mathematics, and often what has passed for abstraction in the computer science literature is simply the removal of implementation details.

exploring, so be it; we three can only try to argue against verification, not blast it off the face of the earth. But we implore our friends and colleagues not to narrow their vision to this one view no matter how promising it may seem. Let it not be the only view, the only avenue. Jacob Bronowski has an important insight about a time in the history of another discipline that may be similar to our own time in the development of computing: "A science which orders its thought too early is stifled. . . . The hope of the medieval alchemists that the elements might be changed was not as fanciful as we once thought. But it was merely damaging to a chemistry which did not yet understand the composition of water and common salt."

References

1. Baker, F. T. Chief programmer team management of production programming. *IBM Syst. J. 11*, 1 (1972), 56–73.

2. Cohen, P. J. The independence of the continuum hypothesis. Proc. Nat. Acad. Sci., USA. Part I, vol. 50 (1963), pp. 1143–1148; Part II, vol. 51 (1964), pp. 105–110.

3. Davis, P. J. Fidelity in mathematical discourse: Is one and one really two? *The Amer. Math. Monthly 79*, 3 (1972), 252–263.

4. Bateman, P., and Diamond, H. John E. Littlewood (1885–1977): An informal obituary. *The Math. Intelligencer 1*, 1 (1978), 28–33.

5. Gelerenter, H., et al. The discovery of organic synthetic roots by computer. *Topics in Current Chemistry 41*, Springer-Verlag, 1973, pp. 113–150.

6. George, J. Alan. Computer Implementation of the Finite Element Method. Ph.D. Th., Stanford U., Stanford, Calif., 1971.

7. Heath, Thomas L. *The Thirteen Books of Eu-clid's Elements*. Dover, New York, 1956, pp. 204–219.

8. Heawood, P. J. Map colouring theorems. *Quarterly J. Math., Oxford Series 24* (1890), 322–339.

9. Hoare, C. A. R. Quoted in *Software Management*, C. McGowan and R. McHenry, Eds.; to appear in *Research Directions in Software Technology*, M.I.T. Press, Cambridge, Mass., 1978.

10. Jech, Thomas J. *The Axiom of Choice*. North-Holland Pub. Co., Amsterdam, 1973, p. 118.

11. Kempe, A. B. On the geographical problem of the four colors. *Amer. J. Math. 2* (1879), 193–200.

12. Kolata, G. Bari. Mathematical proof: The genesis of reasonable doubt. *Science 192* (1976), 989–990.

13. Lakatos, Imre. *Proofs and Refutations: The Logic of Mathematical Discovery*. Cambridge University Press, England, 1976.

14. Manin, Yu. I. *A Course in Mathematical Logic*. Springer-Verlag, 1977, pp. 48–51.

15. Meyer, A. The inherent computational complexity of theories of ordered sets: A brief survey. Int. Cong. of Mathematicians, Aug. 1974.

16. Popek, G., et al. Notes on the design of Euclid. Proc. Conf. Language Design for Reliable Software, SIGPLAN Notices (ACM) *12*, 3 (1977), pp. 11–18.

17. Rabin, M. O. Probabilistic algorithms. In *Algorithms and Complexity: New Directions and Recent Results*. J. F. Traub, Ed., Academic Press, New York, 1976, pp. 21–40.

18. Schwartz, J. On programming. Courant Rep., New York U., New York, 1973.

19. Stockmeyer, L. The complexity of decision problems in automata theory and logic. Ph.D. Th., M.I.T., Cambridge, Mass., 1974.

20. Ulam, S. M. *Adventures of a Mathematician*. Scribner's, New York, 1976, p. 288.

Computer Science and Mathematics

Donald E. Knuth

Donald Ervin Knuth received his Ph.D in mathematics from the California Institute of Technology in 1963. He taught at Cal Tech from 1963 to 1968, and from 1968 to the present he has been with the computer science department at Stanford. He has been a Guggenheim fellow and has received the G. M. Hopper Award and the A.M. Turing Award. Knuth is a member of the National Academy of Sciences.

The relationship between computer science and mathematics is explored in this illuminating essay by a scholar eminently well qualified for the task. Donald Knuth has been introduced to the reader in Volume II in his essay on coping with finiteness. The skill that made that article such an instructive tour of the limits of computing devices serves in this essay to describe how the ideas of mathematics and the challenges of computer science may interact to the mutual enrichment of both disciplines.

An important insight of this essay, which cannot be overemphasized, is that computer science has broadened and enriched the world of mathematics in ways that many mathematicians either do not or will not recognize. Not only have new classes of problems been developed, but old classes have been given new significance because of their potential relevance to problems in computer science. Questions that thirty years ago would have been dismissed as too computational for a serious mathematician's time are now valid topics of research.

Often mathematicians have presented the world with an enormous, sweeping abstract theory and assumed that they need do nothing more with the new creation. However, the specific details of putting the general theory to work in the real world—with incomplete information, finite computing resources, and various algorithmic solutions—often create mathematical questions that are extremely specific. These mathematical questions—specific or not—are unsolved and often do not possess the clean, once-and-for-all solutions that grandiose, unapplied, general theories often provide. While specific problems may seem unimportant in a grand abstract mathematical theory, they may well offer vital insights into some aspect of computer science.

Mathematicians who previously have focused on only the great and abstract mathematical problems may wish to view the addition of these new concrete, practical, significant mathematical problems as they view good deeds; it is impossible to have too many of them.

SINCE COMPUTER SCIENCE is relatively new, I must begin by explaining what it is all about. At least, my wife tells me that she has to explain it whenever anyone asks her what I do, and I suppose most people today have a somewhat different perception of the field than mine. In fact, no two computer scientists will probably give the same definition; this is not surprising, since it is just as hard to find two mathematicians who give the same definition of mathematics.

Source: Donald E. Knuth, "Computer Science and Mathematics," *American Scientist* 61 (1973): 707–713.

Fortunately it has been fashionable in recent years to have an "identity crisis," so computer scientists have been right in style.

My favorite way to describe computer science is to say that it is the study of *algorithms*. An algorithm is a precisely defined sequence of rules telling how to produce specified output information from given input information in a finite number of steps. A particular representation of an algorithm is called a *program,* just as we use the word "data" to stand for a particular representation of "information."[14] Perhaps the most significant discovery generated by the advent of computers will turn out to be that algorithms, as objects of study, are extraordinarily rich in interesting properties and, furthermore, that an algorithmic point of view is a useful way to organize knowledge in general. G. E. Forsythe has observed that "the question 'What can be automated?' is one of the most inspiring philosophical and practical questions of contemporary civilization."[8]

From these remarks we might conclude that computer science should have existed long before the advent of computers. In a sense, it did; the subject is deeply rooted in history. For example, I recently found it interesting to study ancient manuscripts, learning to what extent the Babylonians of 3,500 years ago were computer scientists.[16] But computers are really necessary before we can learn much about the general properties of algorithms; human beings are not precise enough or fast enough to carry out any but the simplest procedures. Therefore the potential richness of algorithmic studies was not fully realized until general-purpose computing machines became available.

I should point out that computing machines (and algorithms) do not only compute with *numbers:* they can deal with information of any kind, once it is represented in a precise way. We used to say that sequences of symbols, such as names, are represented in a computer as if they were numbers; but it is really more correct to say that numbers are represented inside a computer as sequences of symbols.

The French word for computer science is *informatique;* the German is *Informatik;* and in Danish the word is *datalogi.*[21] All of these terms wisely imply that computer science deals with many things besides the solution to numerical equations. However, these names emphasize the "stuff" that algorithms manipulate (the information or data), instead of the algorithms themselves. The Norwegians at the University of Oslo have chosen a somewhat more appropriate designation for computer science, namely, *databehandling;* its English equivalent, *data processing,* has unfortunately been used in America only in connection with business applications, while *information processing* tends to connote library applications. Several people have suggested the term *computing science* as superior to *computer science.*

Of course, the search for a perfect name is somewhat pointless, since the underlying concepts are much more important than the name. It is perhaps significant, however, that these other names for computer science all deemphasize the role of computing machines themselves, apparently in order to make the field more "legitimate" and respectable. Many people's opinion of a computing machine is, at best, that it is a necessary evil—a difficult tool to be used if other methods fail. Why should we give so much emphasis to teaching how to use computers if they are merely valuable tools like (say) electron microscopes?

Computer scientists, knowing that computers are more than this, instinctively underplay the machine aspect when they are defending their new discipline. However, it is not necessary to be so self-conscious about machines; this has been aptly pointed out by Newell, Perlis, and Simon,[22] who define computer science simply as the study of computers, just as botany is the study of plants, astronomy the study of stars, and so on. The phenomena surrounding computers are immensely varied and complex, requiring description and explanation; and, like electricity, these phenomena belong both to engineering and to science.

When I say that computer science is the study of algorithms, I am singling out only one of the "phenomena surrounding computers"; computer science actually includes more. I have emphasized algorithms because they are really the central core of the subject, the common denominator which underlies and unifies the different branches. It might happen that technology someday will settle down and computing machines will change very little. There are no indications of such a stable technology in the near future—quite the contrary—but I believe that the study of algorithms will remain challenging and important even if the other phenomena of computers might someday be fully explored. (For further discussions of the nature of computer science see refs. *17* and *27*, in addition to those cited above.)

Is Computer Science Part of Mathematics?

Certainly there are phenomena about computers now being actively studied by computer scientists which are hardly mathematical. But if we restrict our attention to the study of algorithms, isn't this merely a branch of mathematics? After all, algorithms were studied primarily by mathematicians, if by anyone, before the days of computer science. Therefore one could argue that this central aspect of computer science is really part of mathematics.

I believe, however, that there is just as good an argument for the proposition that mathematics is a part of computer science! It is always difficult to establish boundary lines between disciplines (compare, for example, the subjects of "physical chemistry" and "chemical physics"); but it is possible to distinguish essentially different points of view between mathematics and computer science.

The following true story is perhaps the best way to explain the distinction I have in mind. Some years ago I had just learned a mathematical theorem which implied that any two $n \times n$ matrices A and B of integers have a "greatest common right divisor" D. This means that D is a right divisor of A and of B, i.e. $A = A'D$ and $B = B'D$ for some integer matrices A' and B'; and that every common right divisor of A and B is a right divisor of D. So I wondered how to calculate the greatest common right divisor of two given matrices. A few days later I happened to be attending a conference where I met the mathematician H. B. Mann, and I felt that he would know how to solve this problem. I asked him, and he did indeed know the correct answer, but it was a mathematician's answer, not a computer scien-

tist's answer! He said: "Let $\mathscr{R}$ be the ring of $n \times n$ integer matrices; in this ring, the union of two principal left ideals is principal, so let D be such that

$$\mathscr{R}A \cup \mathscr{R}B = \mathscr{R}D.$$

This matrix D is the greatest common right divisor of A and B." This formula is certainly the simplest possible one: we need only 8 symbols to write it down, and it relies on rigorously proved theorems of mathematical algebra. But from the standpoint of a computer scientist, it is worthless, since it involves constructing the infinite sets $\mathscr{R}A$ and $\mathscr{R}B$, taking their union, then searching through infinitely many matrices D such that this union matches the infinite set $\mathscr{R}D$. I could not determine the greatest common divisor of $\binom{12}{34}$ and $\binom{43}{21}$ by doing such infinite operations. (Incidentally, a computer scientist's answer to this question was later supplied by my student Michael Fredman; see *15*, p. 380.)

One of my mathematician friends told me he would be willing to recognize computer science as a worthwhile field of study as soon as it contains 1,000 deep theorems. This criterion should obviously be changed to include algorithms as well as theorems—say, 500 deep theorems and 500 deep algorithms. But even so, it is clear that computer science today doesn't measure up to such a test, if "deep" means that a brilliant person would need many months to discover the theorem or the algorithm. Computer science is still too young for this; I can claim youth as a handicap. We still don't know the best way to describe algorithms, to understand them or prove them correct, to invent them, or to analyze their behavior, although considerable progress is being made on all these fronts. The potential for "1,000 deep results" is there, but only perhaps 50 have been discovered so far.

In order to describe the mutual impact of computer science and mathematics on each other, and their relative roles, I am therefore looking somewhat to the future, to the time when computer science is a bit more mature and sure of itself. Recent trends have made it possible to envision a day when computer science and mathematics will both exist as respected disciplines, serving analogous but different roles in a person's education.

To quote George Forsythe again, "The most valuable acquisitions in a scientific or technical education are the general-purpose mental tools which remain serviceable for a lifetime. I rate natural language and mathematics as the most important of these tools, and computer science as a third."[9]

Like mathematics, computer science will be a subject which is considered basic to a general education. Like mathematics and other sciences, computer science will continue to be vaguely divided into two areas which might be called "theoretical" and "experimental." Like mathematics, computer science will be somewhat different from the other sciences in that it deals with man-made laws which can be proved, instead of natural laws which are never known with certainty. Thus, the two subjects will be like each other in many ways. The difference is in the subject matter and approach—mathematics dealing more or less with theorems, infinite processes, static relationships, and computer science dealing more or less with algorithms, finitary constructions, dynamic relationships.

Educational Side-effects

A person well-trained in computer science knows how to deal with algorithms—how to construct them, manipulate them, understand them, analyze them. This knowledge prepares him for much more than writing good computer programs; it is a mental tool which will be a definite aid to his understanding of other subjects, whether they are chemistry, linguistics, or music. The reason for this may be understood in the following way: It has often been said that a person doesn't really understand something until he teaches it to someone else. Actually a person doesn't really understand something until he can teach it to a *computer*, i.e. express it as an algorithm. "The automatic computer really *forces* that precision of thinking which is alleged to be a product of any study of mathematics."[7] The attempt to formalize things as algorithms leads to a much deeper understanding than if we simply try to understand things in the traditional way.

Linguists thought they understood languages—until they tried to explain languages to computers; they soon discovered how much more remains to be learned. Many people have set up computer models of things and have discovered that they learned more while setting up the model than while actually looking at the output of the eventual program.

In the late 1940s, there were only three customers signed up to buy a UNIVAC computer, the first large-scale computer to be marketed commercially: the U. S. Census Bureau, the Presidential Life Insurance Company, and the A. C. Nielsen Company, of television rating fame. When the Nielsen people, together with the UNIVAC representatives, analyzed their operations carefully enough to see how they could be computerized, they discovered how to save so much money that they didn't need a computer after all![12]

For three years I taught a sophomore course in abstract algebra, for mathematics majors at the California Institute of Technology, and the most difficult topic was always the study of "Jordan canonical form" for matrices. The third year I tried a new approach, by looking at the subject algorithmically, and suddenly it became quite clear. The same thing happened with the discussion of finite groups defined by generators and relations and, in another course, with the reduction theory of binary quadratic forms. By presenting the subject in terms of algorithms, the purpose and meaning of the mathematical theorems became transparent.

Later, while writing a book on computer arithmetic,[15] I found that virtually every theorem in elementary number theory arises in a natural, motivated way in connection with the problem of making computers do high-speed numerical calculations. Therefore I believe that the traditional courses in elementary number theory might well be changed to adopt this point of view, adding a practical motivation to the already beautiful theory.

These examples and many more have convinced me of the pedagogic value of an algorithmic approach; it aids in the understanding of concepts of all kinds. I believe that a student who is properly trained in computer science is learning something which will implicitly help him cope with many other subjects, and, therefore, there will soon be good reason for saying that undergraduate computer science majors have received a good general education, just as we now believe this of undergraduate math majors. On the other hand, the present-day undergraduate courses in computer science are not yet fulfilling this goal; at least, I find that many beginning graduate students with an undergraduate degree in computer science have been more narrowly educated than I would like. Computer scientists are, of course, working to correct this present deficiency, which I believe is probably due to an overemphasis on computer languages instead of algorithms.

Some Interactions

Computer science has been affecting mathematics in many ways, and I shall try to list the good ones here. In the first place, of course, computers can be used to compute, and they have frequently been applied in mathematical research when hand computations are too difficult; they generate the data which suggest or demolish conjectures. For example, Gauss said that he first thought of the prime number theorem by looking at a table of the primes less than one million. In my own Ph.D. thesis, I was able to resolve a conjecture concerning infinitely many cases by looking closely at computer calculations of the smallest case.[13] An example of another kind is Marshall Hall's recent progress in the determination of all simple groups of orders up to one million.

Secondly, there are obvious connections between computer science and mathematics in the areas of numerical analysis,[28] logic, and number theory; I need not dwell on these here since they are so widely known. However, I should mention especially the work of D. H. Lehmer, who has combined computing with classical mathematics in several remarkable ways; for example, he has proved that every set of six consecutive integers >285 contains a multiple of a prime ≥ 43.

Another impact of computer science has been an increased emphasis on constructions in all branches of mathematics. Replacing existence proofs by algorithms which construct mathematical objects has often led to improvements in an abstract theory. For example, E. C. Dade and H. Zassenhaus remarked, at the close of a paper

written in 1963: "This concept of genus has already proved of importance in the theory of modules over orders. So a mathematical idea introduced solely with a view to computability has turned out to have an intrinsic theoretical value of its own." Furthermore, as mentioned above, the constructive algorithmic approach often has pedagogic value.

Another way in which the algorithmic approach affects mathematical theories is in the construction of one-to-one correspondences. Quite often there have been indirect proofs that certain types of mathematical objects are equinumerous; a direct construction of a one-to-one correspondence shows that, in fact, even more is true.

Discrete mathematics, especially combinatorial theory, has been given a boost by the rise of computer science, in addition to all the other fields in which discrete mathematics is currently being extensively applied. (For references to the influences of computing on mathematics, and for many more examples, see the following sampling of books, each of which contains relevant papers: 1, 2, 4, 5, 20, 23, 26. Peter Lax's article, 19, discusses the effect computing has had on mathematical physics.)

Actually the most important impact of computer science on mathematics, in my opinion, is somewhat different from all of the above. To me, the most significant thing is that the study of algorithms themselves has opened up a fertile vein of interesting new mathematical problems; it provides a breath of life for many areas of mathematics that had been suffering from a lack of new ideas. Charles Babbage, one of the "fathers" of computing machines, predicted this already in 1864[3]:

As soon as an Analytical Engine [i.e. a general-purpose computer] exists, it will necessarily guide the future course of the science. Whenever any result is sought by its aid, the question will then arise—By what course of calculation can these results be arrived at by the machine in the shortest time?

And again, George Forsythe in 1958[25]:

The use of practically any computing technique itself raises a number of mathematical problems. There is thus a very considerable impact of computation on mathematics itself, and this may be expected to influence mathematical research to an increasing degree.

Garrett Birkhoff (*4*, p. 2) has observed that such influences are not a new phenomenon; they were already significant in the early Greek development of mathematics.

I have found that a great many intriguing mathematical problems arise when we try to analyze an algorithm quantitatively, to see how fast it will run on a computer; a typical example of such a problem is worked out below. Another class of problems of great interest concerns the search for best possible algorithms in a given class (see, for example, the recent survey by Reingold, *24*). And one of the first mathematical theories to be inspired by computer science is the theory of languages, which by now includes many beautiful results (see *10, 11*). The excitement of these new theories is the reason I became a computer scientist.

Conversely, mathematics has, of course, a profound influence on computer science; nearly every branch of mathematical knowledge has been brought to bear somewhere. I recently worked on a problem dealing with discrete objects called "binary trees," which arise frequently in computer representations of things, and the solution to the problem actually involved the complex gamma function times the square of Riemann's zeta function.[6] Thus the results of classical mathematics often turn out to be useful in rather amazing places.

The most surprising thing to me, in my experience with applications of mathematics to computer science, has been the fact that so much of the mathematics has been of a particular discrete type, examples of which are discussed below. Such mathematics was almost entirely absent from my own training, although I had a reasonably good undergraduate and graduate education in mathematics. I have naturally been wondering whether the traditional curriculum (the calculus courses, etc.) should be revised to include more of these discrete mathematical manipulations, or whether computer science is exceptional in its frequent application of them.

A Detailed Example

In order to clarify some of the generalizations and assertions made above, I believe it would be useful to discuss a typical computer-science problem in some depth. The particular example I have chosen is the one which first led me personally to realize that computer algorithms suggest interesting mathematical problems. This happened in 1962, when I was a graduate student in mathematics; computer programming was a hobby and part-time job, but I hadn't really ever worn my mathematician's hat and my computing cap at the same time. A friend remarked that "some good mathematicians at IBM" had been unable to determine how fast a certain well-known computer method works, and I thought it might be an interesting problem to look at.

Here is the problem: Many computer applications involve the retrieval of information by its "name"; for example, we might imagine a Russian-English dictionary, in which we want to look up a Russian word to find its English equivalent. A standard computer method, called *hashing*, retrieves information by its name as follows. A rather large number, m, of memory positions within the computer is used to hold the names; let us call these positions $T_1, T_2, \ldots, T_m$. Each of these positions is big enough to contain one name. The number m is always larger than the total number of names present, so at least one of the T_i is empty. The names are distributed among the T_i's in a certain way, described below, which is designed to facilitate retrieval. Another set of memory positions $E_1, E_2, \ldots, E_m$ is used for the information corresponding to the names; thus if T_i is not empty, E_i contains the information corresponding to the name stored in T_i.

The ideal way to retrieve information using such a table would be to take a given name x, and to compute some function $f(x)$, which lies between 1 and m; then the name x could be placed in position $T_{f(x)}$, and the corresponding information in $E_{f(x)}$. Such a function $f(x)$ would make the retrieval problem trivial, if $f(x)$ were easy to compute and if $f(x) \neq f(y)$ for all distinct names $x \neq y$. In practice, however, these latter two requirements are hardly ever satisfied simultaneously; if $f(x)$ is easy to compute, we have

$f(x) = f(y)$ for some distinct names. Furthermore, we don't usually know in advance just which names will occur in the table, and the function f must be chosen to work for all names in a very large set U of potential names, where U has many more than m elements. For example, if U contains all sequences of seven letters, there are $26^7 = 8,031,810,176$ potential names; it is inevitable that $f(x) = f(y)$ will occur.

Therefore we try to choose a function $f(x)$, from U into $\{1, 2, \ldots, m\}$, so that $f(x) = f(y)$ will occur with the approximate probability $1/m$, when x and y are distinct names. Such a function f is called a *hash function*. In practice, $f(x)$ is often computed by regarding x as a number and taking its remainder modulo m, plus one; the number m in this case is usually chosen to be prime, since this can be shown to give better results for the sets of names that generally arise in practice. When $f(x) = f(y)$ for distinct x and y, a "collision" is said to occur; collisions are resolved by searching through positions numbered $f(x) + 1$, $f(x) + 2$, etc.

The following algorithm expresses exactly how a hash function $f(x)$ can be used to retrieve the information corresponding to a given name x in U. The algorithm makes use of a variable i which takes on integer values.

Step 1. Set the value of i equal to $f(x)$.

Step 2. If memory position T_i contains the given name x, stop; the derived information is located in memory position E_i.

Step 3. If memory position T_i is empty, stop; the given name x is not present.

Step 4. Increase the value of i by one. (Or, if i was equal to m, set i equal to one.) Return to step 2.

We still haven't said how the names get into T_1, $\ldots$, T_m in the first place, but that is really not difficult. We start with all the T_i empty. Then, to insert a new name x, we "look for" x using the above algorithm; it will stop in step 3 because x is not there. Then we set T_i equal to x and put the corresponding information in E_i. From now on, it will be possible to retrieve this information whenever the name x is given, since the above

algorithm will find position T_i just as it went to that spot when x was inserted.

The mathematical problem is to determine how much searching we should expect to make, on the average: How many times must step 2 be repeated before x is found? This same problem can be stated in other ways, for example in terms of a modified game of "musical chairs." Consider a set of m empty chairs arranged in a circle. A person appears at a random spot just outside the circle and dashes (in a clockwise direction) to the first available chair. This is repeated m times, until all chairs are full. How far, on the average, does the nth person have to run before he finds a seat?

For example, let $m = 10$ and suppose there are ten players, $A, B, C, D, E, F, G, H, I, J$. To get a random sequence, let us assume that the players successively start looking for their seats beginning at chairs numbered according to the first digits of π, namely, 3, 1, 4, 1, 5, 9, 2, 6, 5, 3. Figure 1 shows the situation after the first six

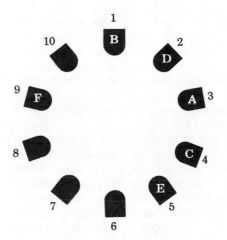

Figure 1   A "musical chairs" game that corresponds to an important computer method.

have been seated. (Thus player A takes chair 3, then player B takes chair 1, $\ldots$, player F takes chair 9.) Now player G starts at chair 2, and eventually he sits down in chair 6. Finally, players H, I, and J will go into chairs 7, 8, and 10.

In this example, the distances traveled by the ten players are respectively 0, 0, 0, 1, 0, 0, 4, 1, 3, 7.

It is not trivial to analyze this problem, because congestion tends to occur; one or more long runs of consecutive occupied chairs will usually be present. In order to see why this is true, consider Figure 1 again, supposing that the next player, H, starts in a random location. He will land in chair 6 with probability 0.6, but he will wind up in chair 7 with probability only 0.1. Long runs tend to get even longer. Therefore, we cannot simply assume that the configuration of occupied vs. empty chairs is random at each stage; the piling-up phenomenon must be reckoned with.

Let the starting places of the m players be $a_1a_2 \ldots a_m$; we shall call this a *hash sequence*. For example, the above hash sequence is 3 1 4 1 5 9 2 6 5 3. Assuming that each of the m^n possible hash sequences is equally likely, our problem is to determine the average distance traveled by the nth player, for each n, in units of "chairs passed." Let us call this distance $d(m,n)$. Obviously $d(m,1) = 0$, since the first player always finds an unoccupied place; furthermore, $d(m,2) = 1/m$, since the second player has to go at most one space, and that is necessary only if he starts at the same spot as the first player. It is also easy to see that $d(m,m) = (0 + 1 + \ldots + (m - 1))/m = (m - 1)/2$, since all chairs but one will be occupied when the last player starts out. Unfortunately, the in-between values of $d(m,n)$ are more complicated.

Let $u_k (m, n)$ be the number of partial hash sequences $a_1a_2 \ldots a_n$ such that chair k will be unoccupied after the first n players are seated. This is easy to determine, by cyclic symmetry, since chair k is just as likely to be occupied as any other particular chair; in other words, $u_1(m, n) = u_2(m, n) = \ldots = u_m(m, n)$. Let $u(m, n)$ be this common value. Furthermore, $mu(m, n) = u_1(m, n) + u_2(m, n) + \ldots + u_m(m, n) = (m - n)m^n$, since each of the m^n partial hash sequences $a_1a_2 \ldots a_n$ contributes one to exactly $m - n$ of the numbers $u_k(m, n)$. Therefore

$$u_k(m, n) = (m - n)m^{n-1}.$$

Let $v(m, n, k)$ be the number of partial hash sequences $a_1a_2 \ldots a_n$ such that, after the n players are seated, chairs 1 through k will be occupied,

while chairs m and $k + 1$ will not. This number is slightly harder to determine, but not really difficult. If we look at the numbers a_i which are $\leq k + 1$ in such a partial hash sequence, and if we cross out the other numbers, the k values which are left form one of the sequences enumerated by $u(k + 1,k)$. Furthermore the $n - k$ values crossed out form one of the sequences enumerated by $u(m - 1 - k, n - k)$, if we subtract $k + 1$ from each of them. Conversely, if we take any partial hash sequence $a_1 \ldots a_k$ enumerated by $u(k + 1, k)$, and another one, $b_1 \ldots b_{n-k}$ enumerated by $u(m - 1 - k, n - k)$, and if we intermix $a_1 \ldots a_k$ with $(b_1 + k + 1) \ldots (b_{n-k} + k + 1)$ in any of the $\binom{n}{k}$ possible ways, we obtain one of the sequences enumerated by $v(m, n, k)$. Here

$$\binom{n}{k} = \frac{n!}{k!(n - k)!}$$

is the number of ways to choose k positions out of n. For example, let $m = 10$, $n = 6$, $k = 3$; one of the partial hash sequences enumerated by $v(10, 6, 3)$ is 2 7 1 8 2 8. This sequence splits into $a_1a_2a_3 = 2\ 1\ 2$ and $(b_1 + 4)(b_2 + 4)(b_3 + 4) = 7\ 8\ 8$, intermixed in the pattern *ababab*. From each of the $u(4, 3) = 16$ sequences $a_1a_2a_3$ that fill positions 1, 2, 3, together with each of the $u(6, 3) = 108$ sequences $(b_1 + 4)(b_2 + 4)(b_3 + 4)$ that fill three of positions 5, 6, 7, 8, 9, we obtain $\binom{6}{3} = 20$ sequences that fill positions 1, 2, 3, and which leave positions 4 and 10 unoccupied, by intermixing the a's and b's in all possible ways. This correspondence shows that

$$v(m, n, k) = \binom{n}{k}u(k + 1, k)u(m - k - 1, n - k)$$

and our formula for $u(m, n)$ tells us that

$$v(m, n, k) = \binom{n}{k}(k + 1)^{k-1}$$
$$\times (m - n - 1)(m - k - 1)^{n-k-1}$$

This is not a simple formula, but since it is correct, we can't do any better. If $k = n = m - 1$, the last two factors in the formula give 0/0, which should be interpreted as 1 in this case.

Now we are ready to compute the desired average distance $d(m, n)$. The nth player must move

k steps if and only if the preceding partial hash sequence $a_1 \ldots a_{n-1}$ has left chairs a_n through $a_n + k - 1$ occupied and chair $a_n + k$ empty. The number of such partial hash sequences is

$$v(m, n - 1, k) + v(m, n - 1, k + 1) + \\ v(m, n - 1, k + 2) + \ldots$$

since circular symmetry shows that $v(m, n - 1, k + r)$ is the number of partial hash sequences $a_1 \ldots a_{n-1}$ leaving chairs $a_n + k$ and $a_n - r - 1$ empty while the $k + r$ chairs between them are filled. Therefore the probability $p_k(m, n)$ that the nth player goes exactly k steps is

$$p_k(m, n) = \left(\sum_{r \geq k} v(m, n - 1, r) \right) / m^{n-1}$$

and the average distance is

$$d(m, \mathrm{n}) = \sum_{k \geq 0} k p_k(m, n)$$
$$= (m - n)m^{1-n} \sum_{r \geq k \geq 0} k \binom{n-1}{r} \times \\ (r + 1)^{r-1}(m - r - 1)^{n-r-2}$$
$$= \frac{(m - n)m^{1-n}}{2} \sum_{r \geq 0} r \binom{n-1}{r} \times \\ (r + 1)^r (m - r - 1)^{n-r-2}$$

At this point, a person with a typical mathematical upbringing will probably stop; the answer is a horrible-looking summation. Yet, if more attention were paid during our mathematical training to finite sums, instead of concentrating so heavily on integrals, we would instinctively recognize that a sum like this can be considerably simplified. When I first looked at this sum, I had never seen one like it before; but I suspected that something could be done to it, since, for example, the sum over k of $p_k(m, n)$ must be 1. Later I learned of the extensive literature of such sums.

Without going into the details I want to point out that such sums arise repeatedly in the study of algorithms. Because I have by now seen literally hundreds of examples in which finite sums involving binomial coefficients and related functions appear in connection with computer science studies, I have introduced a course called "Concrete Mathematics" at Stanford University, in which this kind of mathematics is taught.

Let $\delta(m, n)$ be the average number of chairs skipped past by the first n players:

$$\delta(m, n) = [d(m, 1) + \\ d(m, 2) + \ldots + d(m, n)]/n.$$

This corresponds to the average amount of time needed for the hashing algorithm to find an item when n items have been stored. The value of $d(m, n)$ derived above can be simplified to obtain the following formulas:

$$d(m, n) = \\ \frac{1}{2}\left(2\frac{n-1}{m} + 3\frac{n-1}{m}\frac{n-2}{m} + \\ 4\frac{n-1}{m}\frac{n-2}{m}\frac{n-3}{m} + \ldots \right),$$

$$\delta(m, n) = \\ \frac{1}{2}\left(\frac{n-1}{m} + \frac{n-1}{m}\frac{n-2}{m} + \\ \frac{n-1}{m}\frac{n-2}{m}\frac{n-3}{m} + \ldots \right).$$

These formulas can be used to see the behavior for large m and n: for example, if $\alpha = n/m$ is the ratio of filled positions to the total number of positions, and if we hold α fixed while m approaches infinity, then $\delta(m, \alpha m)$ increases to the limiting value $\frac{1}{2}\alpha/(1 - \alpha)$.

The formula for $\delta(m, n)$ also tells us another surprising thing:

$$\delta(m, n) = \frac{n-1}{2m} + \frac{n-1}{m}\delta(m, n - 1).$$

If somebody could discover a simple trick by which this simple relation could be proved directly, it would lead to a much more elegant analysis of the hashing algorithm and it might provide further insights. Unfortunately I have been unable to think of any direct way to prove this relation.

When $n = m$ (i.e. when all players are seated and all chairs are occupied), the average distance traveled per player is

$$\delta(m, m) = \\ \frac{1}{2}\left(\frac{m-1}{m} + \frac{m-1}{m}\frac{m-2}{m} + \\ \frac{m-1}{m}\frac{m-2}{m}\frac{m-3}{m} + \ldots \right)$$

It is interesting to study this function, which can be shown to have the approximate value

$$\delta(m, m) \approx \sqrt{\frac{\pi m}{8} - \frac{2}{3}}$$

for large m. Thus, the number π, which entered Figure 1 so artificially, is actually present naturally in the problem as well! Such asymptotic calculations, combined with discrete summations as above, are typical of what arises when we study algorithms; classical mathematical analysis and discrete mathematics both play important roles.

We have now solved the musical chairs problem, so the analysis of hashing is complete. But many more problems are suggested by this one. For example, we can consider other ways of probing for empty positions in the table, in order to reduce the congestion which occurs in "musical chairs." An elementary discussion of such questions appears in an expanded version of the present article.[18] It is possible to define generalized hashing schemes whose mathematical analysis leads to interesting computational problems, which in turn lead to interesting mathematical problems. Thus the example of hashing illustrates the typical interplay between computer science and mathematics.

References

1. Amer. Math. Society and Math. Assoc. of America, co-sponsors of conference. 1973. *The Influence of Computing on Mathematical Research and Education.*

2. A. O. L. Atkin and B. J. Birch, eds. 1971. *Computers in Number Theory.* N.Y.: Academic Press.

3. Charles Babbage. 1864. *Passages from the Life of a Philosopher.* London. Reprinted in Philip and Emily Morrison. 1961. *Charles Babbage and His Calculating Engines.* N.Y.: Dover, 1961, esp. p. 69.

4. Garrett Birkhoff and Marshall Hall, Jr., eds. 1971. *Computers in Algebra and Number Theory.* SIAM-AMS Proceedings 4. Amer. Math. Soc.

5. R. F. Churchhouse and J.-C. Herz, eds. 1968. *Computers in Mathematical Research.* Amsterdam: North-Holland.

6. N. G. de Bruijn, Donald E. Knuth, and S. O. Rice. 1972. The average height of planted plane trees. In Ronald C. Read, ed., *Graph Theory and Computing.* N.Y.: Academic Press, pp. 15–22.

7. George E. Forsythe. 1959. The role of numerical analysis in an undergraduate program. *Amer. Math. Monthly* 66:651–62.

8. George E. Forsythe. 1968. Computer science and education. In A. J. H. Morrell, ed., *Information Processing* 68. Amsterdam: North-Holland, pp. 1025–39.

9. George E. Forsythe. 1968. What to do till the computer scientist comes. *Amer. Math. Monthly* 75:454–62.

10. Seymour Ginsburg. 1966. *The Mathematical Theory of Context-Free Languages.* N.Y.: McGraw-Hill.

11. Seymour Ginsburg, Sheila Greibach, and John Hopcroft. 1969. Studies in abstract families of languages. *Amer. Math. Society Memoirs* 87:51 pp.

12. F. E. Holberton and J. Mauchly, personal communication.

13. Donald E. Knuth. 1965. A class of projective planes. *Trans. Amer. Math. Soc.* 115:541–49.

14. Donald E. Knuth. 1966. Algorithm and program: information and data. *Comm. ACM* 9:654.

15. Donald E. Knuth. 1969. *Seminumerical Algorithms.* Reading, Mass.: Addison-Wesley.

16. Donald E. Knuth. 1972. Ancient Babylonian algorithms. *Comm. ACM* 15:671–77.

17. Donald E. Knuth. 1972. George Forsythe and the development of computer science. *Comm. ACM* 15:721–26.

18. Donald E. Knuth. 1974. Computer science and its relation to mathematics. *Amer. Math. Monthly* 81:323–43.

19. Peter D. Lax. 1970. The impact of computers on mathematics. In S. Fernbach and A. Taub, eds. *Computers and Their Role in the Physical Sciences.* N.Y.: Gordon and Breach, pp. 219–26.

20. John Leech, ed. 1970. *Computational Problems in Abstract Algebra.* Elmsford, N.Y.: Pergamon.

21. Peter Naur. 1967. "Datalogy," the science of data and data processes, and its place in education. In A. J. H. Morrell, ed., *Information Processing* 68. Amsterdam: North-Holland, pp. 1383–87.

22. Allen Newell, Alan J. Perlis, and Herbert A. Simon. 1967. Computer science. *Science* 157: 1373–74.

23. Amer. Math Soc. 1963. *Experimental Arithmetic. High-Speed Computing, and Mathematics.* Proc. Symp. Applied Math 15.

24. E. Reingold. 1972. Establishing lower bounds on algorithms—A survey. *AFIPS Conference Proceedings* 40:471–81.

25. Paul C. Rosenbloom and George E. Forsythe. 1958. *Numerical Analysis and Partial Differential Equations.* Surveys in Applied Math 5. N.Y.: Wiley.

26. Slaught Memorial Monograph No. 10. Supplement to the *Amer. Math. Monthly* 72, *Computers and Computing,* Feb. 1965. 156 pp.

27. Peter Wegner. 1970. Three computer cultures. *Advances in Computers* 10:7–78.

28. J. H. Wilkinson. 1971. Some comments from a numerical analyst. *J. ACM* 18:137–47.

Analysis of Algorithms: Coping with Hard Problems

Gina Bari Kolata

Gina Bari Kolata has been an associate editor of *Science* magazine since 1974.

A well-known scientist once observed that "what most people don't understand about exponential growth is that it's the last doubling that gets you!" When the world's population increased from 2,000 to 4,000, overcrowding was no problem. When it grows from 5 billion to 10 billion, there may well be a problem. It is indeed the last doubling that "gets you." Quantities that increase exponentially experience dramatic changes in size, while the growth of polynomial type functions tends to be more stable. For example, compare the values of n^2 and 2^n for some sample values of n:

n	n^2	2^n
1	1	2
2	4	4
3	9	8
4	16	16
5	25	32
6	36	64
⋮	⋮	⋮
100	10,000	1.2677×10^{30}
101	10,201	2.5353×10^{30}

After just 100 steps the polynomial n^2 increases by 201 units as n *increases one unit. But after just 100 steps the exponential expression 2^n increases by 1,267,600,000,000,000,000,000,000,000,000 units as* n *increases by one unit. The quantity 2^n increased by a number much larger than all the grains of sand on all the world's beaches while* n *merely increased from 100 to 101. Imagine what happens when* n *increases from 1,000 to 1,001!*

Another perspective on the growth problem may help. Modern computers approach the ability to do one billion (1×10^9) operations per second. That may seem fast but suppose a process requires 2^n operations for n *trials. If the operator asks for 100 trials, then 2^{100} or 1.2677×10^{30} operations are needed. At a rate of one billion operations per second the computer can do 60×10^9 operations in one minute, 3.6×10^{12} operations in one hour, 8.64×10^{13} operations in one day, and 3.1536×10^{16} operations in one year. It would take just about 4×10^{13} years to complete the requested 100 trials. The universe, by the best modern guesses, has been around for 7×10^9 years. It would therefore take 6,000 consecutive periods of time, each as long as the age of the universe, to complete those 100 trials! By then the computer operator may not care.*

The preceding example should convince even the most devoted skeptic that the search for computer algorithms that operate in polynomial as opposed to exponential time is serious and

Source: Gina Bari Kolata, "Analysis of Algorithms: Coping with Hard Problems," *Science* 186 (1974):520–521. Copyright 1974 by the American Association for the Advancement of Science. (References omitted.)

important. A process in which the number of operations grows as 2^n is just not practical even on the largest modern computers. If, however, a process can be contained within polynomial bounds, then there is some chance that the process can be usefully applied.

This essay discusses the search for convenient and tractable computer algorithms. Kolata suggests that there are many challenging questions still unresolved in this important area of the mathematical sciences.

ALTHOUGH TODAY'S COMPUTERS can perform as many as 1 million operations per second, there are many problems that are still too large to be solved in a straightforward manner. Even with improved solution methods, or algorithms, exact solutions to a wide range of practical problems, from routing of phone calls to scheduling of airplanes, require weeks or months of computer time and are, in effect, not feasible to obtain. Hence the investigation of still more efficient algorithms is of interest to large companies as well as to computer scientists.

The task of finding good ways to solve a large group of important problems has recently, in theory, been simplified. It was shown that many such problems are computationally equivalent, so that a solution for one of them can be used to solve the rest. For example, the problem of determining the best way to schedule events can be converted into the problem of finding the best way to store objects in the minimum amount of space. However, these equivalent problems have so far defied all attempts to solve them without using inordinate amounts of computer time. Since these problems are of great practical importance, many investigators are now devising ways to approximate their solutions and, in some cases, are showing how close certain approximations come to optimum solutions to a problem.

In their search for a good algorithm, computer scientists try to avoid those algorithms in which the number of computational steps (or the amount of computer time) is an exponential function of the size of the problem. (The size of a problem is essentially the number of bits of information required as input for the problem.) Since exponential functions increase very quickly as the size of the problem grows, such algorithms are said to be "inefficient."

The ideal algorithm is one in which the number of computational steps increases only as a polynomial function of the size of the problem. Such algorithms are said to be "efficient." The difference between an efficient and an inefficient algorithm can be dramatic. For example, one algorithm for a problem of size n might require n^2 steps (a polynomial function) while another might require 2^n steps (an exponential function). When n is increased from 10 to 20, the number of steps of an algorithm that requires n^2 steps will quadruple, whereas the number of steps of an algorithm that requires 2^n steps will increase more than 1,000-fold.

A few years ago, Stephen Cook of the University of Toronto analyzed several difficult problems for which no efficient algorithms are known. He showed that all these problems are computationally equivalent in that an efficient algorithm for one of them, if it exists, could be used to solve them all. Richard Karp of the University of California at Berkeley then extended the list of equivalent problems to include many examples in such fields as network optimization, graph theory, and scheduling. Computer scientists decided to call these problems NP-complete. (The symbol NP stands for nondeterministic polynomial time. Complete indicates that a solution to one problem could be applied to all others in the set.)

No one has yet proved that efficient algorithms exist for the NP-complete problems. Many computer scientists consider the question of whether such algorithms exist to be the most important open question in the theory of computations. Since there is no known way to answer this question and since the NP-complete problems are of great practical interest, many computer scientists are choosing to work around the question by finding ways to live with the important problems that are NP-complete. In many practical applications, a special case of an NP-complete problem must be solved. The study of what makes a problem NP-complete can enable computer scientists to recognize when a special aspect of a problem is so restricted that it is no longer NP-complete.

Graph coloring problems are among several kinds of problems that have been recently analyzed to see what features make them NP-complete. According to Donald Knuth of Stanford University, such problems are often used to represent the scheduling of mutually exclusive events. For example, in scheduling classes at a university, a chemistry lecture cannot be scheduled at the same time as its laboratory. In order to represent such a scheduling as a graph coloring problem, each event is denoted by a point. When two events cannot occur at the same time, the points are connected by a line. This collection of points and lines is called a graph. Different times are denoted by different colors. The scheduling problem is then transformed into the problem of deciding whether it is possible to assign all of the different colors to the points of the graph so that no two points connected by a line are assigned the same color. The aim is to find an algorithm to solve this problem without trying out all possible color combinations, since such an algorithm would be inefficient.

Karp showed that graph coloring is NP-complete, but he did not make an analysis as to whether simplified versions of these problems might be solvable by efficient algorithms. Now Larry Stockmeyer of the IBM Research Center, Yorktown Heights, New York, has shown that graph coloring problems in which the number of colors is as small as three and the graph is planar are still NP-complete. Thus even when these problems are greatly simplified, they remain NP-complete. In fact, graph coloring problems are intrinsically so difficult that even the problem of approximating their solution to within a factor of 2 is not any easier than the original problem, according to Michael Garey and David Johnson of Bell Laboratories in Murray Hill, New Jersey.

Another approach to dealing with problems from the set NP is to devise approximate solutions to these problems and then to analyze how close the approximate solutions come to optimal solutions to the problems. Approximate solutions and their analyses have recently been reported for several important problems, including the bin packing problem and the traveling salesman problem.

Approximate Algorithms

In the bin packing problem, n objects are to be packed into the minimum number of bins. Each object takes up a certain amount of space in a bin, and each bin has a certain capacity. For example, the bins could be 1-minute commercial slots on television and the objects could be commercials, each of which takes no more than 1 minute.

Johnson and his associates have recently devised and analyzed two approximate algorithms for this problem: the first-fit algorithm and the best-fit algorithm. In the first-fit algorithm, each object is placed, in succession, into the first bin in which it fits. In the best-fit algorithm, each object is placed in succession, in the most nearly full bin in which it fits. Johnson and his associates showed that, for either algorithm, no more than $[(17/10)L\star] + 2$ bins are used, where $L\star$ is the smallest possible number of bins in which the numbers will fit. Moreover, they showed that if the objects are first listed in decreasing order of size before being assigned to bins, neither algorithm will require more than $[(11/9)L\star] + 4$ bins. Thus the approximate number of bins is always within about 22 percent of the optimum number.

Daniel Rosencrantz, Richard Stearns, and Philip Lewis of General Electric Corporate Research and Development in Schenectady, New York, have recently analyzed approximate algorithms for the traveling salesman problem. This problem, which occurs in many practical situations, involves finding a tour of n cities in which each city is visited at least once and the tour is of the minimum possible length. The traveling salesman problem occurs often in industrial applications, where the cities represent tasks to be done by a machine and the time between cities represents the time it takes to go from one task to the next. The shortest tour of the cities represents the order for performing the tasks that allow all of the tasks to be performed in the shortest possible time.

Various approximation methods for solving the traveling salesman problem are used in practice and often successfully. Rosencrantz and his colleagues compared these approximations to optimal solutions. For one approximate algorithm, the nearest neighbor method, they found that the ratio of the obtained tour to the optimal tour increases logarithmically with the number of cities. For another approximation method, the nearest insertion method, the ratio approaches 2 as the number of cities increases.

Both Johnson and his colleagues and Rosencrantz and his colleagues compared approximate solutions to optimal solutions in the worst case. While such techniques give bounds on how bad the approximate solutions may be, it has been experimentally observed that the average problem may not represent the worst case. Certain algorithms that are commonly used in practice are seldom foiled except by problems purposely designed to make them look bad. Ronald Graham of Bell Laboratories in Murray Hill suggests that analyses of algorithms in terms of average cases could be quite useful, but neither he nor others are yet able to define an average case.

One approach to this problem was taken by Rosencrantz and his associates who tried out approximate algorithms on what they considered to be random traveling salesman problems. They found that, for these random problems, the nearest insertion approximation was much better than the nearest neighbor approximation. In this instance then, the algorithm that performed better in the worst case also performed better in the randomly chosen case.

Although there are as yet no efficient algorithms for any NP-complete problem, progress is being made in finding and analyzing approximate algorithms. The discovery that NP-complete problems are computationally equivalent has enabled investigators to recognize these difficult problems when confronted with them. Now, when asked to solve an NP-complete problem, most computer scientists seek the best probable approximate algorithm rather than attempting what may be the impossible task of finding an efficient algorithm for an exact solution.

The Computer Versus Kepler

Owen Gingerich

Owen (Jay) Gingerich was born in Iowa, did his undergraduate work at Goshen College, and received his Ph.D. in astronomy in 1962 from Harvard. He has been a professor of astronomy and history of science at Harvard since 1969. He is an associate editor of the *Journal of History and Astronomy* and was a Sigma Xi national lecturer in 1971.

The laws of planetary motion were developed over time by a monumental effort involving decades of patient astronomical observations and years of tedious hand calculations of the resulting trigonometric equations. Johannes Kepler was instrumental in the crystalization of this work and is quite properly revered for his framing of the astronomical laws that are, relative to the motion of the planets, essentially unchanged to this day.

Kepler undertook by hand the solution of equations whose number and complexity required months of the most tedious and painstaking effort. In this essay a modern scientist retraces Kepler's tortured path with the digital computer. The result is a confirmation of that heroic effort, which leaves us appreciative of both the dedication of Kepler and the amazing power of modern computational techniques.

WE OFTEN HEAR, in discussions of modern high-speed computers, how an electronic machine can calculate more in a day than a man can calculate in a lifetime by older methods. It occurred to me that a concrete demonstration of some properly chosen specific case would not only be intrinsically interesting, but might shed some light on the historical situation in question, and might also provide a dramatic example of the application of computers in the history of science.

An especially appropriate example is found in the work of Kepler on the orbit of Mars, since he gives some indication of the computational time involved. In *Astronomia Nova*, Kepler describes in detail his attempt to fit a circular orbit to a series of observations of Mars at opposition. Since he wished to investigate a somewhat more general orbit than had been adopted classically, he was led to a thorny trigonometric problem that can be solved only iteratively.

Concerning this involved procedure, Kepler implores his reader: "If you are wearied by this tedious method, take pity on me, who carried out at least seventy trials of it, with the loss of much time, and don't be surprised that this already is the fifth year since I have attacked Mars, although the year 1603 was almost entirely spent on optical investigations."[1]

The implication that this problem required four years must be taken with a grain of salt, but we do get a rough idea of the time involved.

It is this tedious, time-consuming procedure that I have programmed for the IBM-7094 at the Harvard Computing Center. Before describing my quite unexpected results, let me outline Kepler's problem in somewhat greater detail.

Source: Owen Gingerich, "The Computer Versus Kepler," *American Scientist* 52 (1964):218–226. Presented to the History of Science Society, Philadelphia, December 29, 1963. (Some references omitted.)

When Kepler started his investigation on the motion of Mars, in 1601, he was already a convinced Copernican, and therefore he assumed a heliostatic orbit. Nevertheless, at the beginning, he accepted the classical idea of using circles to represent the motion, and not until two years later did he work out the elliptical form of the orbit. The "vicarious orbit" that caused Kepler so much anguish and loss of time was a circle, and in the end was completely abandoned.

Kepler had in hand a dozen observations of Mars at opposition—ten from Tycho Brahe and, later, two of his own. When Mars is at opposition, the sun, earth, and Mars lie in a straight line, so the heliocentric longitude of Mars is immediately known. Figure 1, reproduced from Delambre's *Histoire de l'Astronomie Moderne*, shows us the basic diagram for this problem. In the diagram, the sun is at A, and four observations of Mars, carefully chosen for a reasonably uniform distribution, are laid out from it. Note that the earth does not enter into this discussion. Now the correct elliptical orbit of Mars does not differ very much from a circle, except that the sun is at one focus and reasonably far displaced from the cen-

ter. In this circular approximation, the sun lies off the center of the circle, which is at B.

We know that Mars moves most quickly when nearest the sun and slowest when at aphelion (that is, when farthest from the sun), a fact later expressed in the law of areas. Kepler believed this must be so from physical reasons, and therefore, he was already convinced that the seat of uniform angular motion in the orbit, must lie on the line through A and B, that is, on the line of apsides. In the analogous case, Ptolemy had placed this seat of uniform angular motion, or equant, equally spaced opposite A from the center of the circle. We now know that such a configuration produces the best possible approximation to an ellipse, and when we have the equant at the empty focus of the ellipse, the resulting errors in fitting the observed longitudes reach a maximum of 8' of arc. This is the figure later found by Kepler, which, for him, proved to be such a large discrepancy from Tycho's observations that he felt obliged to abandon the circular orbits.

Kepler, however, wished to keep the spacing of A and C along the line of apsides as an unknown quantity to be determined. Also, he knew the di-

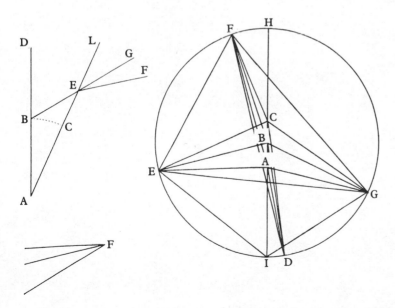

Figure 1

rection of the aphelion fairly well, but he wished to improve its position. Kepler was therefore obliged to use four observations to determine all these quantities. Nowadays, we would try to use all twelve observations, combining them into a least-squares solution. This technique was, of course, unavailable to Kepler. Note that the angles from A are all determined by observation. The angles from C are known relative to one another, because the motion about this point is uniform in time and the times of observations are known. The zero point of this system is to be determined, and also the direction of the aphelion AH.

Kepler starts by assuming these two quantities and solves trigonometrically the various angles of this inscribed quadrilateral. The result tells him whether or not the points lie on a circle. In the first instance they do not, so the direction AH is altered and the solution made again. A comparison of the results of these trials suggests a better position for AH, and the calculation is again repeated. This process I shall call the inner iteration. When it has finally converged, Kepler solves

this triangle EGB to find if the center of circle B lies on the line CA between the sun and the equant. Again in this first instance it does not. This time, the zero point of the mean angles at C is altered, and the inner iteration is repeated. Eventually, the outer iteration also succeeds, and the points A, B, and C are found to lie on a straight line. I am sure Kepler is counting the inner iterations when he tells us that seventy trials were required.

The programming followed Kepler's procedure almost exactly. I was greatly helped by a book by Robert Small,[2] which was recently reprinted through the efforts of William Stahlman. Figure 2 shows how closely the FORTRAN programming followed his notation. The principal difference in my approach is that when Kepler got close to the solution, he jumped to the answer using small corrections made by proportional parts, whereas I found it easier simply to repeat the entire calculation. Also, the program used accuracy criteria somewhat more rigid than Kepler's.

After I had set up and "debugged" this program, I found that the machine could polish off

```
1CCO CCNTINUE
     NICNT=NICNT+1
     WRITE CUTPUT TAPE 6,101,NICNT,N2CNT,ADDS,BCDATE,(CHS,N=1,4),BMEAN,
     WANCM,BAPP,EQN,(AF(N),N=1,4),TAN2,SUM1S,SUM2S
     GC TC K1,(220,230)
C-----ACC ARBITRARY INCREMENT IN FIRST ITERATION.
 220 ACC=RACF(0.,0.,5.,0.C1)
     ASSIGN 23C TO K1
 225 SM1=SUM1
     SM2=SUM2
     SC=SUMC
     CHCLC=CH
     CH=CH+ACC
     GC TC 190
C-----ACC PRCPORTICNAL INCREMENTS IN REMAINING ITERATIONS.
 230 IF(ACF-RACF(C.,0.,0.,10.))235,235,234
 234 ACC=AUC/(SC-SUMC)*SUMC
     IF(NICNT-2C) 2 5,300,300
C
C-----BEGIN CUTER ITERATICN.
 235 EBG= ThCPI-FAF-FAE(4) -SUM1-SUM2
     EAC=FAE(2)+FAF(3)
     AEGAGE=2.*ATANF(TNHSUPF(EAG)*ABAHF(AF(4),AF(2)) )
     AEG=(PI+AFCAGF-EAG)/2.
     EG=AF(4)*SINF(EAG)/SINF(AEG)
     BEG=(PI-EPG)/2.
     BC=EG*SINF(BEG)/SINF(EBG)
     CA=1./PE
     BEA=BEG-AEG
     BAEABE=2.*ATANF(TNHSUPF(BEA)*ABABF(BE,AF(2)) )
     PAF=(PI+BAEABE-BEA)/2.
```

Figure left column (Robert Small commentary):

NOTES.   335

$$\left(\frac{AG + AE}{AG - AE}\right) \xrightarrow{\text{inverted}} = \text{tan. } 19° 37' 40' \left(\frac{103021}{1547}\right) = \text{tan.} 18° 11'';$$

and AEG = 19° 53' 51''; as also EG = $\frac{AG. \sin. EAG}{\sin. AEG}$ =

$\frac{52282.63271}{34.88}$ = 97041.

3. Since the base EG of the isosceles triangle EBG, and the vertical angle EBG are thus found, the angle BEG at the base is given, and = 25° 46' 53''; and, therefore, BE = EG. sin. BEG $\frac{97041 \cdot 43494}{78327}$ = 53860. sin. EBG

4. In the triangle BEA, the angle BEA is given, for it is = BEG — AEG = 5° 51' 2'', and also ½ suppl. = 87° 4' 47''. Therefore. tan. ½ (BAE — ABE) = tan. ½ suppl. BEA $\left(\frac{BE - AE}{BE + AE}\right) = \frac{1957200.51121}{104599}$ = 58402 = tan. 30° 17' 8''; so that BAE = 117° 21' 37''.

But, since in the second operation the aphelion H was found to be too far advanced in longitude, let it now, in consequence of the last correction, be considered as advanced no more than 3' 8'', instead of 3' 20'' beyond the longitude first assumed. Then, since AH is in ½. 28° 47' 8'', and AE in ½. 25° 39' 23'', CAE or HAE will be = 117° 52' 5''; that is, greater by 30° 2''' than BAE; and B is not situated in AC, but on side of it towards E. The suppositions therefore for FAH and FCH, must, one of them, or perhaps both, be false.

But these angles of anomaly cannot be varied by the mere variation of the assumed value of the aphelion; because no other position of it will permit the points D, F, F, G, to be situated in the circumference of the same circle; and before it can be farther varied, the mean longitudes, or the position of the lines FC, FE, &c. must be varied. This, therefore, was the next step of Kepler's procedure; and he tells us, it was not till after a great variety of unsuccessful trials, that he found his purpose would be nearly accomplished by the addition of 2' more to the longitude of the aphelion, and of 30'' at the same time to the mean longitudes. By these additions the mean anomalies FCH, ECH, &c. are all diminished 1' 30'' each; and we have FCH = 32° 9' 36''; KCE = 53° 7' 2''; KCD = 11° 0' 44''; and KCG = 68° 18' 1''. The angles again of equation will become AFC = 5° 8' 26''; AEC = 9° 4' 41''; ADC = 2° 17' 10''; and AGC = 10° 19' 45''; being increased 30'' in the first semi-circle of anomaly, and as much diminished in the second: consequently, the

Figure 2   The comparison of the Robert Small commentary with a portion of the FORTRAN program shows how closely the notations agree.

the entire problem in a little less than eight seconds! This is not too surprising when we realize that only about twenty five trigonometric functions are required in each trial. Unlike Kepler, the computer does not need to look up and laboriously interpolate each of these. Instead, it computes them from scratch as needed, at the rate of 3000 per second!

At least some readers will want to know how long it took *me* to set up the program. When Kepler first arrived at Tycho's establishment, he made a bet that he would have the Mars orbit all cleaned up within eight days. When I agreed to report on this project, I too hoped to finish the calculations very quickly. But I procrastinated, and finally only eight days remained before the Christmas meeting. Thus, circumstances forced me to carry out these computations within that time span. In all, I had nine tries on the computer for this work. In the first two, the computer system detected errors of typography and nomenclature, so those trials "went up in smoke," as Kepler might say (see Figure 3).

This was followed by a series of runs in which other logical flaws were detected—for example, there turned out to be an error in the Robert Small book, which I had blindly followed. By the sixth try, I already had in hand one very interesting result, after a total of eight minutes of computer time. In the ensuing runs, I corrected several more errors and also computed with different initial conditions, as I shall explain. Altogether, I

used 12.4 minutes of IBM-7094 time. Now that the program has been written and "debugged," additional cases require only the eight seconds quoted above. Figure 4 illustrates an example of the output.

The results I have just quoted sound more like a publicity release for electronic computers than a serious paper in the history of science. However, one quite remarkable fact turned up in this investigation. Instead of requiring seventy trials as Kepler did, the computer program, using identical methods, took only nine trials! In fact, we might have anticipated this result without doing any calculations at all, from the following considerations. Suppose the aphelion and the zero point of the mean longitudes are originally known to $1°$ (actually they were much better known than this). Suppose we wish to get these to $30''$ of arc, that is, an improvement by a factor of 120. Since 2^7 is 128, 7 inner iterations should be required in each of 7 outer iterations, if the error is halved each time. This total number of iterations, about 50, should probably be halved because the inner and outer iterations are not independent, and as the outer iteration converges, the inner set will require fewer than 7 tries each time. Furthermore, since the problem turns out to be fairly linear, we can use proportional parts to speed the convergence, and hence we might again halve the number of iterations, making about 12. On the other hand, we make an initial try, then a try with an arbitrary displacement, and finally a try with pro-

Figure 3 FORTRAN diagnostic. A decimal has been mispunched in place of a comma in the format statement.

```
N=  1   ITERATION=  1                    ACD=   0. -0. -0. -0.

                  1587 MAR  6          1591 JUN   8          1593 AUG 25          1595 OCT 31
APHELION          4. 28. 44.  0.0     4. 28. 44.  0.0      4. 28. 44.  0.0      4. 28. 44.  0.0
MEAN LONGITUDE    6.  0. 47. 40.0     9.  5. 40. 19.1     11.  9. 49. 35.8      1.  7.  6. 50.3
MEAN ANOMALY      1.  2.  6. 56.0     4.  6. 56. 19.1      6. 11.  5. 35.8      8.  8. 22. 50.3
APPARENT LONGITUDE 5. 25. 43. -0.     8. 26. 39. 24.2     11. 12. 10. 31.8      1. 17. 24. 21.3
EQUATION OF CENTER C.  5.  7. 56.0    0.  9.  4. 11.0     11. 27. 42. 20.0     11. 19. 45. 45.0
RADIUS VECTOR     5.94300860          5.07040501          4.80596131          5.23072946
TAN(HALF DIFFERENCES) -0.07794160     -0.03456920         0.06613767          0.03087720

                  SUM1   0.  6. 13. 31.0
                  SUM2   0.  5. 45. 49.6


N=  2   ITERATION=  1                    ACD=   0.  0.  5.  0.0

                  1587 MAR  6          1591 JUN   8          1593 AUG 25          1595 OCT 31
APHELION          4. 28. 49.  0.0     4. 28. 49.  0.0      4. 28. 49.  0.0      4. 28. 49.  0.0
MEAN LONGITUDE    6.  0. 47. 40.0     9.  5. 40. 19.1     11.  9. 49. 35.8      1.  7.  6. 50.3
MEAN ANOMALY      1.  2.  1. 56.0     4.  6. 51. 19.1      6. 11.  0. 35.8      8.  8. 17. 50.3
APPARENT LONGITUDE 5. 25. 43. -0.     8. 26. 39. 24.2     11. 12. 10. 31.8      1. 17. 24. 21.3
EQUATION OF CENTER C.  5.  7. 56.0    0.  9.  4. 11.0     11. 27. 42. 20.0     11. 19. 45. 45.0
RADIUS VECTOR     5.92923105          5.07386243          4.77030510          5.22770876
TAN(HALF DIFFERENCES) -0.07627323     -0.04007670         0.07149462          0.03045668

                  SUM1   0.  6.  6. 22.3
                  SUM2   0.  6. 23.  3.8


N=  3   ITERATION=  1                    ACD=  -0.  0.  1. 52.8

                  1587 MAR  6          1591 JUN   8          1593 AUG 25          1595 OCT 31
APHELION          4. 28. 47.  7.2     4. 28. 47.  7.2      4. 28. 47.  7.2      4. 28. 47.  7.2
MEAN LONGITUDE    6.  0. 47. 40.0     9.  5. 40. 19.1     11.  9. 49. 35.8      1.  7.  6. 50.3
MEAN ANOMALY      1.  2.  3. 48.8     4.  6. 53. 12.0      6. 11.  2. 28.6      8.  8. 19. 43.1
APPARENT LONGITUDE 5. 25. 43. -0.     8. 26. 39. 24.2     11. 12. 10. 31.8      1. 17. 24. 21.3
EQUATION OF CENTER C.  5.  7. 56.0    0.  9.  4. 11.0     11. 27. 42. 20.0     11. 19. 45. 45.0
RADIUS VECTOR     5.93441421          5.07386140          4.78371644          5.22834607
TAN(HALF DIFFERENCES) -0.07690100      0.03800140         0.06947503          0.03061499

                  SUM1   0.  6.  9.  3.6
                  SUM2   0.  6.  9.  1.8


OUTER ITERATION =  1                  ADM=   0. -0. -0. -0.      FINAL COMPARISON ANGLES
            ELG=  4.  8. 26. 51.6     EAC=   4. 20. 44. 57.1    HAE=   3. 27. 34. 19.1
            AFG=  0. 19. 55. 57.8     HFG=   0. 25. 46. 34.2    HAE=   3. 27. 52. 17.0
            EG=   5.70434564          HF=    5.38631323
            PA=   0.11485431          CA=    0.18558683
```

Figure 4   Intermediate computer printout. The inner iterations are carried out until SUM1 and SUM2 agree; in the outer iteration angles BAE and HAE are compared, and the process repeated until they match.

portional parts based on the first results. Thus, three tries in each inner iteration, and three outer iterations, give a minimum of nine trials by this method, precisely the number used by the computer.

Why, then, did Kepler require seventy trials? Since Kepler already started with an arbitrary correction to Tycho's zero point on the mean longitudes, we suspect that he may have used many trials to reach the starting point shown in *Astronomia Nova*. Therefore, the calculations were repeated, starting directly from Tycho's figures. Now, thirteen iterations are required, still a very small number.

I can only conclude that Kepler was horribly plagued by numerical errors, that his trials acci-

dently diverged nearly as often as they converged. No wonder he was so frustrated in his attempt to solve this problem, which was apparently just at the limit of his computational ability! Do we have any evidence for this conclusion? Yes. At the very beginning of his calculation, Kepler makes numerical errors in three of his eight starting angles—errors of the same order of magnitude as the corrections he was seeking. These errors were noted both by Small and by Delambre. I therefore programmed the computer to solve the problem both with and without this initial error. The final solution appears comparatively insensitive to these errors, but it is curious to note that Kepler gets about the same answer *with* the errors that the machine computes *without*!

After Kepler completed his solution with four of the twelve oppositions, he carefully calculated the predicted positions for all twelve observations. The results, shown in Figure 5, exhibit several interesting features.

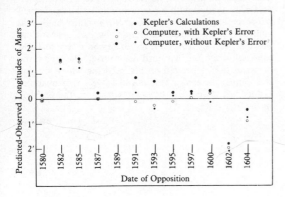

Figure 5

First of all, since the solution was carried out exactly for the oppositions of 1587, 1591, 1593, and 1595, the same observed positions ought to be predicted by the theory. But here, Kepler has taken a very curious step: he corrects each of the positions for the advance of nodes of Mars—a curious step because the correction is made *after* the main calculation instead of *before!* Thus, only the pivotal 1587 opposition must predict exactly the observed position; yet as the graph indicates, Kepler has made a small computational error of 15″. Given a uniform motion of the nodes, the 1591, 1593, and 1595 observations should show increasing errors, yet again this is not the case. Compared to the machine calculations, Kepler's results for 1591 and 1593 show computational errors as large as 1′. One final comment: note from the graph how Kepler's errors generally increase the deviations between observation and prediction, *except* for the most discordant cases!

The best possible solution with this type of model, as stated previously, leaves errors up to 8′ of arc. We see here that Kepler was incredibly lucky in his particular choice of observations—or perhaps we should say unlucky, because, with larger errors, he would probably have recognized

the inadequacy of this construction earlier. As a test, I chose other well-distributed sets of four oppositions as the basis of the solution, and I indeed found larger errors, up to 8′ of arc.

I hope this study has shed some light on the difficulties encountered by Kepler, and perhaps on his computational ability. My thesis, that his calculations were incredibly loaded with numerical errors, has already been observed in another section of *Astronomia Nova* by O. Neugebauer.[3] Perhaps it will someday be further confirmed by a full analysis of the 900 pages of original manuscript computations, still extant in Leningrad. I do not wish, however, to detract in any way from the magnitude of Kepler's scientific achievement. Perhaps the most appropriate conclusion would be a further quotation from *Astronomia Nova:*

> There will be some clever geometers such as Vieta who will think it is something great to demonstrate the inelegance of this method. (As a matter of fact, Vieta has already made this charge against Ptolemy, Copernicus, and Regiomontanus.) Well, let them go solve this scheme themselves by geometry, and they will for me be a great Apollo. For me it suffices to draw four or five conclusions from one argument (in which there are included four observations and two hypotheses), and to have shown by the light of geometry an inelegant thread for finding the way out of the labyrinth. If this method is difficult to grasp, how much more difficult it is to investigate things without any method.[4]

Notes

1. Kepler, J., *Astronomia Nova*, 1609, in *Johannes Kepler Gesammelte Werke*, vol. 3, ed. by M. Caspar, ch. 16, p. 156, Munich, 1927. To this, the French astronomer Delambre replied: "Kepler was sustained by his desire to have a case against Tycho, Copernicus, Ptolemy, and all the astronomers in the world; he has tasted this satisfaction, and I don't believe he deserves our pity for making all these calculations." (Delambre, M., *Histoire de l'Astronomie Moderne*, p. 417, Paris, 1821.)

2. Small, R., *An Account of the Astronomical Discoveries of Kepler*, 1804, reprinted by the University of Wisconsin Press, Madison, 1963.

3. Neugebauer, O., Notes on Kepler, *Comm. on Pure and Applied Math.*, *14*, 593–597, 1961.

4. Kepler, J., *op. cit.*, ch. 16, p. 156.

Six years after writing "The Computer Versus Kepler" I finally gained access to a previously unexamined source, Kepler's own manuscripts preserved at the Academy of Sciences in Leningrad. This new research showed that my original conclusion, that "Kepler was horribly plagued by numerical errors, that his trials accidentally diverged nearly as often as they converged," was unreasonable and quite false. The manuscripts not only showed quite clearly why Kepler carried out at least 70 trials, but they also showed that he iterated almost as efficiently as the computer. The source of his difficulty lay elsewhere, in a direction unimagined in the absence of his working notes. In the first group of iterations, he started with an error in one of the fundamental observations; in a second group a faulty angle was copied out. For further attempts, he had to work out other aspects of his planetary theory in order to know precisely what Martian positions to use, since the times of opposition depended on his knowing where the sun was. Thus, the errors were not in his mathematical procedure but in the data used for setting up the problem in the first place.

Some Moral and Technical Consequences of Automation

Norbert Wiener

Norbert Wiener was born in Columbia, Missouri, in 1894. After graduating from Tufts College at the age of fifteen, he obtained his Ph.D. in mathematics from Harvard at the age of eighteen. He traveled for several years as a Sheldon fellow. From 1918 until his retirement in 1960 he was at the Massachusetts Institute of Technology. He was a Guggenheim fellow and vice-president of the American Mathematics Society. Wiener died in 1964.

Norbert Wiener was a fascinating man. It would be difficult to compile an anthology of twentieth-century works on mathematics or computer science without acknowledging his contributions and influence. While space does not allow an extensive biography, a brief sketch of the man and his life is essential to an appreciation of this essay.

Norbert Wiener was born in Columbia, Missouri, in 1894. His parents, Leo and Bertha Wiener, were Russian immigrants, and from very nearly the day of his son's birth Leo Wiener was determined that Norbert would be somebody. Not long after Norbert's birth Leo decided what sort of somebody young Norbert was to become. He was to become a wunderkind.

In his autobiography Norbert Wiener speaks rather harshly of his father. Leo Wiener's determination that his son become a child prodigy was in outward appearance a success. Norbert entered high school at age nine and graduated at age eleven; at fifteen he was studying zoology at the Harvard graduate school. However, such relentless, almost maniacal parental pressure that impels a child to such achievements must exact a price. Norbert spent the rest of his life paying that price.

At age eighteen Norbert Wiener was awarded a Ph.D. by Harvard University. His original researches in zoology being less than successful, Wiener changed his studies to philosophy, then moved to Cornell University, and finally wandered back to Harvard for a Ph.D. in philosophy with mathematical overtones. From 1913 to 1915 Wiener traveled in Europe. He made the acquaintance of Bertrand Russell, was in residence at both Cambridge and Göttingen, and returned to the United States in 1915, still uncertain where to invest his time and talents. About 1918 Norbert Wiener began to study mathematics in earnest. In 1919 he obtained a position at M.I.T. and the rest, to be trite but accurate, is history. His subsequent mathematical contributions were substantial. His investigations into interactions between humans and machines and into the mathematical foundations of aspects of the nervous system were seminal if somewhat premature. He was an original American genius with an intellect of amazing breadth and facility. Norbert Wiener died in Stockholm, Sweden, on March 18, 1964.

The issues raised by Wiener in this article are relevant to both the specific issue of the

Source: Norbert Wiener, "Some Moral and Technical Consequences of Automation," *Science* 131 (1960): 1355–1358. Copyright 1960 by the American Association for the Advancement of Science. This article is adapted from a lecture the author delivered 27 December 1959 before the Committee on Science in the Promotion of Human Welfare, at the Chicago meeting of the AAAS.

expanding application of digital computers and the broader topic of technology in general. The author's underlying concerns are those of control and prediction. As devices become more complex and capable, the question of who is in control of whom, becomes a relevant one.

An experience almost universal to citizens of the computer age is the computer-generated error that cannot be changed. A machine-produced mislabeled utility bill seems impossible to correct. A dozen telephone calls to as many individuals generates nothing more than an infuriating chorus of helplessness. The machine is doing it and no one seems to know how to make it stop. Now extend that experience to the computer-guided subway car or airplane. Go beyond the horrors implicit in those situations to the computer-directed factory, the machine-regulated national economy, the computer as final arbiter of war and peace. Should we attack first or await the enemy? Let the machine decide.

Even more unsettling is the difficulty of predicting how a machine may behave. If one is dealing with a simple machine—a wristwatch, say—then the range of behavior and the possible consequences are rather easy to predict. But let us move on just a bit in complexity and power, to the self-starting automobile, one programmed to start each day at a specific time or on the voice command of a specific owner. The capacity for harm when such a device malfunctions is substantial. While we can still envision the set of likely outcomes, the potential for damage implicit in some of them makes it very likely that no such device would be built.

But what of devices whose construction is so complex and whose capacities are so varied that no effective catalogue of their patterns of behavior is possible. The self-starting, mobile, seeing, hearing, decision-making robot? Any machine this complex has behavior modes so numerous that we can not begin to catalogue them. How confident can we be that some malfunction will not result in a crazed mechanical monster running amok in a factory or home? And the potential for harm in even more complex systems may be greater. The question is not a trivial one and Wiener brings a lifetime of pioneering investigation to the discussion.

SOME 13 YEARS ago, a book of mine was published by the name of *Cybernetics*. In it I discussed the problems of control and communication in the living organism and the machine. I made a considerable number of predictions about the development of controlled machines and about the corresponding techniques of automatization, which I foresaw as having important consequences affecting the society of the future. Now, 13 years later, it seems appropriate to take stock of the present position with respect to both cybernetic technique and the social consequences of this technique.

Before commencing on the detail of these matters, I should like to mention a certain attitude of the man in the street toward cybernetics and automatization. This attitude needs a critical discussion, and in my opinion it should be rejected in its entirety. This is the assumption that machines cannot possess any degree of originality. This frequently takes the form of a statement that nothing can come out of the machine which has not been put into it. This is often interpreted as asserting that a machine which man has made must remain continually subject to man, so that its operation is at any time open to human interference and to a change in policy. On the basis of such an attitude, many people have pooh-poohed the dangers of machine techniques, and they have flatly contradicted the early predictions of Samuel Butler that the machine might take over the control of mankind.

It is true that in the time of Samuel Butler the available machines were far less hazardous than machines are today, for they involved only power, not a certain degree of thinking and communication. However, the machine techniques of the present day have invaded the latter fields as well, so that the actual machine of today is very different from the image that Butler held, and we cannot transfer to these new devices the assumptions which seemed axiomatic a generation ago. I find myself facing a public which has formed its attitude toward the machine on the basis of an imperfect understanding of the structure and mode of operation of modern machines.

It is my thesis that machines can and do transcend some of the limitations of their designers, and that in doing so they may be both effective and dangerous. It may well be that in principle we cannot make any machine the elements of whose behavior we cannot comprehend sooner or later. This does not mean in any way that we shall be able to comprehend these elements in substantially less time than the time required for operation of the machine, or even within any given number of years or generations.

As is now generally admitted, over a limited range of operation, machines act far more rapidly than human beings and are far more precise in performing the details of their operations. This being the case, even when machines do not in any way transcend man's intelligence, they very well may, and often do, transcend man in the performance of tasks. An intelligent understanding of their mode of performance may be delayed until long after the task which they have been set has been completed.

This means that though machines are theoretically subject to human criticism, such criticism may be ineffective until long after it is relevant. To be effective in warding off disastrous consequences, our understanding of our man-made machines should in general develop *pari passu* with the performance of the machine. By the very slowness of our human actions, our effective control of our machines may be nullified. By the time we are able to react to information conveyed by our senses and stop the car we are driving, it may already have run head on into a wall.

Game-Playing

I shall come back to this point later in this article. For the present, let me discuss the technique of machines for a very specific purpose: that of play-

ing games. In this matter I shall deal more particularly with the game of checkers, for which the International Business Machines Corporation has developed very effective game-playing machines.

Let me say once for all that we are not concerned here with the machines which operate on a perfect closed theory of the game they play. The game theory of von Neumann and Morgenstern may be suggestive as to the operation of actual game-playing machines, but it does not actually describe them.

In a game as complicated as checkers, if each player tries to choose his play in view of the best move his opponent can make, against the best response he can give, against the best response his opponent can give, and so on, he will have taken upon himself an impossible task. Not only is this humanly impossible but there is actually no reason to suppose that it is the best policy against the opponent by whom he is faced, whose limitations are equal to his own.

The von Neumann theory of games bears no very close relation to the theory by which game-playing machines operate. The latter corresponds much more closely to the methods of play used by expert but limited human chess players against other chess players. Such players depend on certain strategic evaluations, which are in essence not complete. While the von Neumann type of play is valid for games like ticktacktoe, with a complete theory, the very interest of chess and checkers lies in the fact that they do not possess a complete theory. Neither do war, nor business competition, nor any of the other forms of competitive activity in which we are really interested.

In a game like ticktacktoe, with a small number of moves, where each player is in a position to contemplate all possibilities and to establish a defense against the best possible moves of the other player, a complete theory of the von Neumann type is valid. In such a case, the game must inevitably end in a win for the first player, a win for the second player, or a draw.

I question strongly whether this concept of the perfect game is a completely realistic one in the cases of actual, nontrivial games. Great generals like Napoleon and great admirals like Nelson have proceeded in a different manner. They have been aware not only of the limitations of their opponents in such matters as materiel and personnel but equally of their limitations in experience and in military know-how. It was by a realistic appraisal of the relative inexperience in naval operations of the continental powers as compared with the highly developed tactical and strategic competence of the British fleet that Nelson was able to display the boldness which pushed the continental forces off the seas. This he could not have done had he engaged in the long, relatively indecisive, and possibly losing conflict to which his assumption of the best possible strategy on the part of his enemy would have doomed him.

In assessing not merely the materiel and personnel of his enemies but also the degree of judgment and the amount of skill in tactics and strategy to be expected of them, Nelson acted on the basis of their record in previous combats. Similarly, an important factor in Napoleon's conduct of his combat with the Austrians in Italy was his knowledge of the rigidity and mental limitations of Würmser.

This element of experience should receive adequate recognition in any realistic theory of games. It is quite legitimate for a chess player to play, not against an ideal, nonexisting, perfect antagonist, but rather against one whose habits he has been able to determine from the record. Thus, in the theory of games, at least two different intellectual efforts must be made. One is the short-term effort of playing with a determined policy for the individual game. The other is the examination of a record of many games. This record has been set by the player himself, by his opponent, or even by players with whom he has not personally played. In terms of this record, he determines the relative advantages of different policies as proved over the past.

There is even a third stage of judgment required in a chess game. This is expressed at least in part by the length of the significant past. The development of theory in chess decreases the importance of games played at a different stage of the art. On the other hand, an astute chess theoretician may estimate in advance that a certain policy currently in fashion has become of little value, and that it may be best to return to earlier modes of play to anticipate the change in policy of the people whom he is likely to find as his opponents.

Thus, in determining policy in chess there are several different levels of consideration which correspond in a certain way to the different logical types of Bertrand Russell. There is the level of tactics, the level of strategy, the level of the general considerations which should have been weighed in determining this strategy, the level in which the length of the relevant past—the past within which these considerations may be valid—is taken into account, and so on. Each new level demands a study of a much larger past than the previous one.

I have compared these levels with the logical types of Russell concerning classes, classes of classes, classes of classes of classes, and so on. It may be noted that Russell does not consider statements involving all types as significant. He brings out the futility of such questions as that concerning the barber who shaves all persons, and only those persons, who do not shave themselves. Does he shave himself? On one type he does, on the next type he does not, and so on, indefinitely. All such questions involving an infinity of types may lead to unsolvable paradoxes. Similarly, the search for the best policy under all levels of sophistication is a futile one and must lead to nothing but confusion.

These considerations arise in the determination of policy by machines as well as in the determination of policy by persons. These are the questions which arise in the programming of programming. The lowest type of game-playing machine plays in terms of a certain rigid evaluation of plays. Quantities such as the value of pieces gained or lost, the command of the pieces, their mobility, and so on, can be given numerical weights on a certain empirical basis, and a weighting may be given on this basis to each next play conforming to the rules of the game. The play with the greatest weight may be chosen. Under these circumstances, the play of the machine will seem to its antagonist—who cannot help but evaluate the chess personality of the machine—a rigid one.

Learning Machines

The next step is for the machine to take into consideration not merely the moves as they occurred in the individual game but the record of games previously played. On this basis, the machine may stop from time to time, not to play but to consider what (linear or nonlinear) weighting of the factors which it has been given to consider would correspond best to won games as opposed to lost (or drawn) games. On this basis, it continues to play with a new weighting. Such a machine would seem to its human opponent to have a far less rigid game personality, and tricks which would defeat it at an earlier stage may now fail to deceive it.

The present level of these learning machines is that they play a fair amateur game at chess but that in checkers they can show a marked superiority to the player who has programmed them after from 10 to 20 playing hours of working and indoctrination. They thus most definitely escape from the completely effective control of the man who has made them. Rigid as the repertory of factors may be which they are in a position to take into consideration, they do unquestionably—and so say those who have played with them—show originality, not merely in their tactics, which may be quite unforeseen, but even in the detailed weighting of their strategy.

As I have said, checker-playing machines which learn have developed to the point at which they can defeat the programmer. However, they appear still to have one weakness. This lies in the end game. Here the machines are somewhat clumsy in determining the best way to give the *coup de grâce*. This is due to the fact that the existing machines have for the most part adopted a program in which the identical strategy is carried out at each stage of the game. In view of the similarity of values of pieces in checkers, this is quite natural for a large part of the play but ceases to be perfectly relevant when the board is relatively empty and the main problem is that of moving into position rather than that of direct attack. Within the frame of the methods I have described it is quite possible to have a second exploration to determine what the policy should be after the number of pieces of the opponent is so reduced that these new considerations become paramount.

Chess-playing machines have not, so far, been brought to the degree of perfection of checker-playing machines, although, as I have said, they can most certainly play a respectable amateur game. Probably the reason for this is similar to the reason for their relative efficiency in the end game of checkers. In chess, not only is the end game quite different in its proper strategy from the mid-game but the opening game is also. The difference between checkers and chess in this respect is that the initial play of the pieces in checkers is not very different in character from the play which arises in the mid-game, while in chess, pieces at the beginning have an arrangement of exceptionally low mobility, so that the problem of deploying them from this position is particularly difficult. This is the reason why opening play and development form a special branch of chess theory.

There are various ways in which the machine can take cognizance of these well-known facts and explore a separate waiting strategy for the opening. This does not mean that the type of game theory which I have here discussed is not applicable to chess but merely that it requires much more consideration before we can make a machine that can play master chess. Some of my friends who are engaged in these problems believe that this goal will be achieved in from 10 to 25 years. Not being a chess expert, I do not venture to make any such predictions on my own initiative.

It is quite in the cards that learning machines will be used to program the pushing of the button in a new pushbutton war. Here we are considering a field in which automata of a nonlearning character are probably already in use. It is quite out of the question to program these machines on the basis of an actual experience in real war. For one thing, a sufficient experience to give an adequate programming would probably see humanity already wiped out.

Moreover, the techniques of pushbutton war are bound to change so much that by the time an adequate experience could have been accumulated, the basis of the beginning would have radically changed. Therefore, the programming of such a learning machine would have to be based on some sort of war game, just as commanders and staff officials now learn an important part of the art of strategy in a similar manner. Here, however, if the rules for victory in a war game do not correspond to what we actually wish for our country, it is more than likely that such a machine may produce a policy which would win a nominal victory on points at the cost of every interest we have at heart, even that of national survival.

Man and Slave

The problem, and it is a moral problem, with which we are here faced is very close to one of the great problems of slavery. Let us grant that slavery is bad because it is cruel. It is, however, self-contradictory, and for a reason which is quite different. We wish a slave to be intelligent, to be able to assist us in the carrying out of our tasks. However, we also wish him to be subservient. Complete subservience and complete intelligence do not go together. How often in ancient times the clever Greek philosopher slave of a less intelligent Roman slaveholder must have dominated the actions of his master rather than obeyed his wishes! Similarly, if the machines become more and more efficient and operate at a higher and higher psychological level, the catastrophe foreseen by Butler of the dominance of the machine comes nearer and nearer.

The human brain is a far more efficient control apparatus than is the intelligent machine when we come to the higher areas of logic. It is a self-organizing system which depends on its capacity to modify itself into a new machine rather than on ironclad accuracy and speed in problem-solving. We have already made very successful machines of the lowest logical type, with a rigid policy. We are beginning to make machines of the second logical type, where the policy itself improves with learning. In the construction of operative machines, there is no specific foreseeable limit with respect to logical type, nor is it safe to make a pronouncement about the exact level at which the brain is superior to the machine. Yet for a long time at least there will always be some level at which the brain is better than the constructed machine, even though this level may shift upwards and upwards.

It may be seen that the result of a programming technique of automatization is to remove from the mind of the designer and operator an effective understanding of many of the stages by which the machine comes to its conclusions and of what the real tactical intentions of many of its operations may be. This is highly relevant to the problem of our being able to foresee undesired consequences outside the frame of the strategy of the game while the machine is still in action and while intervention on our part may prevent the occurrence of these consequences.

Here it is necessary to realize that human action is a feedback action. To avoid a disastrous consequence, it is not enough that some action on our part should be sufficient to change the course of the machine, because it is quite possible that we lack information on which to base consideration of such an action.

In neurophysiological language, ataxia can be quite as much of a deprivation as paralysis. A patient with locomotor ataxia may not suffer from any defect of his muscles or motor nerves, but if his muscles and tendons and organs do not tell him exactly what position he is in, and whether the tensions to which his organs are subjected will or will not lead to his falling, he will be unable to stand up. Similarly, when a machine constructed by us is capable of operating on its incoming data at a pace which we cannot keep, we may not know, until too late, when to turn it off. We all know the fable of the sorcerer's apprentice, in which the boy makes the broom carry water in his master's absence, so that it is on the point of drowning him when his master reappears. If the boy had had to seek a charm to stop the mischief in the *grimoires* of his master's library, he might have been drowned before he had discovered the relevant incantation. Similarly, if a bottle factory is programmed on the basis of maximum productivity, the owner may be made bankrupt by the enormous inventory of unsalable bottles manufactured before he learns he should have stopped production six months earlier.

The "Sorcerer's Apprentice" is only one of many tales based on the assumption that the agencies of magic are literal-minded. There is the story of the genie and the fisherman in the *Arabian Nights*, in which the fisherman breaks the seal of Solomon which has imprisoned the genie and finds the genie vowed to his own destruction; there is the tale of the "Monkey's Paw," by W. W. Jacobs, in which the sergeant major brings back from India a talisman which has the power to grant each of three people three wishes. Of the first recipient of this talisman we are told only that his third wish is for death. The sergeant major, the second person whose wishes are granted, finds his experiences too terrible to relate. His friend, who receives the talisman, wishes first for £200. Shortly thereafter, an official of the factory in which his son works comes to tell him that his son has been killed in the machinery and that, without any admission of responsibility, the company is sending him as consolation the sum of £200. His next wish is that his son should come back, and the ghost knocks at the door. His third wish is that the ghost should go away.

Disastrous results are to be expected not merely in the world of fairy tales but in the real world wherever two agencies essentially foreign to each other are coupled in the attempt to achieve a common purpose. If the communication between these two agencies as to the nature of this purpose is incomplete, it must only be expected that the results of this cooperation will be unsatisfactory. If we use, to achieve our purposes, a mechanical agency with whose operation we cannot efficiently interfere once we have started it, because the action is so fast and irrevocable that we have not the data to intervene before the action is complete, then we had better be quite sure that the purpose put into the machine is the purpose which we really desire and not merely a colorful imitation of it.

Time Scales

Up to this point I have been considering the quasi-moral problems caused by the simultaneous action of the machine and the human being in a joint enterprise. We have seen that one of the chief causes of the danger of disastrous conse-

quences in the use of the learning machine is that man and machine operate on two distinct time scales, so that the machine is much faster than man and the two do not gear together without serious difficulties. Problems of the same sort arise whenever two control operators on very different time scales act together, irrespective of which system is the faster and which system is the slower. This leaves us the much more directly moral question: What are the moral problems when man as an individual operates in connection with the controlled process of a much slower time scale, such as a portion of political history or—our main subject of inquiry—the development of science?

Let it be noted that the development of science is a control and communication process for the long-term understanding and control of matter. In this process 50 years are as a day in the life of the individual. For this reason, the individual scientist must work as a part of a process whose time scale is so long that he himself can only contemplate a very limited sector of it. Here, too, communication between the two parts of a double machine is difficult and limited. Even when the individual believes that science contributes to the human ends which he has at heart, his belief needs a continual scanning and re-evaluation which is only partly possible. For the individual scientist, even the partial appraisal of this liaison between the man and the process requires an imaginative forward glance at history which is difficult, exacting, and only limitedly achievable. And if we adhere simply to the creed of the scientist, that an incomplete knowledge of the world and of ourselves is better than no knowledge, we can still by no means always justify the naive assumption that the faster we rush ahead to employ the new powers for action which are opened up to us, the better it will be. We must always exert the full strength of our imagination to examine where the full use of our new modalities may lead us.

Some Moral and Technical Consequences of Automation—A Refutation

Arthur L. Samuel

Arthur Lee Samuel was born in Kansas in 1901. He did graduate work at M.I.T. and is a fellow of the American Physical Society and a fellow of the Institute for Electrical and Electronic Engineers. He has worked for General Electric, Bell Labs, and the University of Illinois. From 1966 to 1975 he was adjunct professor of computer science at Stanford.

This article is honestly titled. It is an attempt to refute or at least to ameliorate the concerns raised by Norbert Wiener in the previous essay. Samuel's perspective is that of one who is involved in the development of computers. His vantage point clearly presents a somewhat different vista of the future of computers than does that of the research scientist as philosopher. Whether the arguments of this essay will eliminate or assuage the fears engendered by the previous essay only the reader can say. What is not debatable, however, is the necessity of an ongoing debate on such matters. Indeed, it is to be hoped that greater public appreciation of the problems and potential of computers will greatly enlarge the forum in which such debates are conducted. For, like it or not, these are questions that will affect us all.

IN AN ARTICLE entitled "Some Moral and Technical Consequences of Automation," Norbert Wiener has stated some conclusions with which I disagree. Wiener seems to believe that machines *can* possess originality and that they *are* a threat to mankind. In describing a contrary opinion to the man in the street—to wit, "that nothing can come out of the machine which has not been put into it"—he overlooks or ignores the fact that there is a long history of the acceptance of this more reassuring view by scientific workers in the field, from the time of Charles Babbage to the present. Apparently Wiener shares some of the lack of understanding which he ascribes to the public, at least to the extent that he reads implications into some of the recent work which the workers themselves deny.

It is my conviction that machines cannot possess originality in the sense implied by Wiener and that they cannot transcend man's intelligence. I agree with Wiener in his thesis that "machines can and do transcend some of the limitations of their designers, and that in doing so they may be both effective and dangerous." The modern automobile travels faster than its designer can run, it is effective, and the records of highway fatalities attest to the dangerous consequences. However, a perusal of Wiener's article reveals that much more than this is meant, and it is to this extension of the thesis that I wish to take exception.

Wiener's reference to the "Sorcerer's Apprentice," and to the many tales based on the assumption that the agencies of magic are literal-minded, might almost lead one to think that he attributes

Source: Arthur L. Samuel, "Some Moral and Technical Consequences of Automation—A Refutation," *Science* 132 (1960): 741–742. Copyright 1960 by American Association for the Advancement of Science. (References omitted.)

magic to the machine. He most certainly seems to imply an equality between man and the machine when he states "disastrous results are to be expected not merely in the world of fairy tales but in the real world wherever two agencies essentially foreign to each other are coupled in the attempt to achieve a common purpose." In relationships between man and a machine the machine is an agency, but only an agency of man, entirely subservient to man and to his will. Of course, no one will deny that "we had better be quite sure that the purpose put into the machine is the purpose which we really desire and not merely a colorful imitation of it." If we want our house to be at 70°F when we get up in the morning, we had better set the thermostat at 70° and not at 32°. But once the thermostat is set at 70° we can go to sleep without fear that the genie in the furnace controls might, for some reason of his own, decide that 32° was a better figure. In exactly the same way and to the same degree we must anticipate our own inability to interfere when we instruct a modern digital computer (which works faster than we do) and when we instruct a thermostat (which works while we sleep).

Wiener's analogy between a machine and a human slave is also quite misleading. He is right in his assertion that "complete subservience and complete intelligence do not go together" in a human slave with human emotions and needs and with a will of his own. To ascribe human attributes to a machine simply because the machine can simulate some forms of human behavior is, obviously, a fallacious form of reasoning.

A machine is not a genie, it does not work by magic, it does not possess a will, and, Wiener to the contrary, nothing comes out which has not been put in, barring, of course, an infrequent case of malfunctioning. Programming techniques which we now employ to instruct the modern digital computer so as to make it into a learning machine do not "remove from the mind of the designer and operator an effective understanding of many of the stages by which the machine comes to its conclusions." Since the machine does not have a mind of its own, the "conclusions" are not "its." The so-called "conclusions" are only the logical consequences of the input program and input data, as revealed by the mechanistic functioning of an inanimate assemblage of mechanical and electrical parts. The "intentions" which the machine seems to manifest are the intentions of the human programmer, as specified in advance, or they are subsidiary intentions derived from these, following rules specified by the programmer. We can even anticipate higher levels of abstraction, just as Wiener does, in which the program will not only modify the subsidiary intentions but will also modify the rules which are used in their derivation, or in which it will modify the ways in which it modifies the rules, and so on, or even in which one machine will design and construct a second machine with enhanced capabilities. However, and this is important, the machine *will not* and *cannot* do any of these things until it has been instructed as to how to proceed. There is (and logically there must always remain) a complete hiatus between (i) any ultimate extension and elaboration in this process of carrying out man's wishes and (ii) the development within the machine of a will of its own. To believe otherwise is either to believe in magic or to believe that the existence of man's will is an illusion and that man's actions are as mechanical as the machine's. Perhaps Wiener's article and my rebuttal have both been mechanistically determined, but this I refuse to believe.

An apparent exception to these conclusions might be claimed for projected machines of the so-called "neural net" type. These machines were not mentioned by Wiener, and, unfortunately, they cannot be adequately discussed in the space available here. Briefly, however, one envisions a collection of simple devices which, individually, simulate the neurons of an animal's nervous system and which are interconnected by some random process simulating the organization of the nervous system. It is maintained by many serious workers that such nets can be made to exhibit purposeful activity by instruction and training with reward-and-punishment routines similar to those used with young animals. Since the internal connections would be unknown, the precise behavior of the nets would be unpredictable and, therefore, potentially dangerous. At the present time, the largest nets that can be constructed are nearer in size to the nervous system of a flatworm than to the brain of man and so hardly constitute a threat. If practical machines of this type become a reality we will have to take a much closer look at their implications than either Wiener or I have been able to do.

One final matter requires some clarification—a matter having to do with Wiener's concluding remarks to the effect that "We must always exert the full strength of our imagination to examine where the full use of our new modalities may lead us." This certainly makes good sense if we assume that Wiener means for us to include the full use of our intelligence as well as of our imagination. However, coming as it did at the end of an article which raised the spectre of man's domination by a "learning machine," this statement casts an unwarranted shadow over the learning machine and, specifically, over the modern digital computer. I would be remiss were I to close without setting the record straight in this regard.

First a word about the capabilities of the digital computer. Although I have maintained that "nothing comes out that has not gone in," this does not mean that the output does not possess value over and beyond the value to us of the input data. The utility of the computer resides in the speed and accuracy with which the computer provides the desired transformations of the input data from a form which man may not be able to use directly to one which is of direct utility. In principle, a man with a pencil and a piece of paper could always arrive at the same result. In practice, it might take so long to perform the calculation that the answer would no longer be of value, and, indeed, the answer might never be obtained because of man's faculty for making mistakes. Because of the very large disparity in speeds (of the order of 100,000 to 1), on a computer we can complete calculations which are of immense economic value with great precision and with a reliability which inspires confidence, and all this in time intervals which conform to the demands of real-life situations. The magnitude of the tasks and the speed with which they are performed are truly breathtaking, and they do tend to impress the casual observer as being a form of magic, particularly when he is unacquainted with the many, many hours of human thought which have gone into both the design of the machine and, more particularly, into the writing of the program which specifies the machine's detailed behavior.

Most uses of the computer can be explained in terms of simulation. When one computes the breaking strength of an airplane wing under conditions of turbulence, one is, in effect, simulating the behavior of an actual airplane wing which is subject to unusual stresses, all this without danger to a human pilot, and, indeed, without ever having to build the airplane in the first place. The checker-playing program on the I.B.M. 704, to which Wiener referred, actually simulates a human checker player, and the machine learns by accumulating data from its playing experience and by using some of the logical processes which might be employed by a person under similar circumstances. The specific logical processes used are, of course, those which were specified in advance by the human programmer. In these, and in many other situations, the great speed of the computer enables us to test the outcome resulting from a variety of choices of initial actions and so to choose the course with the highest payoff before the march of human events forces us to take some inadequately considered action. This ability to look into the future, as it were, by simulation on a computer is already being widely used, and as time goes on it is sure to find application in more and more aspects of our daily lives.

Finally, as to the portents for good or evil which are contained in the use of this truly remarkable machine—most, if not all, of man's inventions are instrumentalities which may be employed by both saints and sinners. One can make a case, as one of my associates has jokingly done, for the thesis that the typewriter is an invention of the devil, since its use in the nations' war offices has made wars more horrible, and because it has enslaved the flower of our young womanhood. On the whole, however, most of us concede that the typewriter, as a labor-saving device, has been a boon, not a curse. The digital computer is something more than merely another labor-saving device, since it augments man's brain rather than his brawn, and since it allows him to look into the future. If we believe, as most scientists do, that it is to our advantage to increase the rate at which we can acquire knowledge, then we can hardly do otherwise than to assert that the modern digital computer is a modality whose value is overwhelmingly on the side of the good. I rest my case with this assertion.

part two

Mathematics in Art and Nature

SOME 500 YEARS prior to the beginning of the Christian era there came a Greek bearing gifts. Pythagoras of Samos by name, he was philosopher, priest, shaman, charlatan, mystic, magician, and quite possibly the first mathematician. "All is number" was his watchword and mathematics as a distinct and viable discipline was the gift he brought humanity. For it is to Pythagoras and his disciples that all future generations are indebted for the remarkable insight that mathematics may indeed be found in all things.

The history of Pythagoras is shrouded in a mist of legends and anecdotes that most imperfectly reveal to later ages his actual accomplishments. There are, in fact, virtually no documents that tell his story directly. Most of what is known or can be deduced comes from Greek accounts written more than 100 years after the death of Pythagoras. Much of what was written is at best substantially exaggerated, and some of the accounts are demonstrably false. All this notwithstanding, it is fair to assert that a major reason for the importance and reverence that Pythagoras and his followers attached to mathematics was their observation that a few powerful abstract ideas could be applied in an amazing variety of situations. The Pythagoreans found number in music, in architecture, in sculpture, in poetry, in the phenomena of nature, in their perception of beauty, in short, in all that was to them important. The evidence suggests that this revelation had a profound impact on how these scholars-cultists came to view the world. The creation, compilation, and dissemination of an impressive and systematic body of mathematical truths were the results of this almost revelatory insight. The Pythagoreans felt that in their trove of mathematical truths they had obtained an important key that would greatly facilitate their unlocking the secrets of the universe. Whether we of an age some 2,500 years remote from that of Pythagoras would share his wonder at the universality of mathematics and his confidence in its capacity to unmask the face of nature is problematical. But before a quick dismissal of such enthusiasm as the ingenuous babble of minds far more primitive than our own, it's necessary to briefly review some bits of evidence, if only to be polite.

The Pythagoreans discovered that a few integral ratios and some related geometric figures can be used to describe much of what humanity instinctively feels is beautiful. The proportions of leaves and flowers, the shape of waves breaking on a beach, the proportions of the human body, the curves described by parts of the ideal human anatomy, the most pleasing combinations of sounds in music—all of these and much more are connected by and in some sense describable through arithmetic/geometric ideas. This connection between mathematics and beauty struck the Pythagoreans with the power of religious experience. Given the fairly comprehensive ability of Pythagorean mathematics to account for these experiences and given the value that esthetic experience had in Greek society, we can see how the notion that "all is number" was so persuasive.

At this point the modern reader quite naturally observes that the esthetic values of a Greek society some 2,500 years remote from our own are quite probably much less eclectic and diverse than are our own and correspondingly much more easily circumscribed by a few mathematical formulae. The point is granted. A bit more thought leads to the observation that Greek art and mathematics were in some sense interactive. Hence what is beautiful was defined in terms of what Greek mathematics predicted must be beautiful and nonconforming works of art just were not produced. Score another point.

But before discarding the Pythagorean insight completely, the reader should remember that we now have a body of mathematical truths far broader and more comprehensive than that possessed by Pythagoras. Why does it seem so obvious to the cynic that no general mathematical description of esthetic value can be formulated that would validate both classical Greek sculpture and modern abstract expressionism? Because it has not been done? Who knows that much about mathematics and art? Has anyone seriously tried? The essays of this section should at least give the skeptic pause. There is indeed beauty in mathematics and even more surprisingly a great deal of mathematics in both art and nature.

Beauty in Mathematics

François Le Lionnais

François Le Lionnais conceived of his anthology *Les Grandes de la Pensee Mathematique* in 1942 in Marseilles, France. He was a member of a resistance group and in April 1944 was arrested and sent to the concentration camp at Dora where he was forced to work in the underground V-2 factories. He almost lost his life in the camp because of his book. By an unfortunate accident he dropped in front of a guard a piece of paper containing the names of some of the contributors to the anthology. The guard assumed the list of French names was a list of prisoners planning to escape and demanded a confession. When the authorities were finally convinced that there was no escape plan they sentenced Le Lionnais to mandatory lashes of the whip for the crime of using a Nazi pencil on paper of the Third Reich.

Suppose such a being as the "average man" could be found. Suppose further that a gun were placed to his temple and he were given no more than thirty seconds to produce some examples of beauty in mathematics. It has frequently been observed that nothing concentrates the mind so well as the imminence of the termination of one's temporal existence. Thus one might expect that this "average man" would indeed produce some examples of beauty in mathematics. What, one wonders, might they be? Almost surely the first would be geometric figures of fairly regular shape and some symmetry. The circle, perhaps, or an ellipse, or possibly a rectangle of classic Greek proportions might be created. An "average man" of a bit more mathematical insight could suggest a pleasant limaçon or an energetic cardioid.

How likely is it that figures of three dimensions would be mentioned? Not so likely, one guesses, since the geometry of three dimensions is not extensively studied by the "average man" in any country.

Would there be any mention of the elegance and succinctness of "beautiful" proofs in mathematics? Almost surely not. And what of the beauty inherent in mathematical objects themselves? Would the man give a delightful and surprising sequence of whole numbers cunningly embedded in the matrix of integers in a way that stimulates both a sense of discovery and a desire for order? Such aspects of mathematics would almost surely be neglected.

Le Lionnais wrote this essay for the purpose of increasing our appreciation of beauty in mathematics. The number of examples given and the variety of aspects developed may well be rather surprising to those who have felt that mathematics is studied principally for its utilitarian value. For most mathematicians the primary appeal of mathematics is its "beauty." While this term, as used by mathematicians, may have a slightly different meaning than it has in the nonmathematician's everyday language, the experience of creation in mathematics is remarkably parallel to that in the arts. The emotions, the motivations, the physical processes, and the ultimate evocation of self that are typical of the creative process in mathematics are little different from that in music, literature, or painting.

The sense of possession mathematicians have toward their theorems is very much like that any other artist has towards his or her creations. The parallels are so striking that one is compelled to wonder if it is even necessary to justify the use of the word beauty *with respect to mathematics. If beauty is that which is created by the artist at one with his or her craft, then mathematics is beautiful. It remains for us only to gain insight sufficient to appreciate that beauty.*

Source: François Le Lionnais, "Beauty in Mathematics," in F. Le Lionnais, ed., *Great Currents of Mathematical Thought* (New York: Dover Publications, 1971), pp. 121–147. (References omitted.)

Circe never had as much power over her Ulysses as this marvelous science has over the mind, once its first difficulties have been surmounted.—R. BAUDE-MONT

Be on guard against the enchantments and diabolical attractions of geometry.—FÉNELON

Mathematics, rightly understood, possesses not only truth, but supreme beauty.—BERTRAND RUSSELL

BEAUTY OFTEN APPEARS at feasts where only utility or truth have been invited. How then can one remain insensitive to the fascinating charms with which she adorns them? This is true of all activities and all branches of knowledge, but nowhere with more force than in mathematics. Has not the modern Western world confirmed the opinion of ancient Greece, which up to the time of Euclid considered mathematics more art than science? Everything considered, it is most often alluring esthetic satisfactions which have motivated modern mathematicians to cultivate their cherished study with such ardor.

Some of the most cultivated writers have attested to this fascination. Thus Novalis: "The true mathematician is enthusiastic per se. Without enthusiasm there is no mathematics." And, "Algebra is poetry."

Or the Goncourts: ". . . mathematics, and its enthralling power."

But it is the mathematicians themselves who have left the most passionate testimony.

Charles Meray writes:

When we read Gauss's memoirs, whose fresh bloom is still unwithered after nearly a century, do not the details bring to mind those splendid intertwining arabesques conceived by the inexhaustible imagination of artists of the Orient? Does not the overall structure at the same time recall one of those marvelous temples which the architects of Pericles raised to the Hellenic divinities?

See how Painlevé recalls the teaching of Charles Hermite:

Those who have had the good fortune to be students of the great mathematician cannot forget the almost religious accent of his teaching, the shudder of beauty or mystery that he sent through his audience, at some admirable discovery or before the unknown.

The eminent logician Bertrand Russell discerned perfectly this superior quality by virtue of which the queen of the sciences can lay claim to the crown reserved for the arts.

The true spirit of delight, the exaltation, the sense of being more than man, which is the touchstone of the highest excellence, is to be found in mathematics as surely as in poetry.

If some great mathematicians have known how to give lyrical expression to their enthusiasm for the beauty of their science, nobody has suggested examining it as if it were the object of an art—mathematical art—and consequently the subject of a theory of esthetics, the esthetics of mathematics. The study which follows has no intention of establishing the latter; it aspires only to prepare the way for it. The materials that we are going to review will permit us to set up some rough classifications and will merely suggest a provisional basis for more penetrating studies.

Two criteria have guided us in clearing the ground. The first relates to the structure, not of mathematics itself, but of mathematicians' works. The second relates to man's conceptions of beauty.

Without in any way prejudging the real nature of mathematics, one can assume it provides us sometimes with *facts* and sometimes with *methods*. This seems to us a useful distinction and sufficiently justified for an inquiry that is strictly esthetic.

Works of art, too, can be ranged under two grand banners—we do not say which of these we personally prefer: *classicism*, all elegant sobriety, and *romanticism*, delighting in striking effects and aspiring to passion. The two following passages indicate rather well the contrast between these two tendencies:

I was struck by the art with which mathematicians remove, reject, and little by little eliminate everything that is not necessary for expressing the absolute with the least possible number of terms, while preserving in the arrangement of these terms a discrimination, a parallelism, a symmetry which seems to be the visible elegance and beauty of an eternal idea. (Edgar Quinet)

What strikes us first of all, when we compare the mathematics of our times with that of previous epochs, is the extraordinary diversity and the unexpectedness and circuitousness of the paths it has taken; the apparent disorder with which it executes its marches and counter-marches; its maneuvers and constant changes of front. (Pierre Boutroux)

Thus armed with this double-edged blade, we are going to develop our idea with copious examples, each of which will give us an opportunity to provide details we consider important. After considerable hesitation we have chosen to gather this sheaf of examples from the field of elementary mathematics. By so doing, we have been obliged to pass over some of the purest and most vivid examples of beauty in mathematics, in the hope

of reaching a greater number of readers. As Carl Stoermer wrote:

> What one learns about mathematics in primary school corresponds to the alphabet. What one learns in high school corresponds to the sentences of a primer. What one learns in elementary college courses corresponds to simple little stories. Scholars alone are aware of the mathematics that corresponds to literature.

Classical Beauty in Mathematical Facts

We say that a mathematical proposition has classical beauty when we are impressed by its austerity or its mastery over diversity, and even more so when it combines these two characteristics in a harmoniously arranged structure.

Regularity strikes and intrigues us especially when we are expecting a certain disorder. This bounty is all the more delightful in that to some it seems unmerited, to others won after a mighty struggle.

Classicism

There, all is order and beauty,
luxury, calmness and delight.
BAUDELAIRE

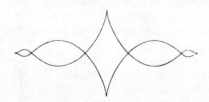

Curve obtained by applying a Joukowsky transformation to an asteroid (= hypocycloid with four cusps).

Romanticism

There are lines which are monsters.
DELACROIX

Some curves satisfying the differential equation:

$$y' = \frac{x[(x - a)^2 + y^2] - y(x^2 + y^2)}{(x - a)(x^2 + y^2) - y[(x - a)^2 + y^2]}$$

Who does not know magic squares? These are cross-ruled squares, filled in as if at random with numbers belonging to a set of consecutive whole numbers. Just as we were resigning ourselves to chaos, we notice the unvarying repetition of a single total for the main directions of this grill. Since one does not need to be endowed with mathematical knowledge to enjoy this pastime, we can understand its having diverted, and sometimes confounded, so many good people all the way back to Renaissance times. We recall the magic square which, like an arithmetic marquetry, Albrecht Dürer introduced into his "Melancholy," in addition to numerous allusions to geometry and mechanics.

One of the most modest branches of the tree of mathematics, the geometry of the triangle, has always had its faithful admirers, because of the graceful ornaments which adorn it. Is it not wonderful to note, throughout this brief episode in the great story of geometry, how often three straight lines meet in a single point, or three points lie on one straight line? I have sometimes thought that it would be worthwhile to begin by offering students pictures wherein the three altitudes of a triangle do not meet (misleading them with an incorrect construction), before teaching them that it is impossible for the lines not to meet.

It is equally surprising to discover more than three points (especially if they come from different definitions) appearing on the same circumference, since three points are sufficient to define a circumference and a fourth is not likely to be on it. In any given triangle the centers of the three sides, the feet of the three altitudes and the centers of the three segments joining the orthocenter (the point in which the altitudes meet) to the three vertices are situated on one and the same circumference, called the *nine-point circle*, or preferably, *Euler's circle*. Thus nine points, furnished by three different definitions, come together on the same circumference, like ballet dancers in a choreographic figure. The acrobatic genius of Euler surely savored this decorative miracle. How he would have marveled had he known how many stars would be added to his original *corps de ballet* in two centuries. These are now 31, and perhaps 43, different points blooming on this mathematical garland.

The study of curves in classical and analytic geometry is equally blessed with harmony. Has not the cycloid, found in so many natural phenomena, been called the "Helen of geometry"?

The logarithmic spiral, discovered by Descartes and studied chiefly by Jacques Bernoulli in a treatise on the differential calculus published in 1698, possesses numerous astonishing properties, notably that of being equal to its caustics by reflection and refraction, to its evolute, and to numerous other derived or conjugate curves. For this reason Bernoulli requested that on his tombstone be engraved a logarithmic spiral, above the following inscription: *eadem numero mutata resurgo*. "This marvelous spiral," he wrote, "gives me such overwhelming pleasure by virtue of its singular and wonderful properties that I can scarcely satisfy my desire to contemplate it."

Similar bursts of fireworks shoot forth and disperse, as if spontaneously, at each step of the theory of functions. Who has not been amazed to learn that the function $y = e^x$, like a phoenix rising again from its own ashes, is its own derivative?

We appreciate that these various examples are very unequal in value. The value of each of them depends on the depth of the mathematics required to prove it. Let us recollect that what we are studying here is the subjective character of the beauty in mathematics; we are not concerned with the objectivity of the mathematics itself. A fact which overwhelms us the first time we meet it, comes to appear trite in the end. Thus the mysterious novelty of the preceding example is dissipated to a large extent as soon as we realize that it is not very surprising for the differential equation $y = y'$ to have a solution. Still a certain margin of wonderment remains when one realizes the economy of this solution.

Imagine my surprise (I was going to say, my disbelief) when I learned as a schoolboy that the product of the least common multiple of two numbers and their largest common divisor is exactly equal to the product of these two numbers. My wonderment completely disappeared when I realized a little later that this property obviously results from the definition of the least common multiple and the largest common divisor based on the composition in terms of the prime factors of the initial numbers. Awareness of a mechanism dethroned the impression of finality and extinguished its iridescence.

This impression of finality often plays a large role in the esthetic enjoyment which the sciences can provide us. There is, to be sure, no finality in mathematics, any more than there is in nature, but the very frailty of our intelligence engenders these illusions which so stir our emotions.

Without as yet leaving the empire of classical beauty, we can add the delightful Ionian slenderness to the rigid simplicity of the Doric order. But at this stage of our inquiry, we shall invoke diversity only when it is not excessive and when monotony seems to threaten.

This is what happens in plane trigonometry when one runs into the formulas for the addition of arcs; the rhythmic complexity of their structure agreeably shatters the anticipated poverty. And what shall we say of the celebrated hypergeometric series, this Proteus of mathematics, whose ability to metamorphose itself into highly varied functions by means of trifling modifications of its coefficients is veritably unbelievable?

It is always impressive to emerge from a long, wearisome trek underground into the blue open, among the high peaks. The view encompasses horizons revealing unsuspected surroundings. Is it such a sentiment which inspired Gauss to describe his celebrated theorem "on quadratic reciprocity," relating to prime numbers, with the phrase "the jewel of arithmetic"? What is more startling than this theory, on whose reefs the efforts of the cleverest mathematicians have gone aground? Every prime number seems immobilized by a tight girdle of steel which prevents all communication with the other numbers. We must keep this rigorous restriction in mind if we wish to appreciate fully the importance of Gauss's discovery, which permits two prime numbers to exchange roles, for all the world like two trapeze artists crossing in mid-air.

Pascal's arithmetic triangle, also, which is very easily constructed, provides a most remarkable link to the coefficients of Newton's binomial expansion, to the important notions of "combinations" and "permutations" encountered in combinatorial analysis, and consequently to the calculus of probability.

When the same mathematical notion can be defined in two different ways, this very fact introduces a correlation between the subjects of these varying definitions that often would not have been suspected. This is notably the case with the number π whose geometric definition everyone knows and which can be equally well expressed by formulas from analysis, or by very different series of numbers.

The same is true of the number e. Sometimes its definition is encountered at the beginning of the study of the theory of functions, sometimes at the beginning of the study of logarithms. Like the little phrase in Vinteuil's sonata, it later reappears in unexpected series.

After numerical series, there are functional series. What student has not been dazzled upon first meeting the Taylor and Maclaurin series, whose gold and silver chains link together the sparkling gems of the successive derivatives of the same function, on up to infinity?

Euler's formula $\sqrt{-1}^{\sqrt{-1}} = e^{-\pi/2}$ (which can also be written $e^{\pi\sqrt{-1}} - 1 = 0$), establishes what appeared in its time to be a fantastic connection between the most important numbers in mathematics, 1, π, and e. It was generally considered "the most beautiful formula of mathematics." The brilliance of this expression is due to the nearly perfect elimination of every element foreign to the three numbers just cited. Today the intrinsic reason for this compatability has become so obvious that the same formula now seems, if not insipid, at least entirely natural.

Sometimes rather simple transformations can alter one of a pair of traditional curves into the other though they had appeared quite unrelated. The sudden revelation of their kinship is truly a treat.

There are relationships even more monumental, such as that bridging the gap between algebra and geometry: this striking dualism, which associates a figure with every equation and vice versa, each of them holding a mirror wherein the other is reflected, is one of the most distinctive in all of mathematics; truth, utility and beauty, joined in intimate marriage, give birth to the most glorious and vital perfection.

Next in turn, infinitesimal analysis reveals to us the sublime interdependence between the area and tangent of a curve. The relationship which unites the curve and its tangent at a given point is expressed analytically by the derivative of the

On a strange whim I had banished irregular plant forms from these scenes.
CHARLES BAUDELAIRE

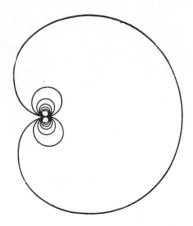

Cochleoid: $\rho = \alpha \dfrac{\sin \theta}{\theta}$

It was an endless palace full of pools and waterfalls tumbling into dull and burnished gold.
CHARLES BAUDELAIRE

Rhodane: $\rho = \frac{3}{10} \theta + \frac{1}{5}$

. . . the Wonderland so sweetly dreamed of.
LEWIS CARROLL

Differential equation:
$$\rho \frac{d\theta}{dp} = \tan\left(4 \text{ arc tan sin } 4\theta + \frac{\pi}{4}\right)$$

Her caresses were so light that pathways sprang up by themselves at each instant.
PAUL ELUARD

Differential equation:
$$y' = \frac{\left(y \tan \frac{\pi}{6} - x + a\right)(x^2 + y^2) + \left(x - y \tan \frac{\pi}{6}\right)[(x - a)^2 + y^2]}{[(x - a) \tan \frac{\pi}{6} + y](x^2 + y^2) - \left(y + x \tan \frac{\pi}{6}\right)[(x - a)^2 + y^2]}$$

function which describes the curve. Moreover, the relationship which unites the curve and the area bounded by it is expressed analytically by the integral of this function. Now, by definition, integration is nothing but the reverse of differentiation. The result is that the tangent to a curve and its area are only inverse modifications of each other with respect to the law describing the inherent structure of the curve itself.

Romantic Beauty in Mathematical Facts

By contrast with classic mathematical beauty we are now going to examine another sort of beauty which can be described as romantic. Its underlying principle is the glorification of violent emotion, nonconformism and eccentricity.

The notion of the asymptote, with which we shall open this new series of examples, has as it were fallen into the public domain. Thus it requires an effort to appreciate to what extent an entire epoch could have been intrigued by its discovery. Montaigne writes,

Jacques Peletier was telling me at my house that he had found two lines approaching each other, which, however, he established could never succeed in meeting except at infinity.

One must guard against automatic judgments; more conscientious investigation will sometimes bring unexpected confutations. Ask a high school student what would be the result of raising a given number to the zero power. He will respond with assurance that the result is zero, but then discover to his shame that it is 1, no matter what number the base is. One experiences the same kind of surprise—as Silvanus P. Thompson notes—upon realizing

how, often, there is little resemblance between a differential equation and its solution. Who would suppose that an expression as simple as

$$\frac{dy}{dx} = \frac{1}{a^2 - x^2}$$

could be transformed into

$$\frac{1}{2a} \log_e \left(\frac{a + x}{a - x} \right) + C?$$

This resembles the transformation of a chrysalis into a butterfly!

Amazement can turn into something still more violent, producing what seem to be completely illogical results repugnant to common sense.

One of the most difficult branches of mathematics, *analysis situs*, that spring whose waters lose themselves in the ocean of modern topology, abounds in spells and charms. Certain of these, like the one-sided Möbius strip, are as amusing to children as conjuring tricks, even though arising from serious problems.

One always experiences some difficulty in getting those uninitiated in the calculus to appreciate the mechanical properties possessed by the cycloid, whose classic beauty was mentioned above. These properties were discovered by Jacques and Jean Bernoulli and Christian Huygens; some malice must be concealed in the barbarous names given these properties, brachistochronism and tautochronism. The a priori conceptions of common sense burst into pieces under the hammer blows of mathematical analysis, and in a harsh light their fragility becomes apparent.

The propensity of the mathematical spirit for escaping physical reality on the wings of its rational imagination often provokes it to fashion concepts in which the uninitiated are prone to see insane nightmares rather than the fruits of logical activity. Of course, in the end one grows accustomed to anything; in short, it is their success which sanctions these innovations, at the same time that it robs them of their charm.

To someone who knows how to raise a number to the 2nd, 3rd, 4th, etc., power, i.e., multiply it 1, 2, 3, etc., times by itself, what indeed would raising it to a fractional or negative power, like ⅗ or − 4, correspond to? To nothing, evidently, as long as we have not agreed to extend the original definition in such a way as to permit its adaptation to new situations. But what could be said about a power whose exponent is imaginary, i.e., contains $\sqrt{-1}$? How could one hope to exorcise such a phantasm? Happily this is possible and by no means involves a gratuitous rule of the game. It is indispensable in obtaining the previously mentioned Euler's formula, which plays an essential role not only in pure mathematics but also in the application of science to technology.

Luxury, oh hall of ebony, where garlands of renown writhe in their death throes to beguile a king.

STÉPHANE MALLARMÉ

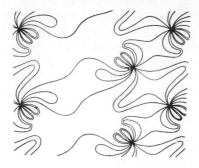

Pascal's limaçon transformed by elliptic functions

From monster to monster, from caterpillars to giant larvae, I went, clutching my way.

HENRI MICHAUX

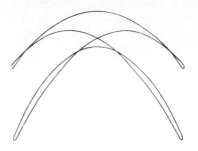

Algebraic equation

$$20y = (8 + x \pm \sqrt{16 - x}) \\ \times (8 - x) \pm \sqrt{16 + x}$$

. . . worlds of a sardonic reality brushing against whirlpools of feverish nightmares.

HOWARD PHILLIPS LOVECRAFT

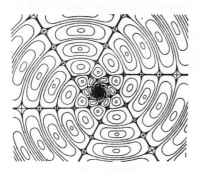

Simultaneous differential equations:

$$\frac{du}{dt} = \frac{\tan u}{\tan t};$$

$$u = \theta - \rho; t = \theta - \frac{1}{\rho}$$

. . . algebra danced madly.

ALDOUS HUXLEY

Simultaneous differential equations:

$$\frac{du}{dt} = \tan 2u; u = \sin \rho - \theta;$$

$$t = \int \frac{d\rho}{\rho^2 \cos \rho} + \theta$$

At the beginning of the 19th century, Poncelet was led by the study of the intersections of two ellipses to introduce the notions of *circular points* and *isotropic straight lines*. These last enjoy extraordinary properties which cause students much delight: any two given circles intersect in the circular points; every isotropic straight line forms any angle with itself and in particular, a right angle—the last property being frequently used; the distance between any two points on this straight line is always zero, etc. We are not dealing here with jokes in questionable taste. Mathematics remains perfectly serious even when it affects these lunatic airs.

For centuries the impossibility of proving Euclid's parallel postulate was "the scandal of geometry and the despair of geometers" (d'Alembert). Its replacement by other postulates, those of Lobachevsky-Bolyai or those of Riemann, seemed an intolerable *coup d'état*. And yet without this replacement could we have developed the general theory of relativity, which plays so powerful a role in explaining the universe?

Many people would have bet against the appearance of the number π in the calculus of probabilities. True, a little reflection will destroy this impression if one is familiar with the experiment known as Buffon's needle. In fact, one finally realizes that the figure needed to illustrate this experiment has something to do with circumferences and their diameter. To penetrate the enigma of how the number π enters into the probability that two integers picked at random will be prime with respect to each other, a knowledge not of elementary geometry, but of advanced analysis, becomes indispensable.

Does not the modern theory of sets take as its point of departure conceptions which seemed an insolent defiance of common sense when Cantor defended them? This exuberant theory had to enjoy repeated successes in other disciplines already classic like arithmetic and analysis before we would accept the existence of quantities "greater than infinity" (Cantor's expression) plus that startling number ω situated *on the other side of infinity*. Theologians were not the last to protest certain ideas as unfair competition.

After the paradoxes come the anomalies, the irregularities, indeed the monstrosities. They arouse some people's indignation and to others bring delight.

The extension of the notion of multiplication introduced a whole series of related notions, in mathematics that for convenience we still call multiplication; but these sometimes have the annoying property of no longer being commutative, with the result that the product of two factors is no longer the same but depends on the order in which they are multiplied. What perversity indeed!

Certain transpositions do not appear to be necessarily introducing anything unexpected. However we must not rush into stating this as a certainty before carefully verifying it. Are not the essentials of the straight line and the circumference contained in the respective properties of shortest distance between two points and equal distance from a central point? Look at the ravages produced when they are uprooted from the plane and transplanted onto the pseudosphere; the straight line twists into an elegant loop; the circle penetrates its own interior, then breaks apart in hysterical contortions, and finally explodes into a spiral. And lastly the triangles, those humble assemblages of three straight line-segments, metamorphose into alarming hydras, the sum of whose angles is always less than 180° and may even become zero.

The following example is no less subversive. It concerns the generalization of the notion of circle in the geometry of n dimensions, n being equal successively to 2, 3, 4, 5, etc. The definition of such a figure always remains the same: A "hypercircle" in a space of n dimensions will be formed by the figure bounded by all the points situated at an equal distance from an interior point called the center. For each of these successive spaces, it is easy to calculate the formula for the measurement of a hypercircle in a space of any given number of dimensions. For simplicity, let us suppose that the length of the radius is always equal to unity. It is disconcerting to note that the measurement of the hypercircle first keeps increasing, reaches a maximum, and then constantly decreases and approaches zero. The most disturbing aspect of this business is that the maximum is located in a space the number of whose dimensions is not an integer and lies between 7 and 8.

Yes, these are reflections, negative images
Tossing themselves about like a motionless object
Throwing their active multitude into the nothingness
And composing a counterpart for every truth.
RAYMOND QUENEAU

HERE IS WHAT BECOMES OF THE FOLLOWING WHEN THEY ARE EXILED TO A PSEUDOSPHERE

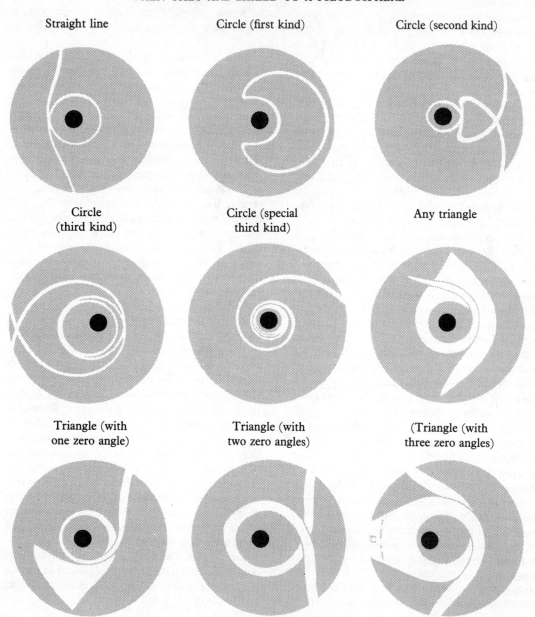

Straight line

Circle (first kind)

Circle (second kind)

Circle (third kind)

Circle (special third kind)

Any triangle

Triangle (with one zero angle)

Triangle (with two zero angles)

(Triangle (with three zero angles)

With Riemann and Weierstrass made known the existence of continuous functions without derivatives, what an outcry came from the mathematicians against these newcomers. "I turn with fright and horror from this lamentable plague of continuous functions having no derivatives," exclaimed Charles Hermite. If it is difficult to reason about such functions, it becomes impossible to visualize fully the infinite caprices of the curves representing them. The arcs joining two points of such curves are always infinite in length, however close together these points are located! But for a century the menagerie of functions has collected so many equivocal and fantastic inmates that we have ended up by becoming acclimated to the deformities of functions without derivatives, which all in all are rather unobtrusive.

Is there any need to emphasize that we consider the division into classical and romantic beauty only a convenient method for understanding and analyzing beauty in mathematics and by no means an absolute and rigid frame? Many of the examples just given have a complex esthetic nature containing side by side several of the categories discussed above.

The romantic wildness of continuous functions without derivatives could evoke in the mystical Hermite the impression that he was battling demons escaped from some mathematical hell. Observe, however, the case of one of these functions, the celebrated Koch curve or *homunculus*. Every arc of this curve, no matter how short, is similar to the entire curve, whose exquisite arabesque it chisels into infinity with unfailing regularity. What could be more classical?

The beauty in mathematical methods will lead us to a still more legitimate distinction between endeavors. This distinction reduces essentially to the antithesis between a desire for equilibrium and a yearning for lack of balance.

Before coming to the actual mathematical methods, it is well to recall that every mathematician possesses a style that can be enjoyed for its esthetic value independently of the scientific results that it permits him to obtain. Whence the well-known parallels between Euler's tactical sinuosities and Lagrange's linear strategy, between Riemann's original lightning flashes and Weierstrass's systematic method of construction, between Kronecker's positivism and Cantor's apocalypse, etc., parallels which for the most part reduce to the inevitable contrast between classicism and romanticism.

Classical Beauty in Mathematical Methods

It seems to us that a method earns the epithet of classic when it permits the attainment of powerful effects by moderate means.

A proof by recurrence is one such method. What wonderful power this procedure possesses! In one leap it can move to the end of a chain of conclusions composed of an infinite number of links, with the same ease and the same infallibility as would enter into deriving the conclusion in a trite three-part syllogism.

Certain notations and algorithms have a rare felicity. We must acknowledge how much we owe to positional notation and the use it makes of zero. Without it arithmetic would doubtless never have emerged from its Greek cocoon. And who knows what level civilization would have been able to reach had it been deprived of this lubricating fluid? Does not its beneficent influence make itself felt in much of the mechanism, not only of mathematical technique, but also of those techniques upon which the power of the great modern states is based?

Vast areas of the theory of functions of complex variables, that formidable continent discovered by Cauchy, ran the risk of being passed over almost unnoticed because the appropriate instrument for exploring them in all their convolutions was lacking. By grafting upon analysis tissues taken from topology, Riemann surfaces permitted us to unravel difficulties which would otherwise have remained inextricable, and caused order and clarity to reign there.

Equally classic are the methods which cast a new light on previously known facts, bringing together and unifying discoveries formerly considered disparate.

On the face of it, the circle and the ellipse have no similarity apart from the fact that they are both simple closed curves, nor the hyperbola and the parabola apart from the fact that they are both simple open curves; and the first two do not seem to have much more in common with the latter two.

Now, a single definition introducing the notion of focus, in which only one word is changed (the word addition is changed to subtraction) permits the close linking of ellipse and hyperbola. A little reflection will now show that the circle is a special case of the ellipse.

One can go even further and define the ellipse, hyperbola and parabola together, as the locus of points, the ratio of whose distances to a fixed point and a fixed straight line is constant and less than, greater than, or equal to 1, respectively.

When the same protagonists are rediscovered in their different roles as intersections of a plane or cone, their unification will receive a new boost. The circle, ellipse, hyperbola and parabola are all now called *conics*, a name properly given to them to call attention to their family ties. Projective geometry, of which the plane and cone mentioned above are only a sort of materialization, illuminates still more profoundly the relationships between the properties of these various figures.

A complete merger was finally established, when thanks to analytic geometry, it could be shown that the equations of the above four curves are all algebraic expressions of the second degree, and reciprocally, that nothing but conics are obtainable from the general and complete second degree equation.

It is hard to imagine that there could be any connection between two curves as different from each other as the Cornu spiral (or clothoid) and Fresnel's integrals. However, they both can be obtained by projecting a sort of conical helix, whose equation is rather simple, on three planes each of which is perpendicular to the other two. If this helix is illuminated by suitably directed, parallel light sources, the shadows it projects on planes parallel to its axis will be Fresnel's integrals, and the shadow it projects on the plane perpendicular to its axis will be a Cornu spiral. As a Platonist I could not have wished a better illustration of the allegory of the cave. It goes without saying that this does not provide an argument in defense of the Platonic theses, for our helix has no more and no less reality or intelligibility than the two plane curves whose shadows it forms [p. 84].

Certain mathematical disciplines—most especially the theory of groups, abstract algebra and general analysis—are unrivaled in their aptitude for centralizing; precisely this constitutes their best raison d'être.

We had to wait for the theory of groups to reveal the relationship which unites mathematical phenomena drawn from completely different chapters such as algebra, geometry and analysis. The following example, cited by Emile Borel, has since become classic:

When Klein makes us see that the algebraic theory of equations of the fifth degree is notably simplified by a prior study of the properties of the regular icosahedron and that this comparison also permits a fruitful study of certain differential equations of the second order, we are lost in admiration at how this overall view illuminates the scattered facts.

We must not think that mathematics progresses only via the royal road of classicism. The directions of research, the scientific ideal and perhaps even the affective climate of certain schools of modern mathematics are without a doubt based on this lucid, passionate and at times somewhat narrow quest for unity. But the dialectics—and also the drama—of mathematical progress consist essentially in an ever-renewed antagonism between this desire for unity and the rebellions which erupt at every new attempt to get to the heart of material reality.

Romantic Beauty of Mathematical Methods

Certain types of proofs could be considered romantic because of their indirect character. This would be the case for a *reductio ad absurdum* proof. While just as convincing as other proofs, these actually do not shed any light on the structure of the propositions they establish. A quite characteristic state of dissatisfaction results from this.

There are elementary proofs such as the proof of the irrationality of $\sqrt{2}$ which please as much, if not more, by the nature of the procedures em-

AN EXAMPLE OF A PROGRESSION TOWARD UNITY: THE CONICS

. . . these are not spring flowers, at the mercy of the changing seasons, but rather never-fading amaranths, gathered from the most beautiful flower-beds of geometry.

BLAISE PASCAL: letter to M. DE SLUSE

I. The natural disparity

Circumference   Ellipse

Parabola

Hyperbola

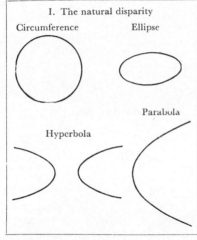

II. Unification by means of a focus

Ellipse +   Hyperbola –

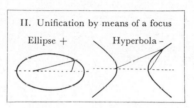

III. Unification by means of a directrix

Ellipse   Parabola   Hyperbola

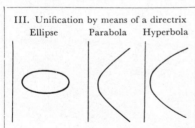

IV. Unification through projection

Circle

Ellipse

Parabola

Hyperbola

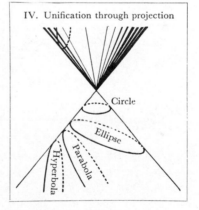

V. Unification through algebra

$$f(x, y) = Ax^2 + 3Bxy + Cy^2 = 2Dx + Ey + F = 0$$
$$AC - B^2 > 0: \text{elliptic}$$
$$AC - B^2 = 0: \text{parabolic}$$
$$AC - B^2 < 0: \text{hyperbolic}$$

A certain position of the bolt which positively closes the lock.

PAUL VALÉRY

TO ILLUSTRATE PLATO

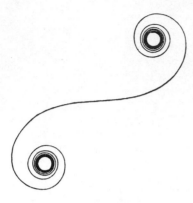

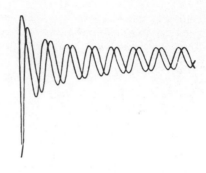

Clothoide, or Cornu spiral   Fresnel's integrals

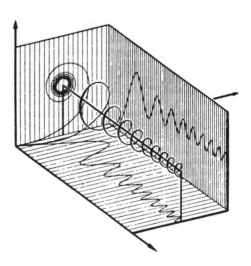

Relief of Fresnel's equation   The objects and their shadows

*. . . if they could converse with one another, do you not think that
they would suppose that they were naming the real objects themselves
when naming the shadows that they were actually seeing?*

                                                        PLATO

ployed as by the facts which result. For example, the proof that the elevation of any real number whatsoever to the zero power always gives 1 merely takes advantage of an ingenious trick. And are not the tricks delightful that Roberval and Pascal employ to calculate the area of a cycloid (by means of wheels which somehow lose their spokes or their chords while turning)? These artifices, which Sergescu reminded us of at a conference in 1947, are proscribed in today's teaching because they revive the excommunicated method of *indivisibles*.

From the pedagogical point of view romanticism (in methods of proof) is very often synonymous with difficulty. The discouragement to which so many pupils yield must be imputed chiefly to the employment of casuistic ruses; while these do honor to the intuitive perspicacity of their authors, they nonetheless strew the labyrinths of comprehension with obstacles.

Elementary algebra—which already normally rebuffs the beginner with its abtractness—could often be expounded with more clarity. It is not always as easy to remain straightforward in elementary geometry. The truths there are skittish; they do not let themselves be approached easily and fall victim only to ambushes whose ingenious inventiveness is far from obvious. Hegel understood this very well, and he stated his criticism— one may not generalize from a single occurrence—in clear language in the two following passages:

[Construction, in geometry] is thoroughly ordered and one must blindly obey the instructions and draw just the lines in question, although one could draw an infinite number. . . . After it is done, one also recognizes that these lines were adapted to the end sought, but the adaption to this purpose is only superficial. (*Phenomenologie.*)

Mathematical representation is a tortured representation. (*Naturphilosophie.*)

The proof of the Pythagorean theorem currently used is certainly very clever, with its method of drawing straight lines joining the vertices of the fundamental triangle to the vertices of the squares constructed on the sides, and comparing certain of the new triangles thus obtained. However, the students who cannot assimilate so Byzantine a maneuver have a very good excuse. So also do those students who are confused by the employment of that peculiar technique of calculating the volume of a triangular pyramid by adding to it a quadrangular pyramid whose volume is double that of the initial pyramid, the combined figures forming a readily measurable prism.

There is only too much to choose from in higher mathematics. A few examples will suffice to make apparent the extraordinary divinatory gifts of the great mathematicians.

There is a certain collection of points and straight lines called the *figure of Veronese*, which can be formed from Pascal's *mystical hexagram*, i.e., any hexagon inscribable in a conic. This figure is perturbing enough by itself. It calls for a tropical profusion of elements, one branching off from another, that we could have chosen to describe in the first part of this study. Kirkman's 60 points, Steiner's 20, Salmon's 15, Pascal's 60 lines, the 20 of Cayley-Salmon, the 15 of Steiner-Plücker, and others still, cross in disorder in this singular jungle. How would one imagine being able to untangle such a wilderness by resorting to a surface of the third degree, and then finding the properties of this latter in a section of hexastigmal space? We call hexastigmal the simplest definable figure having any six points and located in a *four-dimensional space!*

The theory of numbers and *analysis situs*, these high points of arithmetic and geometry, are justly considered two of the altars at which the most secret masses of the cult of mathematics are celebrated. The rites hardly change save for unexpected inventions that are sometimes of spell-binding virtuosity. For example, does it not seem inconceivable that we have to employ the two faces of a single plane to prove the simple proposition that two Jordan curves located on a single surface necessarily intersect in an even number of points?

How can we convey the level of genius that was necessary for certain applications of analysis to the theory of numbers? One is overcome with admiration upon reading Riemann's famous paper "On the Number of Prime Numbers Smaller than a Given Number (1859)." This introduces that

The terrifying realms of worlds in formation.

Jean Paul Righter

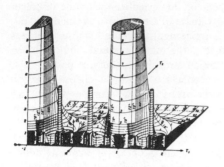

Relief of the elliptic modular
function

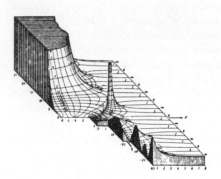

Relief of Reimann's zeta function

ideal catalyst in the laboratory of prime numbers, the fantastic zeta function.

Seeing a certain method succeed regularly every time it is employed makes it more disconcerting to discover its inefficacy in a new instance, and increases all the more the enthusiasm with which we greet an entirely original and successful procedure. This is what occurs, for example, when the theory of composite functions is employed to calculate certain derivatives, that of $y = x^x$ among others.

Extraordinary acts of daring accompanied the birth of elliptic functions. Why did elliptic integrals resist the assaults of the best mathematicians at the end of the 18th and the beginning of the 19th centuries? Because analysts of Legendre's caliber did not think of anything besides time-worn tactics to storm this citadel. How could one doubt that even more darkness would be cast on these questions by investigating the *inverse* functions of these recalcitrant integrals, and particularly by shifting them from the real to the *complex* field? Far from aggravating the difficulties of the problem, this audacious double twist permitted the magical trumpet blast that sent the walls of this mathematical Jericho tumbling down. Abel and Jacobi victoriously entered the city and set

about delivering the keys to a treasure whose value would be shown by the energetic development of the theory of functions in the 19th century. Mittag-Leffler writes:

> The best works of Abel are true lyric poems of sublime beauty, whose perfection of form allows the profundity of his thought to show through, while at the same time filling the imagination with dream visions of a remote world of ideas, raised farther above life's commonplaces and emanating more directly from the very soul than any poet, in the ordinary sense of the word, could produce.

The Beauty of Mathematics and of Its Development

The flaming iridescence of a rose window in a Gothic cathedral should not hide from us the grand architectural unity of the whole. In the same way there is a geometry of mathematics as a whole; it is in its totality that it is beautiful, with a splendor surpassing the most ineffable visions.

No other area of human thought or intelligence operates with such light-headed intrepidity. E. T.

Bell could write, "The essence of mathematics is its eternal youth." And Gonseth does not hesitate to declare, "It is not a paradox; the spirit of adventure, a sort of heroism, animates the mathematician far more than his formulas."

An epic breath unceasingly swells and expands the notions of number, space and function that have been outlined in this study. This fluttering of wings in the sky of abstraction always upsets the best minds. Aside from many declarations of a sometimes mystic cast, the scars this has left are to be seen in the very names given the successive generalizations of whole numbers: irrational, complex, ideal, transcendent, etc. Do not these designations reveal a rather unscientific state of mind seeking to eternalize esthetic emotions rather than the elements of a clear definition?

We know how, by repeated generalizations, geometers have increased the value of their initial capital, the usual space of three dimensions. With an eye on algebraic models they first framed the concept of four-dimensional space. Then by repeating the same operation over and over, they produced spaces of ever-increasing dimension, ending up by passing beyond the geometry of n dimensions (n being any number whatsoever, variable or unknown) to the geometry of spaces with an infinite number of dimensions. Why then be limited to a denumerable infinity? It took but a little time to cross this Rubicon and fashion spaces with dimensions greater than infinity.

If a romantic excess seems to characterize the style of these efforts to outbid their precursors, we discern a classic order in the famous *"Erlangen program"* proposed by Klein in 1872. This classification of particular geometries, which constitute as it were the important ministries of the empire of geometry, associates with each geometry a group of transformations that characterize it. As we go from a group of transformations to a more general group, which includes the former as a subgroup, we correspondingly go from one geometry to a more general geometry. Thus, by successive distillations we extract from metric geometry—which preserves translations, rotations and symmetries—Euclidean geometry, which preserves similarity properties; then, projective geometry, which preserves properties under projec-

tions and sections; then algebraic geometry, which preserves properties under birational transformations; and finally topology, which preserves properties only under homeomorphisms.

These are solemn moments of prestigious and significant beauty, when disciplines up to then distinct establish contact with each other and, making various assorted matches, are wed, each one preserving its own individuality even while being absorbed into a higher unity.

A new breath was infused into the whole of ancient thought when arithmetic met geometry under the sign of Pythagoras. Let us listen to Edgar Quinet celebrate the marriage of algebra and geometry under the sign of Descartes:

If I was smitten by algebra, I was dazzled by the application of algebra to geometry. . . . The idea, the possibility of expressing a line, a curve, in algebraic terms, by an equation, seemed to me as beautiful as the *Iliad*. When I saw this equation function and solve itself, so to speak, in my hands, and burst into an infinity of truths, all equally indisputable, equally eternal, equally resplendent, I believed I had in my possession the talisman which would open the door of every mystery.

The marriage of the theory of functions and the theory of surfaces under the sign of Monge is of the same character. And calling to mind the introduction of the theory of groups of substitutions into the domain of algebraic equations under the sign of Evariste Galois, the introduction of the theory of groups of transformations into geometry under the sign of Felix Klein, and the merger of these two theories with the theory of abstract groups under the sign of Sophus Lie, are not these sufficient to make us believe that we are hearing the three fateful knocks which announce the raising of the curtain upon the drama of 20th-century mathematics?

This is how beauty evidences itself in mathematics, as in the other sciences, in art, in life and in nature.

Sometimes the emotions it stirs up are comparable to those of pure music, great painting or poetry, but usually they are different in character, and can scarcely be comprehended by one who has not felt their glow within him. To be sure, the beauty of mathematics guarantees neither its truth nor its utility. But to some it brings the gift of being able to live matchless hours, to others the certainty that mathematics will continue to be cultivated for the greatest good of all and for the greatest glory of the human adventure, by men who expect no material profit for themselves.

Architecture and the Mathematical Spirit

Le Corbusier

Charles-Edouard Jeanneret Le Corbusier was born in Switzerland in 1887. He never obtained formal university training in architecture or mathematics. Le Corbusier left art school to work for architects in Paris and Berlin. He then traveled through Europe analyzing architectural shapes. Until the outbreak of World War II he devoted himself to town-planning projects. After World War II he was able to implement his earlier ideas for multistoried living centers that allow maximum privacy to be combined with most efficient use of space. Le Corbusier died in 1965.

The American poet Robert Frost once observed that writing poetry without rhyme was about the same as playing tennis without a net. Frost, it seems, felt that the imposition of a rhyme scheme provides an important discipline without which the creative impulse could degenerate into meaningless self-indulgence. For those sympathetic with Frost's view that the exigencies of external rules are essential to good art, architecture may well be the ultimate form of serious artistic expression. The reason for this is really quite simple: In architecture the same rules apply to all architects. No matter how much the architect may wish to alter, abandon, or modify the rules that limit freedom of expression, he or she cannot do so. These rules are, naturally, the laws of physics. The billowy castles of the architect's imagination must be rendered in extant materials and must be fashioned in such a way as to resist forces, such as gravity, that would reduce them to a tangle of rubbish. Although tennis players may agree to take down the net and still play a game of tennis, architects can never agree to eliminate the laws of physics.

This article suggests the influence of mathematics in the creative life of one of this century's most famous and creative architects. Le Corbusier's empathy with the creative nature of mathematics and the mathematical aspects of architectural creation is not surprising. While there is much art in mathematics, it is—as is the art in architecture—an art subject to a rigorous set of rules that cannot be broken or altered at the artist's whim. Mathematicians also can't take down the net, that is, not if what they intend to create is mathematics.

We are inclined to believe that the literature and arts of our time have ignored two aspects of the civilizing function of mathematics. They have sacrificed the rigor which represents the part that clear consciousness plays in anything creative; and they have ignored one of the most original sources of lyricism.

OUR EDITOR, LE LIONNAIS, addressed these lines to the authors from whom he solicited contributions to this book.

Here are some additional lines excerpted from a contribution of mine to a forthcoming issue of *L'Architecture d'aujourd'hui* to be devoted to the synthesis of the major arts:

Source: Le Corbusier, "Architecture and the Mathematical Spirit," in F. Le Lionnais, ed., *Great Currents of Mathematical Thought* (New York: Dover Publications, 1971), pp. 175–188. (References omitted.)

To take possession of space is the first act of living things, men and beasts, plants and clouds; it is a fundamental manifestation of equilibrium and of duration. The first proof of existence is the occupation of space.

The flower, the plant, the tree, the mountain are upright, living in an environment. If one day they attract attention by their truly reassuring and sovereign attitude, it is because they appear limited by their shape but induce resonances all around them. We stop, realizing that there is so much natural interrelationship; we look and are stirred by so much concordance orchestrating so much space, and we measure while what we observe is irradiating.

Architecture, sculpture and painting are specifically dependent upon space; they each have to manage space by appropriate means. The essential point I will make here is that the key to esthetic feeling is a concern with space.

Action of the work of art (architecture, statue or painting) upon the surroundings; waves, shouts or outcries (the Parthenon on the Acropolis in Athens), beams shooting forth like those caused by radiation or an explosion; the land near or distant is shaken by it, affected, dominated or caressed by it. Reaction of the environment: the walls of the room, its dimensions; the public square with its façades of varying weights; the sweep of the land or its slopes, and even the bare horizons of the plain or the rugged horizons of mountains: the whole environment imposes its weight upon this place possessing a work of art, this mark of man's will, and imposes upon it its depths or its protrusions, its hard or fuzzy densities, its violence or its tenderness. We are presented with a phenomenon of concordance, exact as mathematics and a true manifestation of plastic acoustics; thus we are allowed to invoke one of the most subtle orders of phenomena, the bearer of joy (music) or of oppression (cacophony).

Without making the slightest special claim, I shall make a statement about the "magnification" of space that artists of my generation ventured upon around 1910 under the influence of the prodigiously creative spirit of cubism. They spoke of a *fourth dimension*, whether more or less intuitively and clairvoyantly does not matter. A life devoted to art and especially to the search for harmony, has permitted me, through the practice of the three arts of architecture, sculpture and painting, to observe the phenomenon in my turn.

The fourth dimension seems to be the moment of complete escape, brought about and triggered by an exceptionally close harmony among the plastic means employed.

This is not due to the theme chosen but is a victory of proportion in all physical aspects of the work as well as for the efficiency with which intentions are carried out—intentions which may or may not be under control and apprehended, but which do exist and are due to intuition, that miraculous catalyst of acquired, assimilated and even forgotten knowledge. For in a work that is completed successfully there lie buried numerous intentions, a veritable world of them, revealing themselves to those entitled to them, that is, those worthy of them.

Then a bottomless well opens up, wipes out walls, drives contingent presences away and *accomplishes the miracle of ineffable space.*

I do not know about the miracle of faith, but I often live the miracle of ineffable space, the crowning of plastic emotion.

We are quite alive to the fact that the precision required in all these acts meant to trigger a superior emotion is of a mathematical order. One word expresses the product: harmony. Harmony is the happy coexistence of things. Coexistence implies a double or multiple presence; consequently it calls for relationships and accords. What kind of accords could these be, to interest us? Accords between us and our environment, between man's spirit and the spirit of things, between the mathematics which is a human discovery and the mathematics which is the secret of the world.

This can lead to trances or religious transports. At the other extreme, simple and solid, is our daily work as artists. The reality and ingenuity of precise, measured and measurable relationships go into this work which fills the plastic artist's day. The plastic artist will be a poet, that is, able to stir the emotions, only when his materials are of unquestionable quality, made with the unrelenting rigor of striking relationships.

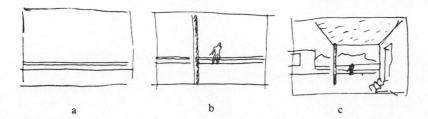

a   b   c

Figure 1

Unrelenting rigor of striking relationships. . . . Allow me to cut short the insatiable dialectic of words in order to explain some material, experimental facts.

I. The Right Angle

In 1923 I built a small house. The grounds were minuscule. There was a low retaining wall at the edge of the lake (Figure 1a). When the house was finished, a plastic phenomenon compelled attention: the crossing of the wall at right angles by a narrow column consisting of a simple metal pipe (Figure 1b). The scanty grounds were deliberately enclosed within walls to mask the horizon. A view of the lake and mountains was permitted at just one specific spot where means of measurements existed that could make one feel strong relationships: the intersection of the right angle, which can be sublime; the backlighting and the luminous expanse of water; the complete sobriety of the architectural lines and the sharply engraved outline of the mountains (Figure 1c).

Man and his measuring tool: the intersection of the right angle. Nature and her discourse: space, the horizontal plane of the water, the narrative told by geographic and geological profiles. . . .

Two alternatives presented themselves:

the scribble or the orthogonal.

II. The Need for Mathematical Expression

I built my first house at the age of 17; it was decorated from top to bottom. I was 24 when I did my second; it was white and bare: I had traveled. It is 1911, and the plans for this second house are on the drawing board. The arbitrariness of the holes in the façade (the windows) becomes startlingly obvious. I blacken them with charcoal. At once the black spots speak a language, but this language is incoherent. The absence of rules and laws is obvious. I am overwhelmed: I realize that I am working in complete chaos. Here is when I discover the necessity for the intervention of mathematics, the need for a monitor. From now on this obsession will occupy a corner of my brain.

III. Memories Are Awakened

I am an apprentice engraver of watch cases. It is around 1900; decoration inspired by natural elements is in style. I am in the mountains, drawing an old fir tree that stands in the pasture. I discover a law. "Look," I say to my master, "you can tell the age of the tree from its oldest branch."

Here are the three growths of the year, each with its three buds (Figure 2a); the left-hand bud will provide next year's growth; the other buds will angle off, each in turn yielding three growths with three buds apiece. The law is enunciated. The oldest branch, the one closest to the ground, almost surely initiates a series of growths (Figure 2b).

And the entire tree (Figure 2c) is a pure math-

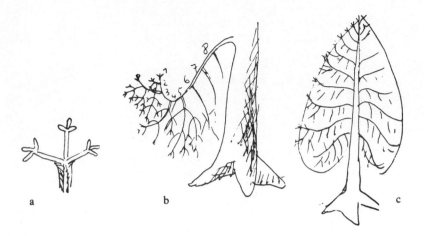

Figure 2

ematical function. (This is not an assertion of fact; I have never had the opportunity to prove it.)

IV.   Equilibrium Through Equivalence

This same year the cook in the Alpine inn where I am spending my vacation has served chamois. I come down to see him, anxious to carry off the waste trimming of the head—the horns. Too late! "Take the hoofs at least!" I remained several days skinning the chamois hoofs with my pocket knife, and musing on their slenderness, as well as on the

formidable number of ligaments joining the bones, insuring articulation and attachment to the muscles.

The chamois leaps from rock to rock, its entire powerful body coming to rest on four small supports (Figure 3).

A day arrived later when I was studying about reinforced cement, in books and on the job simultaneously.

Another day came, later still, when I was meditating on a series of concomitant facts (urbanism, the esthetics of reinforced concrete, economy, the joyous exploitation of the dazzling resources of the new material), and I arrived at some stimulating, through scandalously heterodox, conclusions concerning plastic form and doctrine; free-standing skeletal structure, glass faces, stilts, etc. in violent contrast to architectural traditions, usages and attitudes, namely: stilts (Figure 4a), free bearing-structure and free façade (Figure 4b), in

Figure 3

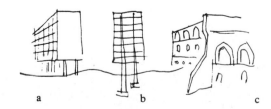

Figure 4

opposition to the previous harmonies springing from stone and wood (Figure 4c).

The hoof of the chamois and the stilts of reinforced cement take into account the material that goes into their making, creating balanced wholes that are intense, nimble and intelligent. Ideas to enchant the mind and overwhelm the conformists; and finally to repudiate Vignola!

V.   All Things Are Subject to, Proclaim or Demand a Law

Thus are organisms created and shaped, guided to their form by evolution and selection.

Let us suppose a dwelling or office building, in short a shelter for man.

In 1922 (at the Salon d'Automne, "A contemporary city of three million inhabitants"), there was an exhibit of a "Cartesian skyscraper" which presented a contrast to the arbitrary forms, dimensions and ground plans of the American skyscraper. The law here was to meet the requirements for light, something which had preoccupied me from the very beginning.

This was the *cruciform* skyscraper, a veritable radiator of light (Figure 5).

But in resuming these studies around 1930, I estimated that at least a quarter of the façades would thus have a northern exposure, and this appeared absolutely atrocious to me. Consequently the form of the skyscraper undergoes a change:

The sun's course is represented by the two solstices (Figure 6a). Illustrated is a desirable form for the building, the sun striking it at the east, south and west (Figure 6b). Another in the shape of a thorn, with the sun striking from the east and west (Figure 6c). Another form, the whole facing

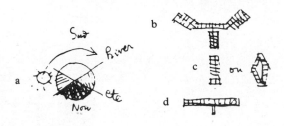

Figure 6

front, with the sun at the south (Figure 6d). These are not the whole story.

According to studies as well as experience, the law of the sun imposes new arrangements:

The sun of the dog days coming through glass façades is overpowering; yet glass façades are a masterly gift of modern technology, not to be rejected. Certainly at the south and west, and probably at the east, we must "break" the summer sun. But in winter the solar rays must be able to penetrate the building. The summer trajectory is high and the brise-soleil (sun-control louvre; Figure 7) in front of the glass façade will shade the glass while permitting diffuse light to enter. The low winter trajectory is not affected by the summer brise-soleil, and direct sunlight penetrates the interior.

At the east or south the sun is harmful only in the later hours of the day when infrared waves are present. A brise-soleil placed in a predominantly horizontal position will be sufficient (m in Figure 7).

To the west, the sun's heat is at a maximum at sunset, that is, when it is near the horizon. The brise-soleil will be predominantly vertical: h with relatively narrow and close vertical slats; b with wide vertical slats spaced farther apart.

We have here demonstrated an increasingly precise biology; buildings to be used for business or dwellings are to adapt their form in accordance with the law of the sun, the master of life. A law will govern the very essence of architectural substance.

VI.   Harmony Is an Act of Consonance

If, in order to house 100,000 inhabitants of Algiers, I once proposed occupying the site called

Figure 5

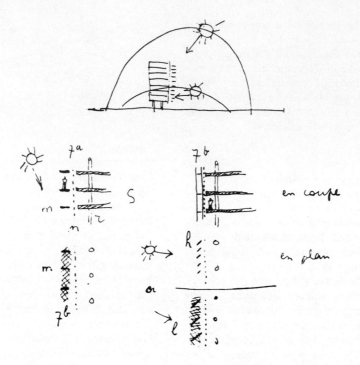

Figure 7 m = horizontal brise-soleil; n = glass façade; r = bearing stanchions; S = floors.

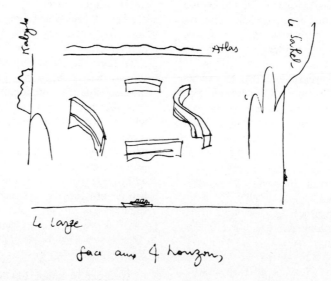

Figure 8

"The Heights of Algiers" (which hangs precipitously over the harbor 400 meters as the crow flies from the center of town) with volumes of construction which aroused enthusiasm as well as indignation throughout the world, it was because I was dominated by the imperative and deep-seated need to enter into a harmonious relationship with the surrounding universe, that is, with the site, the sun and the topography. These considerations gave rise to forms conditioned by, and wholly responsive to, this triple objective. This is what might be called *situating* something: harmonizing a human work with its environment, bringing man's mind into accord with nature's laws. To make them resound, make them sound good together, to produce consonance. To establish the reign of harmony. To accomplish, if successful, the miracle of ineffable space.

VII.

Ineffable space, produced by mathematical rigor applied to the whole complex of problems one faces. The senses transmit to the mind the action of the forms which determine the extent of the sensation. To appreciate that the measure of the latter has absolutely no relation to size, we need only consider the humblest sea shell. Human enterprise can, in turn, embody in the purity and harmonious arrangement of the shell a vast number of concordant elements and events, and thus achieve radiance.

The hall of the Palace of Soviets (1931) was to hold 14,000 spectators and auditors. One possible source of conflict was eliminated at the outset; the problem of statics was separated from visual and auditory problems. All three could have been combined, but incompatibilities in the systems would have rendered the attempt hazardous. Bearing and supporting members obey laws of gravity and statics and are subservient to materials and construction processes. The phenomenon of acoustics is something else again; sound waves ricochet off reflecting surfaces, and the intensity with which they are transmitted is a function of the distance covered. We are no longer dealing with a static order but rather with a biological order—mouth or ear, emitter, transmitter and re-

verberator. Finally the visual phenomenon in the very difficult conditions considered here, where distance chops up the spectacle, prompts us to seize upon whatever advantages we can. We shall see how.

The listener-viewers were installed in a concave amphitheater permitting everyone to have a good view of the stage but also giving a real view of the mass in attendance. For if the amphitheater had been required only to provide visibility of the stage, the seats would have been arranged in horizontal rows, and the plane thus determined by the spectators would become tangent to their line of sight, and the view of the crowd itself would be reduced to practically nothing. The concavity of the amphitheater, on the contrary, provided a display of the occupied surfaces, and each spectator could see with his own eyes the tremendous crowd intent upon the action on the stage. This is in itself a powerful and moving source of emotion.

The techniques of sound led us to a solution of great purity. The direct sounds—speakers, singers, orchestra and all other sources (j in Fig. 9)—were picked up by microphones (Fig. 9, h) placed above the stage. The stage walls were made absorbent: A "gulf" of eleven meters was created between the first sound sources and the first listeners. Then, the undistorted sound was entrusted to a single loudspeaker (Fig. 9, f) placed in front of the stage, which thus became the only emitter. The problem was being simplified: carry this sound emitted from a single point to 14,000 pairs of ears (Fig. 9, o–p). All that would be needed thereafter would be to establish the necessary reflecting surfaces, taking into account a loss of sound proportional to the square of the distance; consequently, to construct a reflecting membrane (Fig. 9, k) mathematically proportioned to take into account the location of every listener present and his distance from the loudspeaker. The ceiling of the hall would satisfy this requirement.

First of all choose a concave form for the amphitheater; here is a fragment cut out of a basin (Fig. 9, a).

Next, agree that the seat of every listener (Fig. 9, l) will be sprinkled with droplets of sound emanating from a mouth (the loudspeaker; Fig. 9, g)

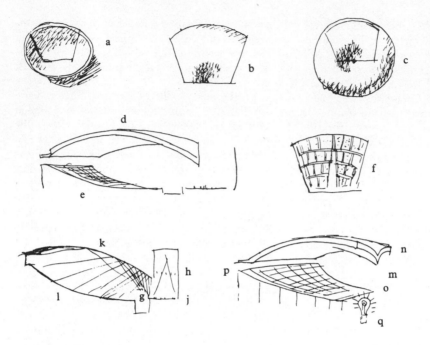

Figure 9

and reflected mathematically by the ceiling (Fig. 9, k), with the direction and intensity of the reflection entering into the mathematics. Where shall we get a serviceable form (Fig. 9, b). In a torus whose inner circle is reduced to a point (Fig. 9, c). The farther along the reflecting ceiling the droplets of sound strike, the more numerous they should be, and as a result the more extensive the ceiling surface will have to be. In this way good acoustics are achieved; the seats at o and the seats at p in the figure enjoy practically the same harvest of sound waves. This is verified in a mock-up through the use of electric lighting. A small lamp was placed at q. From o to p the amphitheater was illuminated evenly by reflection from the ceiling, with the same intensity at every point. A phenomenon of perfect concordance.

Elements of the solution became apparent: the 14,000 seats (e); the reflecting shell, an acoustic phenomenon (d). The amphitheater (l) and stage (j), a visual phenomenon. At this point I have a question: in principle I am hostile to gigantic programs; they lose sight of the human scale. If, by precise methods, sound can be transmitted infinitely farther than was imagined, there are still severe limits to visibility. My question then is as follows: To look for a needle in a haystack or a pile of dirt is unrealistic. But finding a needle becomes possible in a place where all points—the floor of the amphitheater, the lateral partitions, the back, each point of the vault—are in mathematical agreement, establishing a close and harmonious relationship between the immense hall and the stage. The needle (in this instance, the actors on the stage) becomes the fateful target. I shall answer my own question. We have to admit that a strong feeling of unity and coordination comes into play; the senses are swept towards a single objective, and the result is that spectators, listeners and actors find themselves united in the same unique and intense adventure.

The hall has become a place of harmony.

One readily understands that without bold initiative it would have been difficult to counterpoint the matter with considerations of statics and the resistance of materials.

The ceiling (the reflecting shell) can be made of a slab of reinforced cement from three to five centimeters thick. At a distance of two meters from this membrane there will be a second slab serving as an umbrella. A scheme of very delicate, trellised small beams will serve to join and solidify the two conches. Various results are achieved: acoustic quality of the lower slab, impermeability of the upper slab, possibility of inspection and repair, lightness, etc.

At this point it is only necessary to suspend this double keel from above. Support on the ground: eight pylons at the back of the hall (Fig. 10a). Another support: a parabolic arch of reinforced concrete 100 meters high, whose two feet rest outside the building. Hanging from king posts is a beam, a sort of binding joist (b). At the top of the pylons (a) and on this latter joist (b) rest eight large latticed girders of reinforced concrete, fitted with king posts from which the vault will hang. This immense ceiling, like Holofernes' head, will be held by its hair! So that the phenomenon of "the law of gravity and methods of construction" will be in evidence outside the building itself, *on the exterior*. The interior is like a pure sea shell. And save for errors, we are adhering to the most authentic tradition of cathedrals except for the fact that we are dealing with reinforced cement whereas the Gothic builders used dressed stone without binding material.

We cannot bring this study of the hall of the Palace of Soviets to a more fitting conclusion than by repeating once again the remark so pointedly phrased by Le Lionnais:

. . . The arts of our time have ignored two aspects of the civilizing function of mathematics. They have sacrificed the rigor which represents the part that clear consciousness plays in anything creative; and they have ignored one of the most original sources of lyricism.

To the artist, mathematics is not just the subject matter of mathematics. Mathematics is not a question of calculation perforce but rather the presence of royalty: a law of infinite resonance, consonance and order. Its rigor is such that truly a work of art results, be it a drawing by Leonardo, the startling exactitude of the Parthenon, the cutting of whose marble can be compared with the work done by a machine tool, the implacable and impeccable construction of a cathedral, the unity which Cezanne achieves, the law determining a tree, the unifying splendor of the roots, trunk, branches, leaves, flowers and fruit. There is nothing haphazard in nature. If one has understood what mathematics is in the philosophical sense, all of the works of nature will henceforth reveal it. Rigor, exactitude are the means to a solution, the source of character, the reason for the harmony. "The lion is recognized by the blow of its paw."

The mark of measure. Giving a measurement, taking a measurement, making measurement reign: these acts are necessary to establish order and the means of order.

The traditional measurements of a finger's breadth, inch, foot and cubit are expressions of natural mathematics. A great crime was committed against the domain of human construction when the metric unit was imposed upon it, that ridiculous and pointless forty-millionth of the earth's meridian!

Dimensions and measure lead to the establishment of proportions in things. Laws administer the proportions which produce character. In the domain of construction attention to proportion has, since the Renaissance, declined to the point of disappearance. I feel the idea of proportion as part of me, and my mind as well as my hand never cease to be occupied with it. In architecture sketches are guides; in painting, too, sketches are guides. You can attain such mastery in this mathematics of the plastic arts that you are no longer obliged to make calculations and preliminary drawings; your hand will perform them automat-

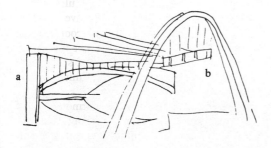

Figure 10

ically. It remains for our modern world to free itself from the arbitrary metric measurement in construction to replace it with the tremendous resources of numbers, particularly the fruitful and inexhaustible golden section. . . .

I have been dreaming for a long time of a mathematical unity resulting from a golden rule applied to projects dealing with urban problems, architecture and furnishings in our machine civilization.

After twenty years of study, I believe that I have lighted upon, not the rule, but one of the rules capable of triggering a prodigious flowering and abundance of harmonious forms. In the United States as well as in France, in the U.S.S.R., in England and everywhere else, this rule could serve as a tool for determining the dimensions of any prefabrication or any construction. I am announcing this discovery here to whet the curiosity of the seekers and so that this rule, investigated and perfected by all, may before too long aid in projecting unity and harmony into the projects of this second era of machine civilization now underway. Deep-seated and universal harmony, part of our epoch's potential, charged with the mission of eradicating the chaos in which the machine civilization was born.

January 4, 1946, in the Azores,
aboard the cargo boat *Vernon S. Hood.*

Mathematics and Music

Henri Martin

Henri Martin was principal inspector of technical instruction at the time this article was originally written.

As was noted in the introduction to this section the Pythagoreans were overwhelmed by their discovery that the music of their time could be described mathematically. The relationship between music and mathematics has, if anything, expanded, and yet most educated music lovers have little if any knowledge of this connection. In this article Henri Martin provides a brief review of the numeric character of the most popular musical scales and suggests that there is a connection between successful musical composition and the mathematics of symmetry and proportion.

A point that Martin does not develop, but which deserves at least passing interest, is the apparent relationship between mathematical and musical talent. Substantial evidence, admittedly anecdotal in character, suggests that there is a positive correlation between the two talents. Whether serious scientific study would confirm this suspicion and account for it remains to be seen, but it is an intriguing aspect of the mathematical mind.

LEIBNIZ ONCE WROTE:

> Music is a secret arithmetical exercise and the person who indulges in it does not realize that he is manipulating numbers.

He could have added, and a person playing the harpsichord does not realize that he is manipulating logarithms. Indeed the connection between music and certain parts of mathematics is very close, primarily for the following reasons:

1. The effect of a musical sound upon our ears depends first and foremost upon its pitch (physicists speak of its "frequency," i.e., the number of vibrations per second of the body emitting the sound). To say that we hear middle *c*, or to say that our ear registers 256 vibrations per second, means the same thing. Therefore a number is associated with each sound, and conversely, with each number, whether integer or not, is associated a sound.

2. Hearing two sounds simultaneously is equivalent to perceiving two numbers and a relationship between them. To hear the first and fifth tones of the same scale is equivalent to "hearing" the ratio 3/2, which is the ratio of their frequencies. Now experience with music shows that the esthetic effect of a chord depends almost exclusively on the ratio of frequencies; the whole question of harmony is therefore a question of the choice of ratios.

3. To these two reasons we add rhythm, which is by its nature essentially arithmetical. We shall put this question aside because it is at once too important to be mixed in with another and too removed from the study of sounds which we propose to undertake.

Source: Henri Martin, "Mathematics and Music," in F. Le Lionnais, *Great Currents of Mathematical Thought* (New York: Dover Publications, 1971), pp. 189–196.

Let us now note that colors, which are also differentiated by their frequencies, play the same role with respect to sight that sounds play with respect to hearing. Our eyes and our ears are *counters of frequencies*. However, there is an enormous difference between the way colors and sounds are used: A painter can put colors of any frequency whatever on his canvas, while a composer cannot place sounds of arbitrary pitch in his work. Why is this?

First of all, because he must write his music. There would have to be an infinite number of symbols to designate all the pitches; deciphering such notation would be almost impossible and very slow in any case. Next, music is made to be played, and the large majority of our instruments can produce only a limited number of sounds.

Furthermore, our ear is incapable of discerning two sounds that are too close. This "power of separation" obviously varies a great deal among individuals, but it scarcely permits one to distinguish a shift of the fingers on the violin of the order of two millimeters, for example. This therefore makes it fruitless in any case to use all the frequencies. However, it is agreed that a practiced ear can distinguish about 300 sounds in one octave; this is still too much for musical notation and for the capacity of the instruments (a piano of eight octaves would have 2400 keys).

Therefore, for musical purposes, we are led to employ only a limited number of sounds in each octave, which is the natural basic interval. Let us recall that two notes are said to be an octave apart if the frequency of one is double the frequency of the other; or, what comes down to the same thing, if a string produces a certain note, half the length of string will produce the octave.

The following question was asked as soon as music became a social art: Among the 300 discernible sounds in an octave, how does one choose the scale of sounds to use?

We would like the reader to grasp the importance of this question; in a way, it committed music for millennia, if not for eternity.

Once a scale was adopted, it became in fact practically impossible to change it. Let us take an example. Suppose that the musicians of a certain era had decided to divide the octave into 10 intervals in the following fashion: The fundamental

sound is given by a string one meter long, then its octave by a string 50 centimeters long; the intermediate sounds will be given by strings of 55, 60, 65, etc. centimeters, with five-centimeter intervals. A priori there is nothing disturbing in this. Ah, well! A piece written in this scale cannot be transcribed with our present notation, even with the aid of sharps, flats, double sharps or double flats. In any event, only certain instruments, the violin among them, could perform such a piece.

The music of such an era would be completely unavailable to us, therefore "dead."

The continuity of musical life thus requires, assuming that conditions pertaining to the instruments be such as have prevailed up to now, the continuing use of the same scale or those with practically negligible differences—which in fact is what has happened in the course of the history of our music.

Were musicians and philosophers to reflect about all this, they would be alarmed at the responsibility assumed by the first musical theorists when they cut up the octave into definite units. In no area of art did a decision have such importance; it is perhaps the Greeks' most splendid and most eternal claim to glory that they created the scale *at the same time that they created mathematics* (the coincidence is worth noting).

If another scale, audibly different, had later been revealed to be more esthetic, efforts would have been made to establish it, and despite the difficulties we have indicated, the centuries would have won out over a division of the octave judged outworn. Now, nearly 2500 years have passed and the present-day scales, which we shall investigate, are in fact only variations of the Greek scale; a single notation serves them all; their notes have the same name, and a piece is composed, written down, played and sung without specification of the scale.

If they are not entirely equivalent physically, they are used and regarded as such.

From the point of view of philosophy and esthetics, the question of the timeless value of the Greek scale is accordingly disturbing! Let us try to clarify this mystery partially; to do this we must first specify the nature of the three most frequently employed scales: the diatonic Pythagorean scale, the Zarlin or physicists' scale and the tempered scale immortalized by J. S. Bach.

We shall frequently speak of the interval determined by two notes; we should understand by this the ratio of the frequencies of these two notes. Take, for example, the notes corresponding to 400, 600 and 800 vibrations per second; the interval of the first two is 600 to 400 or 3/2; the interval of the latter two is 800 to 600, or 4/3.

The difference between the frequencies is the same, but the intervals are not equal; we must not lose sight of this concept in what follows.

1. The Greek Scale

Let us take a string which produces the sound f and let us regard this as the beginning of an octave. Two-thirds of this string's length will produce a higher-pitched note, which by definition will be called the fifth above f: This will be our c of the same octave. Two-thirds of the c string will again produce a new fifth, the g of the octave immediately above; by doubling this g string we shall come back to the g of the initial octave, and so forth from fifth to fifth. The notes obtained will be in the order: f–c–g–d–a–e–b when transposed to the original octave, they appear in the order: c–d–e–f–g–a–b–c. Continuing this series of fifths beyond b does not give us f again, but a note called f-sharp, then c-sharp, etc., and when the series is continued on the other side of the initial f, it gives flats.

The concept of this scale is therefore extremely simple and coherent, and well within the Pythagorean tradition.

2. The Zarlino or Physicists' Scale

The principle here is entirely different. It consists of the a priori assumption that two sounds will be the more agreeable to the ear, especially if heard simultaneously, to the extent that they offer harmonics in common. Let us recall that an initial sound has harmonics, that is, sounds which correspond to doubled, tripled and quadrupled frequencies, etc., and are thus called second, third, fourth, etc., harmonics.

Let us take, for example, the frequencies 400 and 500 which correspond to an interval of 5/4; the fifth harmonic of the first sound will coincide with the fourth harmonic of the second (i.e., 2000 vibrations per second). Their harmonics, 10 and 8 respectively, will again coincide, etc. Complex intervals thus correspond to coinciding higher harmonics, and if the frequencies are incommensurable, the two sounds will not have harmonics in common.

A rather small number of intervals are thus determined. Among these we find some that figure in the Greek scale (9/8 for the interval of the second (c–d), 3/4 for the fourth (c–f), 3/2 for the fifth (c–g)). Others do not figure in it but are close enough to Pythagorean intervals to be substituted for them and receive the same name.

The interval of the third (c–e) in the two scales is not the same, but the difference is practically unnoticeable.

Multiplying its frequency by 25/24 sharps a note; multiplying by 24/25 flats it; this produces sharps and flats that are very close to the corresponding sounds of the Greek scale.

3. The Tempered Scale

It must be added that the two preceding scales, by lumping together the very close notes c-sharp and d-flat, etc., defined twelve slightly unequal intervals. The tempered scale also divides the octave into twelve intervals, but makes them equal a priori.

As a result of this the twelfth power of each of these intervals is equal to 2, the interval of the octave. In other words, the fundamental interval is the twelfth root of 2, and the frequencies of the twelve notes are in geometric progression. If the first note is c, the second will be called both c-sharp and d-flat, etc., and will be the identical note in this scale.

The simplest way to determine the fundamental interval, the twelfth root of 2, is to make use of logarithms. This fundamental interval is an irrational number; as a result, the tempered scale *does not possess any simple interval*, a fact which would have driven Pythagoras to despair; and the notes of which it is composed *have no harmonics in com-*

mon, which is very far from the physicists' conception of the affinity of sounds. Nevertheless, the notes of this scale are close enough to those of the two preceding scales to receive the same names; but none of them coincides exactly with its homonym.

Thus the tempered scale is clearly based upon a more complicated mathematical conception than the others and could not have been conceived before the invention of logarithms.

Johann Sebastian Bach, who was the first to employ the "tempered scale," was able to do so only because Napier had invented logarithms before him, shortly after 1600. This scale has become, naturally, the one in accordance with which instruments of fixed pitch are tuned.

Other scales in addition to these three have been conceived. Fanatic partisans of the golden section have tried to apply it to the lengths of strings. These attempts, although very interesting, have not dethroned the standard scales, which remain the only ones in use; the plural "scales" is, as we have seen, to all intents and purposes a singular, and Bach's scale is in fact merely the daughter of the Greek scale, from which it is not distinguished in practice.

It remains for us to attempt a mathematical-philosophical critique of these three scales to see if it would not be possible for mathematics to play a role in reconstituting the art of sound.

Their esthetic value is not to be disputed; it is an established fact by virtue of the emotional power of music. So we ask the following questions:

1. Where does this esthetic value come from?
2. Do these scales exhaust the possibilities of musical expression?
3. Would it be possible and interesting to use other sounds than those which they impose on us?

The Pythagorean and Zarlino scales are, as far as mathematicians are concerned, identical conceptions; they reduce to simple ratios. The tempered scale, which uses irrational ratios, can only account for its emotional value with the feeble argument that its intervals are equal. In that case its creators could have been asked: "Why twelve intervals in the octave, rather than seven or fifteen,

etc?" The answer seems obvious to me: "Because, by the division into twelve, we find ourselves with sounds that are practically identical with those of the Greek scale." The tempered scale was thus created to resemble the Greek scale. The same remark goes for the Zarlino scale, which chooses only those sounds already defined by Pythagoras, from among all those available to it.

The problem of the esthetics of the scales comes down entirely to a consideration of the Greek scale.

Its artistic value resides in the following concept, which has already been found to be true for the arts in general: Simple relationships create beauty. Moreover, it is *a fact,* established by the existence of works of art that have been conceived in accordance with this principle. Therefore we can state (with all the caution that should accompany such assertions): Our scales are beautiful because they partake of the Greek principle of harmony, the use of simple ratios.

Here the mathematician at once asks us whether the converse of this assertion also holds: "Can beauty be created only by simple ratios?"

The answer is no. Let us examine from a musical point of view some facts of a personal or general nature which will bear out this assertion.

I remember a climb in the Alps when there suddenly came to us from both slopes of the mountain the sound of cow-bells belonging to two herds, a sound which could scarcely be made out in the valley some hundred meters below. The great variety of the sounds which reached us constituted an astonishing euphony, without rhythm or classical harmony. I am unable to remember this without strong emotion. And yet, it consisted of sounds that cannot be transcribed in our music; no composer could have put them down on paper, and no orchestra could have attempted to recreate them. I venture to add that even an uncultured, but normally constituted, human being could not have remained unmoved by this music.

And the song of birds? It is a cliché, but true nevertheless, that the long phrases of the nightingale's song are beautiful; yet it is not possible to write them down in our scale.

In his *Voyage to the Congo,* Gide spoke of Negro melodies; he affirmed that the sounds employed in them do not correspond to those of our scale and that the transcriptions he attempted with our symbols were only approximate (he said so himself). However, these melodies stir the Negroes; therefore they are beautiful. It is true that this music eludes us (2500 years of musical atavism cannot so easily be uprooted!) but we do not have the right to deduce from this that it is deficient in esthetics.

As concerns another category of ideas, our scales and the majority of our instruments do not allow the use of sounds with continuous pitch variation, examples of which are modulations of the wind in the trees and under a door, or, in the area of rather disagreeable sounds, a siren.

As a result of all this our music does not and cannot exhaust the resources of the art of sound. Let us not conclude that our musical art is tainted with inherent poverty; there are more than 400 million ways of grouping the twelve notes of the scale (not taking into account possible repetitions or variations in rhythm); composers therefore have plenty of elbow room.

However, nothing prevents us from conceiving a new utilization of sound. To make ourselves clear, we are not considering here the creation of a new scale that will dethrone the one to which all our musical tradition has tied us much too much. We are concerned with supplementing the present possibilities with other possibilities in which mathematics could play its role.

Nothing prevents a musician from asking a mathematician to design for him, for example, a scale of equal intervals, but with fourteen notes instead of twelve. The problem is easily solved, as we have seen, with the aid of logarithms. After an adaptation that a good artist should be capable of making, the musician could play a piece in such a scale; string instruments and some wind instruments could be tuned in accordance with this scale. We do not underestimate the difficulty, but men have surmounted worse ones. Such an effort would at least be undeniably original in character, and perhaps one of the scales which could be obtained in this manner is that of the nightingale, or of birds in general.

Let us note by the way that musical notation is nothing but a graph with two variables, since it indicates the length of a note and its pitch.

Conversely, a graph drawn on a musical staff can be played. Let us draw a curve on a musical staff: The points where this curve intersects the lines of the staff shall define a note whose length can be indicated by the horizontal distance which separates two neighboring points of intersection. Mathematical considerations might well be an aid in plotting such curves.

To sum up, 2500 years ago music was identified with the mathematics of that period: The Pythagorean school created them both on the same principles. Then there was a slackening in the relations between music and mathematics, the tempered scale of 250 years ago being the last important result of their collaboration. There is no reason to conclude that we have seen the last of this collaboration, in fact there are unquestionable possibilities which future musicians will perhaps put to use.

Does Pure Mathematics Have a Relation to the Sciences?

Felix E. Browder

Felix Browder was born in Moscow, Russia, in 1927. He received his doctorate from Princeton in 1948. He served as chairman of the mathematics department at the University of Chicago from 1972 to 1977. He has been a Guggenheim fellow, a Sloan fellow, a National Science Foundation senior fellow, a fellow of the American Academy of Arts and Sciences, and a member of the Institute for Advanced Study. He was editor of the *Bulletin of the American Mathematical Society* from 1960 to 1967. He is a member of the National Academy of Arts and Science.

With this essay our passage through the world of mathematics in art and nature begins to deflect from those pleasant if unpragmatic considerations of the esthetic to the more prosaic topic of mathematics as the language of science. We have explored much of the abstract quality of mathematics and of the artistic single-mindedness with which its most successful creators produce it. But we have been reminded of the surprising interaction between nature and mathematics, a genuinely symbiotic relationship that lends marvelous clarity and precision to the explanations of science and provides discipline and inspiration for mathematics. Browder addresses this article to this special relationship. The author, himself an eminent mathematician, persuasively argues that modern mathematics has not outstripped the capacity of science to use its ideas. He suggests that this fact is important not only to the progress of science but to mathematics as well.

THE TITLES GIVEN to lectures and articles are designed usually for advertisement or seduction. They are supposed either to give a glamorous aura to the subject by identifying it with something that is already attractive to the prospective audience or to use the preconceptions of the audience to predispose it to accept a particular point of view. The title of the present essay was chosen for an almost opposite purpose—to use ordinary terms in a slightly puzzling way to jar the reader from the automatic reflex of standard preconceptions. It is intended as a sort of provocation, not to emotion but to careful thought. It uses familiar terms in an unfamiliar way as an introduction to an attempt to show that our customary way of using very familiar categories of thought is misleading. The intention is to make the point, which I shall try to develop in detail, that the way we usually analyze that part of the intellectual and practical world we call *mathematical* blinds us to some of the most important aspects of that world.

My title contains an apparent paradox, or, more precisely, as we shall see, several layers of paradox. The first and most obvious is this: Doesn't the term *pure mathematics*, with the emphasis on the adjective *pure*, denote exactly that part of mathematical activity that does not have anything to do with the sciences, or indeed with anything outside its own autonomous domain? This is a view that is held by many, including

Source: Felix E. Browder, "Does Pure Mathematics Have a Relation to the Sciences?" *American Scientist* 64 (1976): 542–549.

many mathematicians, and that was most eloquently set forth thirty-odd years ago by the eminent British mathematician G. H. Hardy in his autobiographical essay, *A Mathematician's Apology*. I should like to suggest that this view is false, or at least very partial. To do so, I need to give an alternative general definition of pure mathematics: Pure mathematics is that part of mathematical activity that is done without explicit or immediate consideration of direct application to other intellectual domains or domains of human practice. This new definition points to the distinction between the short-run application of mathematics with forethought, on the one hand, and the long-run and surprising application of mathematics, on the other.

Let me give one of the best-known examples to illustrate the point. In 200 B.C., the Greek geometer Apollonius of Perga wrote his celebrated Treatise on Conic Sections. Though Apollonius was himself a major contributor to the Greek study of mathematical astronomy, his geometrical discussion of the conic sections (the ellipse, parabola, and hyperbola) was an exercise in pure mathematics in the strict sense since no applications of his results were considered or made in the classical world. In 1604, 1,800 years later, the German mathematician and mathematical physicist Johannes Kepler read the writings of Apollonius and applied them in optics and the study of parabolic mirrors. In 1609, he made the brilliant observation (impossible without the focal function of the ancient theory) that the orbits of the planets should be described as ellipses, not by means of circles and epicycles, thereby laying the principal foundation for Newton's later theory of gravitation.

The example is somewhat extravagant, since most important advances in pure mathematics rarely wait 1,800 years for application. Yet in this case, we can surely say that the magnitude of the application made it worth waiting for. As a generalization, I should say that with the increasing momentum of mathematical and scientific activity (and contrary to some people's impressions) the speed of application has also increased. Thus, it took 60 years from the development of matrix theory as a part of pure mathematics in 1860 to its application as the fundamental mathematical tool of matrix mechanics to describe atomic systems in 1925, thirty-odd years from the development of tensor calculus by the geometers of Italy in the 1870s to its application as the basic mathematical tool of relativity theory by Einstein in the 1910s, 20 years from the development of the eigenfunction expansions of differential and integral operators by David Hilbert in 1906–10 (following on the theory of Sturm-Liouville of 1840) to its application in wave mechanics in 1927.

On the theme of the surprising application, let me give an outstanding historical example of a slightly different character. In 1931, the young Austrian mathematician Kurt Gödel proved his celebrated incompleteness theorem, one of the greatest achievements in the development of mathematical logic. If there ever was a mathematical result that was pure in the purest sense, this was it. The great German mathematician Hilbert, in answer to the criticisms of the school of L.E.J. Brouwer, had proposed a program of proving the consistency of such classical mathematical systems as the whole numbers by constructive, step-by-step procedures. By an amazing logical tour-de-force, Gödel had shown that such proofs were impossible and that, paradoxically, all they could prove was that mathematics was inconsistent.

The great abstract logical work of Gödel had a striking outcome. In analyzing the formal machinery of Gödel's description of what could be obtained by step-by-step procedures, the brilliant young English logician Alan Turing identified the results of such procedures—the general recursive functions—with the outcomes of what could be computed on a *machine in general*. It is with this analysis, and its impact on the minds of such men as John von Neumann and others, that the theoretical concept and the analysis of the digital computer in the modern sense began. It remains true to this very day that the theoretical description of what can be computed in general and its more penetrating analysis are rooted in that soil of mathematical logic which Gödel turned over for the first time in his memoir of 1931.

What kinds of conclusions should be drawn from examples like the one just cited? I should like to suggest some that I believe are validated by a broad range of experience.

1. The potential usefulness of a mathematical concept or technique in the advance of scientific understanding has very little to do with what one can foresee before the concept or technique has appeared.
2. Such usefulness has very little to do with the pure or applied character of the motivation underlying the creation of the technique or concept, or with its degree of logical or formal abstraction.
3. Concepts or techniques are useful only if they can eventually be put in a form that is simple and relatively easy to use in a variety of contexts. Putting them in such a form is not always an obvious task in terms of their original appearance, and often requires innovative originality of a very high order.
4. We do not know what will be useful (or even essential) until it has been used. We cannot rely upon the concepts and techniques that have been applied in the past without ruling out the possibility of significant innovation.

To use an industrial metaphor, mathematics (and especially pure mathematics) is the machine-tool industry of the sciences, and we cannot use only the tools manufactured in the past unless we believe that science will never again have significantly new problems to solve—a belief that is clearly false.

Contemporary Mathematical Research

If we consider the various areas of contemporary research in mathematics on a theoretical level, some of the most active and fruitful in terms of their development toward their own self-generated goals are also those having the most obvious and potentially significant links with the future development of the sciences. I shall try to give a brief survey of a number of conspicuous examples of this kind. I have already mentioned one case implicitly—the study of the theoretical process of computation based upon Turing's concept of a machine. The problems of the theory of computability have been formulated as asking whether a given problem can be solved in a number of steps that grows no faster than a fixed power of its number of components. The basic achievements of this study of the complexity of *computation* are fully in the spirit of Gödel—namely, there are simple, significant, explicitly stated basic problems that cannot be so solved.

Let me note in passing that the theory of automata—i.e. the abstract description of how a *machine in general* operates—is one of those domains to which a number of very abstract algebraic logical theories have been applied, such as categorical algebra, a form of very general algebraic logic derived originally from the application of algebra to topology.

A second example is the relation between topology and the study of the long-term or asymptotic properties of differential equations. Since the time of Newton, the basic laws describing physical processes have been set forth in the form of differential equations—i.e. equations prescribing the rate of change of the state variables of a physical system in terms of the given state of the system. Consider for example the system for two variables x and y in the form:

$$\frac{dx}{dt} = f(x,y)$$
$$\frac{dy}{dt} = g(x,y).$$

In the decade before World War I, the great French mathematician and mathematical astronomer Henri Poincaré introduced a mode of analysis of such equations in two unknowns that described the ultimate properties of their solutions:

$$x = x(t), \; y = y(t)$$

as t becomes very large. He showed that each such pair of functions when plotted as a point in the (x,y)-plane converges either to a singular point (x_0,y_0) for which $f(x_0,y_0) = 0$ and $g(x_0,y_0) = 0$ or to a *limit cycle*, a solution $\{u(t),v(t)\}$ such that $u(t + T) = u(t)$, $v(t + T) = v(t)$. He also gave conditions for the mutual relations of a number of singular points and limit cycles (e.g. each limit cycle must contain at least one singular point). The results obtained (the Poincaré-Bendixson theory) were applied in subsequent decades to a variety of problems in science and engineering, especially in the theory of servomechanisms and control processes, and more recently as one of the principal tools in formulating models in developmental biology. The extension of these results to more than 2 variables:

$$(x_1, \cdots, x_n)$$
$$\frac{dx_j}{dt} = f_j(x_1, \cdots, x_n), (1 \le j \le n)$$

was first attacked seriously in the past two decades and offers significant topological difficulties. The most important results were those obtained by Stephen Smale in the theory of the Morse-Smale systems. Even greater difficulties arise in the study of functional differential equations.

The asymptotic properties of such systems as those obtained from solutions of differential equations may be considered from another point of view, that of the theory of probability. In its modern form, the theory of probability was developed as a precise and powerfully sophisticated mathematical discipline on the basis of the theory of the Lebesgue integral and measure. This theory was invented by the French mathematician Henri Lebesgue in 1902 as the answer to the difficult pure mathematical problem of finding a simple system for integrating and computing the Fourier coefficients of very general real-valued functions. Probability theory developed in this century using ideas and techniques introduced by pure mathematicians such as the Russian André Kolmogoroff, the American Norbert Wiener, and the Frenchman Paul Levy. In 1931, George D. Birkhoff and John von Neumann proved the first two general ergodic theorems, giving a sharp mathematical formulation to the often-debated ergodic hypothesis of Ludwig Boltzmann and Josiah Willard Gibbs. This hypothesis on the long-run behavior of mechanical systems that contain a large number of components relates the temporal and spatial averages of a function f of a wandering point $u(t)$ on a constant energy surface Ω in phase space:

$$T^{-1} \int_0^T f(u(s))ds \to \int_\Omega f(w)dw.$$

An important example of an ergodic (or metrically transitive) system is given by the model of Bernoulli trials, which in the simplest form is the statistical result of tossing a fair coin. Starting around 1960, Kolmogoroff and some of his students, especially Jakov Sinai, generalized the physical concept of entropy in a subtle way to serve as a mathematical tool for the study of the transformation of probabilistic systems. The development of ergodic theory in this new and sophisticated form created the tools for the much deeper analysis of the statistical behavior of mechanical systems. In work initiated by Sinai and carried to completion by the American mathematician Donald Ornstein, surprising conclusions have been obtained to show that a few relatively crude statistical hypotheses imply that any such system is completely equivalent from the probabilistic point of view to one of the standard systems of Bernoulli trials.

The description of physical phenomena in a continuous form (of wave motion and diffusion as well as of equilibrium phenomena), has been given since the eighteenth century in the form of partial differential equations—i.e. equations prescribing rates of change in various spatial directions as well as in time in terms of the state variables. The pure mathematical theory of the solutions of partial differential equations, especially of those solutions that satisfy further conditions called boundary conditions on given regions of space-time in which they are defined, was begun by the celebrated German mathematician Bernhard Riemann in the 1850s and developed in conjunction with the whole framework of methods and concepts in mathematical analysis since that time. Since World War II, in particular, this theory has undergone intensive development through its interaction with two other broad mathematical theories. The first of these was the theory of (linear) functional analysis—i.e. of infinite dimensional vector spaces of functions with prescribed norms or topologies and linear operators or mappings on such spaces, where $T:X \to Y$ is said to be linear if

$$T(c_1 \mathbf{x}_1 + c_2 \mathbf{x}_2) = c_1 T(\mathbf{x}_1) + c_2 T(\mathbf{x}_2).$$

Using these basic ideas, the French mathematician Laurent Schwartz created a new theory of *distributions*, or generalized functions, through which new classes of solutions could be generated and a much more effective apparatus of calculating solutions could be created. The second such theory (created before World War II by men like

Michel Plancherel, Salomon Bochner, Norbert Wiener, Torsten Carleman, and others) was the theory of the Fourier transform, which in the n-dimensional case is

$$\hat{f}(\xi) = F(f)(\xi) =$$
$$(2\pi)^{-n/2} \int_{R^n} \exp(-i\langle x,\xi\rangle)f(x)dx$$

where

$$\langle x, \xi \rangle = x_1\xi_1 + \cdots + x_n\xi_n$$
$$x = (x_1, \cdots, x_n),$$
$$\xi = (\xi_1, \cdots, \xi_n)$$
$$dx = dx_1 \cdots dx_n$$

The classical problems concerning all the usual classes of partial differential equations have been solved in a simple and systematic way by the use of these tools. Broad new classes involving the foundations of relatively inaccessible theories, such as the theory of analytic functions of several complex variables, have also been attacked. Some very sophisticated tools have been invented in recent years that enable the rapid transformation of problems and their solutions—such tools as the theory of pseudodifferential operators of the form

$$Af(x) = \int_{R^n} \exp(-i\langle x,\xi\rangle) \, a(x,\xi)\hat{f}(\xi)d\xi$$

developed from the work of Alberto Calderon and Antoni Zygmund, and the more general theory of Fourier integral operators of the form

$$A(f)(x) = \int_{R^n} \exp(-i\phi(x, \xi)) \, a(x,\xi)\hat{f}(\xi)d\xi$$

introduced and studied by the Swedish mathematician Lars Hörmander and the Russian mathematician Dmitri Egoroff.

One of the most fertile classical pure-mathematical theories of the nineteenth century, which has been the center of a thousand applications, is the classical theory of analytic functions of a single complex variable. Let $w = f(z)$ be a complex function of a complex variable, i.e.

$$z = x + iy, \quad w = u + iv$$

with x and y, u and v real. Suppose that for each z in the disk around z_0, the function f is defined. Then f is said to be analytic if its components satisfy the system of partial differential equations (the Cauchy-Riemann equations):

$$\frac{\partial u}{\partial x} = \frac{\partial v}{\partial y}, \quad \frac{\partial v}{\partial x} = -\frac{\partial u}{\partial y}$$

The theory of analytic functions of a single complex variable was the masterwork of nineteenth-century mathematics. Its impact on physics can be measured by the opening sentence of the 1966 volume by the British physicists Eden, Landshoff, Olive, and Polkinghorne, *The Analytical S-Matrix*: "The great discovery of theoretical physics in the last decade has been the complex plane." One of the major pure-mathematical themes of the past three decades has been the extension (begun by Karl Weierstrass, Henri Poincaré, and Friedrich Hartogs at the end of the nineteenth century) of this theory to the theory of analytic functions of several complex variables:

$$w = f(z_1, \cdots, z_n)$$

where f is analytic in $(z_1, \cdots, z_n)$ if it is analytic in z_j for each j with all the others held fixed. One of the most important topics in this theory from the point of view of applications is the generalization of the theory of residues. Suppose $f(z_0) = 0$, and f vanishes nowhere else inside the curve C. Then

$$\int_C \frac{1}{f(z)} \, dz = c_{z_0}(f)$$

where $c_{z_0}(f)$ can be calculated by a systematic process from f and its derivatives at the point z_0. The generalization of this sort of conclusion to integrals over hypersurfaces in n-variables demands deep general results from the algebraic geometry of n-variables, such as the Picard-Lefschetz theory of algebraic varieties. While the theory of analytic functions of several complex variables has pressed forward in recent decades, mathematicians and physicists in the past decade have used such sophisticated results to calculate Feynman integrals involved in quantum field theory.

In addition to the rapid advances in the theory of linear partial differential equations during the past three decades, an equally intense development has taken place in the more difficult terrain of nonlinear partial differential equations and nonlinear problems. The applications, achieved and potential, of such a development encompass most of the key areas of the physical and biological sciences. One especially conspicuous application during the past decade has been in the theoretical description of nonlinear dispersive wave motion—the Korteweg-De Vries equation

$$\frac{\partial u}{\partial t} + u\frac{\partial u}{\partial x} + \frac{\partial^3 u}{\partial x^3} = 0$$

whose detailed investigation has shown the existence of solitons—permanent waves that move around and interact without losing their identity or vitality.

The study of nonlinear equations, partial differential equations, integral equations, or more general forms has demanded the development of a systematic study of nonlinear functional analysis, considering nonlinear operators on spaces of functions and studying the properties of solutions of equations involving such operators. Nonlinear problems form one of the most vital frontiers of future mathematics and theoretical science. The development of nonlinear functional analysis or operator theory has involved tools from algebraic topology, from the topology of differentiable manifolds, and from the theory of convexity, as well as the sharpest tools developed in the study of normed linear spaces. It has had a keen impact over the past decades in the study of a broad variety of nonlinear boundary value problems as well as in creating theories of new and more general problems relevant to applications not describable in terms of partial differential equations, such as variational inequalities and quasivariational inequalities.

An extremely promising program that proposes to apply sophisticated mathematical tools to a broad variety of problems in the sciences, and especially the domain of developmental biology, has been put forward by the French mathematician René Thom in his theory of *catastrophes*, presented in his book *Structural Stability and Morphogenesis*. As the title of Thom's book suggests, the key concept in his approach is that of structural stability, a topological concept introduced by the Russian mathematicians Ivan Andronov and Leon Pontrayagin in 1935. This concept can be described briefly as follows: Consider, for example, m functions of n real variables $(x_1, \cdots, x_n)$

$$y_j = f_j(x_1, \cdots, x_n), \; 1 \leq j \leq m$$

for $m \leq n$, defined for $|x| = (x_1^2 + \cdots + x_n^2)^{1/2} \leq r$. Write, for brevity,

$$y = f(x).$$

Then the system of functions f is said to be structurally stable if any function f_1, nearby in the sense that $f - f_1$ and all derivatives of order $\leq r$ (r given) are small, has the property that after an (invertible) change of variables

$$w = g(y)$$
$$u = h(x)$$

with x near the origin, and both f and g near the identity, the equation $y = f_1(x)$ is equivalent to $w = f(u)$.

In his mathematical theory of singularities, Thom initiated the study of structurally stable mappings, which was considerably extended by the French mathematician Benard Malgrange and the American mathematician John Mather. Thom's general thesis in his theory of catastrophes is to use the classification of structurally stable singularities as a model for the description of stable or repeatable forms in nature, which he insists must be structurally stable in order to exist in a persistent form. The applications of this thesis by Thom and his disciples have given rise to much discussion in theoretical biology and more recently in other disciplines, such as economics.

Although I do not have the space to present in detail other points of contact between sophisticated pure-mathematical concepts and techniques and interesting potential scientific applications, I will simply list a few of them here:

1. The use of concepts of Riemannian geometry in the large and differential topology by Roger Penrose, Stephen Hawking, Robert Geroch, etc., in the study of singularities in the general theory of relativity and the cosmological consequences.
2. The study of simple graded Lie algebras as a description of *supersymmetries* and *superselection* rules in elementary particle physics.
3. The application of results on the structure of large finite simple groups in algebraic coding theory.
4. The application of bifurcation theory, a branch of nonlinear functional analysis, to the description of flow problems, chemical reactions, fracture and buckling problems, etc.

5. The application of sophisticated results in combinatorial analysis, especially in connection with the packing of spheres, to various theoretical problems in crystallography.

6. The development of a rigorous, mathematically sophisticated constructive quantum field theory using formal analogies between field theory and statistical mechanics.

These certainly do not exhaust the possibilities; they do, however, provide a vivid illustration of the lively interchange of stimuli and ideas that already goes on between sophisticated domains in contemporary mathematics and important areas of contemporary scientific activity—an interchange that must continue and be raised to a continually higher level if mathematics and the sciences are to achieve their full potential.

Some Fundamental Questions

In the light of these examples, is there any reason why we should deny ourselves the pleasure of answering the question, Does pure mathematics have a relation to the sciences? with an emphatic *yes*? There is a very simple reason to deny us such an easy outcome, which tells us that in some perspectives the answer might well be *no* or, at the very least, *maybe*. This is the reason embodied in the preconceptions with whose analysis I began the discussion and with which we must deal at a more fundamental level before we can satisfactorily understand the question we have posed. We must see the nature of the question as a significant fact within the context of the intellectual history of our century as a part of the whole of conscious human history. We can learn a good deal more by looking at the same time at some closely related questions.

Why are the physical sciences so mathematical in their basic conceptual and theoretical underpinnings? To use the language of a famous essay by Eugene Wigner, why has mathematics proved so unreasonably effective in the physical sciences? If the theoretical side of the physical sciences is as fundamentally mathematical as it appears to be, why has there come to be such an apparent alienation or mutual estrangement between scientific and mathematical research as that which is incarnated in the ideal of *purity* of mathematics, in the sense of the negative connotations of sharp and irreducible separation?

I propose to discuss this complex of questions and suggest some answers of my own. Answers to questions of this sort, of course, do not fall within the scope of a sharply defined system of verified objective knowledge such as one asks for in the classical ideal of scientific knowledge or in the very similar, if even more idealized, form of mathematical knowledge. We must exercise an irreducible amount of individual judgment, and reason (as Pascal remarked) in the spirit of subtlety rather than in the spirit of geometry. Moreover, the answers I propose are somewhat unorthodox in their nature and will tend to disturb the taste of a certain type of dogmatic mathematician as much as of the dogmatic natural scientist.

The Historical Background

The conscious development of mathematical knowledge as well as the recognition of scientific knowledge as such began with the ancient Greeks. With the Greeks as well as the Babylonians before them, the development of mathematical ideas and techniques took place in parallel with the development of the first explicitly rational science—descriptive and predictive astronomy. For the Pythagoreans, who gave mathematics its name in sixth-century Greece, the universality of mathematical relationship in the cosmos was shown by numerical relations in the movement of the heavenly bodies and by those that govern musical tones. In the more sophisticated and logically critical intellectual milieu generated by the Greek philosophical schools, and particularly by the Eleatics and Plato, mathematics was transformed into a logically deductive a priori discipline of geometry and number. Yet its close relation to the study of the physical cosmos continued in the work of mathematicians like Eudoxus and Archimedes, who were also great astronomers and mathematical physicists. Even Plato, the greatest a priorist in human history, for whom mathematics was a knowledge of transcendents, found a role for mathematics in his *Timaeus* in the formation of the physical elements and the structure of the heavens.

In the creative period of physical science and of mathematics that began in Western Europe in the latter years of the sixteenth century and continued on to become what has been called the Seventeenth-century Scientific Revolution, the revolutionary program of the "analytic" in mathematics of men like Vieta and Descartes went hand in hand with the revolutionary program of Copernicus in astronomy and Galileo in physics and merged with them in the great achievement of the century—Newton's mathematical cosmology based on Newtonian mechanics. The "modern" science of the seventeenth century was modern precisely in its mathematical character, and it remains the permanent and irreplaceable paradigm of what scientific knowledge should be to the present day (no matter how little resemblance scientific knowledge sometimes bears to this paradigm). The "modern" mathematics of the seventeenth century—the program of the analytic that culminated in the systematic treatment of the differential and integral calculus by Newton, Leibniz, and their successors—was modern precisely in its focus on solving problems and reaching the unknown in a spirit designed to penetrate and clarify the concepts of the newly arising mathematical physics.

How much some of the great figures of the scientific renaissance were seriously involved in the process of purely mathematical development of the time is little known or appreciated. Many of us know for example that Kepler as an ardent Platonist found his celebrated three laws of planetary motion by trying to inscribe the five regular Platonic solids in the orbits of the planets. Few know that the title of one of Kepler's substantial books was *On Calculating the Volume of Barrels*, i.e. in the language of the succeeding period, a treatise on integral calculus. Fewer still are aware of the role of Galileo and his pupils in the early development of the calculus, or of Kepler's contributions to the treatment of infinite processes.

Mathematics and physics in the seventeenth century were two distinct but related forms of objective knowledge, as they had been for Archimedes 2,000 years earlier. In fact, one might even venture to say that, for the seventeenth cen-

tury at least, the concept of scientific knowledge in the domain of physics was more or less identical with the results of applying a mathematical way of thinking to the study of physical problems and phenomena.

What I have just said raises an important and difficult problem. What do we mean when we speak of a mathematical way of thinking? There is little doubt that, in some senses at least, we are speaking of a historically conditioned phenomenon just as we do if we speak of a pattern of thought of a physicist or of a biologist. We have a strong tendency to believe and to argue that the patterns of thought we can observe in the works of our professional predecessors are simply imperfect variants of our own way of thought. This is fairly clearly not the case, at least in the following sense: though there are more or less permanent or cumulative technical developments in all these fields, this cumulativeness or permanence does not extend to the subjective images or self-concepts of the principal practitioners. Each generation of mathematicians or scientists reacts to a different body of accumulated knowledge and a vastly different body of accumulated problems. Each generation is molded most forcefully by its own direct experience in trying to confront and master the problems of its own time.

Mathematics undeniably has had a stable repertoire of basic themes. Some that it has accumulated over the centuries include number, geometry and its application to space, the solution of algebraic equations, infinite processes and the mathematics of changing quantities, continuity, and probability. It has a stable component of method: the primacy of deductive argument and the use of symbolic representation. During the past two centuries it has generated newer and even more forceful central themes and ideas: the study of groups and other algebraic systems, the study of analytic functions of a complex variable, the study of solutions of ordinary and partial differential equations as well as the more inclusive study of operations on spaces of functions we now call functional analysis, differential geometry, and the theory of manifolds, as well as all the varied forms taken in the twentieth century by topology. Finally, mathematics in the past century has begun to study its own methods of reasoning and its own structure as the objects of new mathematical methods and disciplines.

In the first decade of the twentieth century, fundamental attitudes toward mathematics were transformed in the discussion of the foundations of mathematics. Under the impetus of problems generated by one of the most original innovations in the mathematics of modern times—Cantor's theory of infinite sets—an intense division of opinion developed among leading mathematicians and logicians as to the legitimate basis for justifying the validity of mathematical knowledge. Three major currents of ideology arose and fought for supremacy—intuitionism, logicism, and formalism. Logicism, first formulated by Frege and popularized by Russell, argued for founding mathematics upon the transparencies of logical truth. It turned out that logical truth is not transparent, and this program, which was the favorite of logicians rather than mathematicians, collapsed. Intuitionism, founded and led by Brouwer, denied the validity of most reasoning about infinite processes, classical as well as Cantorian. If it had prospered, it would have made mathematical activity in most mathematical fields impossibly difficult. It did not prosper.

The third movement, formalism, endorsed and led by the most prestigious German mathematician of the time, David Hilbert, won a victory by default (though Hilbert's technical program collapsed under Gödel's analysis). The formalist doctrine in foundations justified the correctness (not the significance) of mathematical theories by trying to show that they did not lead to contradictions. By its accession to the position of an orthodoxy, it achieved effects that its rather sophisticated originators certainly never dreamed of.

In its most vulgar form (and it is the vulgar form of sophisticated intellectual doctrines that tend to sweep across the intellectual landscape), the formalist doctrine was taken to say that mathematics consists simply of the formal manipulation of uninterpreted symbols, or of reasoning by formal deduction (itself reduced simply to symbolic manipulation) from any assumptions whatever as long as they could be presented in an explicitly symbolic form. (To quote a well-known aphorism of Russell: "Mathematics is the subject in which we do not know what we are talking about, and we do not care whether what we are saying is true.") Taken in this form (and it is clear from his explicit statements that Hilbert would have found the thesis horrifying), the vulgar formalist doctrine argues against even the possibility of any objective content for any part of mathematics, and indeed (very effectively from its own assumptions) against the significance and the content of the historically conditioned mathematical fields as well as against their intuitions and central problems. In the context of applying mathematics to the analysis of the phenomena of the natural world, this view tends to make any significant application a miracle on principle and a triumph of will over content. It is in terms of this vulgar formalist conception of mathematics that Wigner's phrase about the unreasonable effectiveness of mathematics in the physical sciences gains its psychological force for most people (though clearly the sense that Wigner intended was simply to emphasize the surprising applications of mathematical ideas such as symmetry). Indeed, how could a game with meaningless symbols bear any intrinsic or significant relation to the processes of the physical world?

Instrumentalism and Quantum Mechanics

An important aggravation of vulgar formalism took place as a consequence of one of the major turning points in the history of modern physics— the creation of quantum mechanics and its transformation of physics during the late 1920s and early 1930s. Perhaps the most thoroughly mathematical in form of all physical theories that had developed up to that time, quantum mechanics and its mathematical machinery failed to achieve an easy rapprochement with conventional physical intuition and failed to obliterate the classical ideal of physics which it officially replaced. What it did succeed in doing was to destroy the strong influence of *rationalism* as a cornerstone of physical theory. Perhaps the most fruitful in detailed application of any of the major physical theories, quantum mechanics might justify the words of G. K. Chesterton: "I have seen the truth, and it makes no sense."

In the subsequent development of theoretical physics, the disjunction between mathematical formalism and the demands of a confining intuition has become ever greater as the theories have grown more elaborate. While the vulgar formalist attitude toward mathematics has never achieved a totally dominant influence upon mathematical research, the very similar instrumentalist viewpoint of the contemporary theoretical physicist toward mathematics became dominant in the domain of basic physical concepts, the very domain in which, until the quantum mechanical revolution, the most creative interaction had taken place between mathematics and the physical sciences.

Certainly in the past decade, if not over a longer period, the influence of formalist doctrines in any form has waned in terms of the attitudes of mathematicians carrying on research on a significant level. This has not been accompanied by any great thrust of counterideology. Indeed, over the same period, vulgar formalism has been spread on a much more explicit level and to a much wider public than it ever reached before, through the formalist thrust of a large part of the new curricula in the elementary and secondary schools.

"Formalism" in this sense has a natural root within the trivial common-sense assumptions of our present-day culture: it is a trivially natural way to do mathematics if one disbelieves in universals. We find it easy to believe in the reality of physical things and (except for the behaviorists) in the reality of thoughts in people's heads. We find it difficult in principle, except after long conditioning, to believe in formal or mathematical relations as objective realities independent of a conscious mind. The fact that the most fundamental and firmly accepted parts of our general scientific knowledge of the world involve mathematical relations as complex and sophisticated as those involved in Newtonian mechanics, in the Maxwell electromagnetic theory, in special relativity, or in the operator formalism of quantum mechanics seems to elude us even when we take these doctrines for granted.

The answer I seem to be producing for the questions I listed earlier may seem perverse to some. Mathematics in its own distinct way is an objective science dealing with certain basic intuitive themes of human experience and practice by a continually more ingenious apparatus of technical devices and simplifying concepts. Because of its origins and its nature, mathematics is not unreasonably effective in the physical sciences: it is simply (though surprisingly) effective. With a certain amount of ingenuity and insight (amounting perhaps to genius), someone will probably even make it reasonably effective in the biological sciences.

Mathematics is being ever more extensively applied and in a way that fulfills its basic character. Every serious contribution to mathematical thought is fundamentally applicable since it represents, if it is serious, a new insight into relations of a fundamental kind. (By an extension of the principle of plenitude, one might even venture the assertion that every significant mathematical relation must have a significant role within the phenomena of the physical, biological, or social worlds. Of course, I am begging the metaphysical question by the use of the adjective *significant*, but not the practical question.)

Indeed, who at the time of the writing of Apollonius's book on conic sections in the third century B.C. would have dreamed that almost 2,000 years later, Kepler would have employed his results to describe the motion of the planets? Who would have thought in 1831, when Galois introduced the concept of the *group* into the study of the solvability properties of algebraic equations in terms of radicals, that a century and more later the fundamental principles of physics would be formulated in terms of concepts from group theory? Who (except for Leibniz, of course) might have foreseen that the development of mathematical logic and of proof theory in the first thirty-odd years of the twentieth century would make it the basic conceptual tool for the introduction of digital computers and the basis for their great transformation of modern technology?

Why has there been a tendency to estrangement between most fields of scientific research and some of the main currents of mathematical research during the past fifty years? In part, this is due to the influence of formalist currents in mathematics and an instrumentalist view of mathematics in the physical sciences. A role, though somewhat smaller, has been played by the pressures of specialization and the enormous complexities generated in the technical development of the individual fields of science and mathematics. The most damaging effect of this lies in the tendency to treat the education of students in any field as a process of indoctrination in the given field to the exclusion of openness to other types of experience and insight.

Within mathematics itself, we cannot neglect the role in this estrangement played by the emphasis upon the primacy of new fields of mathematical research that have originated from more classical domains of mathematics rather than from areas whose problems and insight are connected with the natural sciences. The most important examples of such fields have been mathematical logic, the theory of numbers and especially algebraic number theory, algebraic topology, and algebraic geometry. Such emphasis has been strongly buttressed by the role of influential groups of mathematicians stressing this position, particularly mathematicians associated with the Bourbaki group in France. It is not the case, however, that in their consequences, the development of such disciplines needs to remain permanently irrelevant to applications in other scientific disciplines. Examples to the contrary are numerous and important.

Is there any serious reason to believe that the future will bring closer relations between mathematical research and research in the natural sciences? In answering this question, the problem lies in the adjective *serious*. A fairly wide range of promising new tendencies have begun to close the gap that has existed between mathematics and various sciences. One is the growing respect for and diminished hostility to those individuals who have made a conscious and explicit effort to assimilate new and relatively sophisticated developments in mathematics and adapt them to a useful role in theoretical physics. A second important tendency is the rise of a class of mathematicians of the highest talent who are interested in dealing with fundamental problems in various theoretical sciences and actively involved in resolving their mathematical difficulties—such as James Glimm, Arthur Jaffe, and many others in constructive field theory, and a whole host led by René Thom in biology. A third very promising tendency is the

growing interaction in certain areas of mathematical applications of mathematicians of varying degrees of "purity." One can point to significant examples in fluid mechanics, stochastic processes, numerical analysis of partial differential equations, control theory and dynamical systems, and mathematical economics. We may see in this last tendency a hopeful antidote to the negative development during the past few years of a systematic separation of (and in many cases of organized conflict between) opposed groups of mathematicians labeled *pure* and *applied*.

On the basis of objective criteria, there is no single field called applied mathematics having the same relative unity of background and ethos provided to mathematics as a whole by its historical tradition. The current varieties of application of mathematics are quite different from one another in content and method and are certainly not based upon any common methodological core. Applied mathematics can be most accurately described as a family of subfields each of which starts with the methods of one or another mathematical discipline and concerns itself with a field of application external to mathematics proper. The generation of organized opposition and separation between pure and applied mathematical factions in American universities has given rise to an unprincipled factionalism and exaggerated confrontations between fictitious ideals of mathematical purity on the one side and equally fictional slogans of extramathematical relevance on the other.

Mathematics and Contemporary Society

During the past year, I presented some remarks on the theme of the present article to a meeting of science journalists. The manager of the meeting, having looked casually at the manuscript of an earlier treatment of this question, plucked from it the Chesterton quotation I cited above and presented it as his description of mathematics. I observed then and I observe now that whether or not Chesterton's aphorism, which he puts in the mouth of his detective Father Brown, applied to the world at large, it cannot be true of mathematics at all. By the principles by which it forms itself, mathematics is *the truth that makes sense.*

However, Chesterton's aphorism and its use by that conference organizer do provide an important commentary and a moral on the role of mathematics in the world.

Contemporary society is becoming increasingly mathematicized in a number of essential ways. On the level of everyday life and social practice, we see the dominant role of the quantitative approach and the digital computer as the central organizing instruments of the technological mass society. In the practice of an ever-widening variety of intellectual disciplines, whether in the physical, biological, or social sciences, or even in the humanities, an increasingly dominant role has long been held or is being assumed by systems of concepts formulated in mathematical terms and involving the use of relatively sophisticated mathematical techniques. At the same time, there is little general understanding in society at large, even among the well-educated, of what mathematics is and how it functions. It is this disparity between what is and what people understand that is illuminated by Father Brown's aphorism. It illuminates as well the sense of alienation that this disparity creates by making it impossible for most educated members of our society to have the knowledge and understanding necessary for a meaningful critical assessment of the social practices and intellectual disciplines based upon such uses of mathematics. It is to the effort to transform and abolish this alienation that the present exercise in the "rectification of names" is dedicated.

The Unreasonable Effectiveness of Mathematics in the Natural Sciences

Eugene P. Wigner

Eugene Paul Wigner was born in Budapest, Hungary, in 1902. In 1925 he received his doctorate from the Technische Hochschule in Berlin. He received twenty-one honorary degrees within twenty-four years (between 1949 and 1973) and has held academic appointments at Göttingen, Wisconsin, and Princeton. Since 1971 he has been an emeritus professor of physics and astronomy. He has received a Nobel Prize in physics, the Medal of Merit, the Franklin Medal, the Fermi Award, the Atoms for Peace Award, the Max Planck Medal, the National Medal of Science and the Albert Einstein Award. He was president of the American Physical Society and is a member of the National Academy of Science.

Samuel Johnson, the British lexicographer and essayist, on seeing a dancing dog is reputed to have observed that "the remarkable thing is not that it was not done well but that it was done at all!" The author of this essay has essentially the same feeling about the role of mathematics in natural science. The remarkable thing, in his view, is that one is able to explain anything at all. The unreasonable effectiveness to which the title refers is the rather amazing ability of modern science to form mathematical models of natural phenomena that not only accurately describe current empirical events but also predict phenomena that no one had previously observed. For example, Newton's theory predicted the possibility of artificial satellites, Einstein's theory predicted the possibility of atomic bombs, and modern cosmology predicted the possibility of black holes.

There is no fundamental reason that explains such effectiveness. Indeed it is easy to conceive of a variety of hypothetical eventualities that would forever shatter our confidence in the ability of science to rationally account for the empirical. Wigner describes how such a faith-shattering event might occur. He then observes, however, that our confidence in the methodology of science and its language of mathematics has endured no such trauma to the present. And that is truly remarkable.

. . . and it is probable that there is some secret here which remains to be discovered—C. S. PEIRCE

THERE IS A story about two friends, who were classmates in high school, talking about their jobs. One of them became a statistician and was working on population trends. He showed a reprint to his former classmate. The reprint started, as usual, with the Gaussian distribution and the statistician explained to his former classmate the meaning of the symbols for the actual population, for the average population, and so on. His classmate was a bit incredulous and was not quite sure whether the statistician was pulling his

Source: Eugene P. Wigner, "The Unreasonable Effectiveness of Mathematics in the Natural Sciences," *Communications in Pure and Applied Mathematics,* 13(1960):1–14. Reprinted by permission of John Wiley & Sons, Inc.

leg. "How can you know that?" was his query. "And what is this symbol here?" "Oh," said the statistician, "this is π." "What is that?" "The ratio of the circumference of the circle to its diameter." "Well, now you are pushing your joke too far," said the classmate, "surely the population has nothing to do with the circumference of the circle."

Naturally, we are inclined to smile about the simplicity of the classmate's approach. Nevertheless, when I heard this story, I had to admit to an eerie feeling because, surely, the reaction of the classmate betrayed only plain common sense. I was even more confused when, not many days later, someone came to me and expressed his bewilderment[1] with the fact that we make a rather narrow selection when choosing the data on which we test our theories. "How do we know that, if we made a theory which focuses its attention on phenomena we disregard and disregards some of the phenomena now commanding our attention, that we could not build another theory which has little in common with the present one but which, nevertheless, explains just as many phenomena as the present theory." It has to be admitted that we have not definite evidence that there is no such theory.

The preceding two stories illustrate the two main points which are the subjects of the present discourse. The first point is that mathematical concepts turn up in entirely unexpected connections. Moreover, they often permit an unexpectedly close and accurate description of the phenomena in these connections. Secondly, just because of this circumstance, and because we do not understand the reasons for their usefulness, we cannot know whether a theory formulated in terms of mathematical concepts is uniquely appropriate. We are in a position similar to that of a man who was provided with a bunch of keys and who, having to open several doors in succession, always hit on the right key on the first or second trial. He became skeptical concerning the uniqueness of the coordination between keys and doors.

Most of what will be said on these questions will not be new; it has probably occurred to most scientists in one form or another. My principal aim is to illuminate it from several sides. The first

point is that the enormous usefulness of mathematics in the natural sciences is something bordering on the mysterious and that there is no rational explanation for it. Second, it is just this uncanny usefulness of mathematical concepts that raises the question of the uniqueness of our physical theories. In order to establish the first point, that mathematics plays an unreasonably important role in physics, it will be useful to say a few words on the question "What is mathematics?" then, "What is physics?" then, how mathematics enters physical theories, and last, why the success of mathematics in its role in physics appears so baffling. Much less will be said on the second point: the uniqueness of the theories of physics. A proper answer to this question would require elaborate experimental and theoretical work which has not been undertaken to date.

What Is Mathematics?

Somebody once said that philosophy is the misuse of a terminology which was invented just for this purpose.[2] In the same vein, I would say that mathematics is the science of skillful operations with concepts and rules invented just for this purpose. The principal emphasis is on the invention of concepts. Mathematics would soon run out of interesting theorems if these had to be formulated in terms of the concepts which already appear in the axioms. Furthermore, whereas it is unquestionably true that the concepts of elementary mathematics and particularly elementary geometry were formulated to describe entities which are directly suggested by the actual world, the same does not seem to be true of the more advanced concepts, in particular the concepts which play such an important role in physics. Thus, the rules for operations with pairs of numbers are obviously designed to give the same results as the operations with fractions which we first learned without reference to "pairs of numbers." The rules for the operations with sequences, that is with irrational numbers, still belong to the category of rules which were determined so as to reproduce rules for the operations with quantities which were already known to us. Most more advanced mathematical concepts, such as complex numbers, algebras, linear operators, Borel sets—and this list could be continued almost indefinitely—were so devised that they are apt subjects on which the mathematician can demonstrate his ingenuity and sense of formal beauty. In fact, the definition of these concepts, with a realization that interesting and ingenious considerations could be applied to them, is the first demonstration of the ingeniousness of the mathematician who defines them. The depth of thought which goes into the formation of the mathematical concepts is later justified by the skill with which these concepts are used. The great mathematician fully, almost ruthlessly, exploits the domain of permissible reasoning and skirts the impermissible. That his recklessness does not lead him into a morass of contradictions is a miracle in itself: certainly it is hard to believe that our reasoning power was brought, by Darwin's process of natural selection, to the perfection which it seems to possess. However, this is not our present subject. The principal point which will have to be recalled later is that the mathematician could formulate only a handful of interesting theorems without defining concepts beyond those contained in the axioms and that the concepts outside those contained in the axioms are defined with a view of permitting ingenious logical operations which appeal to our aesthetic sense both as operations and also in their results of great generality and simplicity.[3]

The complex numbers provide a particularly striking example for the foregoing. Certainly, nothing in our experience suggests the introduction of these quantities. Indeed, if a mathematician is asked to justify his interest in complex numbers, he will point, with some indignation, to the many beautiful theorems in the theory of equations, of power series and of analytic functions in general, which owe their origin to the introduction of complex numbers. The mathematician is not willing to give up his interest in these most beautiful accomplishments of his genius.[4]

What Is Physics?

The physicist is interested in discovering the laws of inanimate nature. In order to understand this statement, it is necessary to analyze the concept "law of nature."

The world around us is of baffling complexity and the most obvious fact about it is that we cannot predict the future. Although the joke attributes only to the optimist the view that the future is uncertain, the optimist is right in this case: the future is unpredictable. It is, as Schrödinger (1933) has remarked, a miracle that in spite of the baffling complexity of the world, certain regularities in the events could be discovered. One such regularity, discovered by Galileo, is that two rocks, dropped at the same time from the same height, reach the ground at the same time. The laws of nature are concerned with such regularities. Galileo's regularity is a prototype of a large class of regularities. It is a surprising regularity for three reasons.

The first reason that it is surprising is that it is true not only in Pisa, and in Galileo's time, it is true everywhere on the Earth, was always true, and will always be true. This property of the regularity is a recognized invariance property and, as I had occasion to point out some time ago (Wigner, 1949), without invariance principles similar to those implied in the preceding generalization of Galileo's observation, physics would not be possible. The second surprising feature is that the regularity which we are discussing is independent of so many conditions which could have an effect on it. It is valid no matter whether it rains or not, whether the experiment is carried out in a room or from the Leaning Tower, no matter whether the person who drops the rocks is a man or a woman. It is valid even if the two rocks are dropped, simultaneously and from the same height, by two different people. There are, obviously, innumerable other conditions which are all immaterial from the point of view of the validity of Galileo's regularity. The irrelevancy of so many circumstances which *could* play a role in the phenomenon observed, has also been called an invariance (Wigner, 1949). However, this invariance is of a different character than the preceding one since it cannot be formulated as a general principle. The exploration of the conditions which do, and which do not, influence a phenomenon is part of the early experimental exploration of a field. It is the skill and ingenuity of the experimenter which shows him phenomena which depend on a relatively narrow set of relatively easily realizable and reproducible conditions.[5] In the present case, Galileo's restriction of his observations to relatively heavy bodies was the most important step in this regard. Again, it is true that if there were no phenomena which are independent of all but a manageably small set of conditions, physics would be impossible.

The preceding two points, though highly significant from the point of view of the philosopher, are not the ones which surprised Galileo most, nor do they contain a specific law of nature. The law of nature is contained in the statement that the length of time which it takes for a heavy object to fall from a given height is independent of the size, material and shape of the body which drops. In the framework of Newton's second "law," this amounts to the statement that the gravitational force which acts on the falling body is proportional to its mass but independent of the size, material and shape of the body which falls.

The preceding discussion is intended to remind, first, that it is not at all natural that "laws of nature" exist, much less that man is able to discover them.[6] The present writer had occasion, some time ago, to call attention to the succession of layers of "laws of nature," each layer containing more general and more encompassing laws than the previous one and its discovery constituting a deeper penetration into the structure of the universe than the layers recognized before (Wigner, 1950). However, the point which is most significant in the present context is that all these laws of nature contain, in even their remotest consequences, only a small part of our knowledge of the inanimate world. All the laws of nature are conditional statements which permit a prediction of some future events on the basis of the knowledge of the present, except that some aspects of the present state of the world, in practice the overwhelming majority of the determinants of the present state of the world, are irrelevant from the point of view of the prediction. The irrelevancy is meant in the sense of the second point in the discussion of Galileo's theorem.[7]

As regards the present state of the world, such as the existence of the earth on which we live and on which Galileo's experiments were performed,

the existence of the sun and of all our surroundings, the laws of nature are entirely silent. It is in consonance with this, first, that the laws of nature can be used to predict future events only under exceptional circumstances—when all the relevant determinants of the present state of the world are known. It is also in consonance with this that the construction of machines, the functioning of which he can foresee, constitutes the most spectacular accomplishment of the physicist. In these machines, the physicist creates a situation in which all the relevant coordinates are known so that the behavior of the machine can be predicted. Radars and nuclear reactors are examples of such machines.

The principal purpose of the preceding discussion is to point out that the laws of nature are all conditional statements and they relate only to a very small part of our knowledge of the world. Thus, classical mechanics, which is the best known prototype of a physical theory, gives the second derivatives of the positional coordinates of all bodies, on the basis of the knowledge of the positions, etc., of these bodies. It gives no information on the existence, the present positions, or velocities of these bodies. It should be mentioned, for the sake of accuracy, that we have learned about thirty years ago that even the conditional statements cannot be entirely precise: that the conditional statements are probability laws which enable us only to place intelligent bets on future properties of the inanimate world, based on the knowledge of the present state. They do not allow us to make categorical statements, not even categorical statements conditional on the present state of the world. The probabilistic nature of the "laws of nature" manifests itself in the case of machines also, and can be verified, at least in the case of nuclear reactors, if one runs them at very low power. However, the additional limitation of the scope of the laws of nature[8] which follows from their probabilistic nature, will play no role in the rest of the discussion.

The Role of Mathematics in Physical Theories

Having refreshed our minds as to the essence of mathematics and physics, we should be in a better position to review the role of mathematics in physical theories.

Naturally, we do use mathematics in everyday physics to evaluate the results of the laws of nature, to apply the conditional statements to the particular conditions which happen to prevail or happen to interest us. In order that this be possible, the laws of nature must already be formulated in mathematical language. However, the role of evaluating the consequences of already established theories is not the most important role of mathematics in physics. Mathematics, or, rather, applied mathematics, is not so much the master of the situation in this function: it is merely serving as a tool.

Mathematics does play, however, also a more sovereign role in physics. This was already implied in the statement, made when discussing the role of applied mathematics, that the laws of nature must be already formulated in the language of mathematics to be an object for the use of applied mathematics. The statement that the laws of nature are written in the language of mathematics was properly made three hundred years ago;[9] it is now more true than ever before. In order to show the importance which mathematical concepts possess in the formulation of the laws of physics, let us recall, as an example, the axioms of quantum mechanics as formulated, explicitly, by the great mathematician, von Neumann (1955), or, implicitly, by the great physicist, Dirac (1947). There are two basic concepts in quantum mechanics: states and observables. The states are vectors in Hilbert space, the observables self-adjoint operators on these vectors. The possible values of the observations are the characteristic values of the operators—but we had better stop here lest we engage in a listing of the mathematical concepts developed in the theory of linear operators.

It is true, of course, that physics chooses certain mathematical concepts for the formulation of the laws of nature, and surely only a fraction of all mathematical concepts is used in physics. It is true also that the concepts which were chosen were not selected arbitrarily from a listing of mathematical terms but were developed, in many if not most cases, independently by the physicist and recognized then as having been conceived before by the mathematician. It is not true, how-

ever, as is so often stated, that this had to happen because mathematics uses the simplest possible concepts and these were bound to occur in any formalism. As we saw before, the concepts of mathematics are not chosen for their conceptual simplicity—even sequences of pairs of numbers are far from being the simplest concepts—but for their amenability to clever manipulations and to striking, brilliant arguments. Let us not forget that the Hilbert space of quantum mechanics is the complex Hilbert space, with a Hermitean scalar product. Surely to the unpreoccupied mind, complex numbers are far from natural or simple and they cannot be suggested by physical observations. Furthermore, the use of complex numbers is in this case not a calculational trick of applied mathematics but comes close to being a necessity in the formulation of the laws of quantum mechanics. Finally, it now begins to appear that not only numbers but so-called analytic functions are destined to play a decisive role in the formulation of quantum theory. I am referring to the rapidly developing theory of dispersion relations.

It is difficult to avoid the impression that a miracle confronts us here, quite comparable in its striking nature to the miracle that the human mind can string a thousand arguments together without getting itself into contradictions or to the two miracles of the existence of laws of nature and of the human mind's capacity to divine them. The observation which comes closest to an explanation for the mathematical concepts' cropping up in physics which I know is Einstein's statement that the only physical theories which we are willing to accept are the beautiful ones. It stands to argue that the concepts of mathematics, which invite the exercise of so much wit, have the quality of beauty. However, Einstein's observation can at best explain properties of theories which we are willing to believe and has no reference to the intrinsic accuracy of the theory. We shall, therefore, turn to this latter question.

Is the Success of Physical Theories Truly Surprising?

A possible explanation of the physicist's use of mathematics to formulate his laws of nature is that he is a somewhat irresponsible person. As a result, when he finds a connection between two quantities which resembles a connection well-known from mathematics, he will jump at the conclusion that the connection *is* that discussed in mathematics simply because he does not know of any other similar connection. It is not the intention of the present discussion to refute the charge that the physicist is a somewhat irresponsible person. Perhaps he is. However, it is important to point out that the mathematical formulation of the physicist's often crude experience leads in an uncanny number of cases to an amazingly accurate description of a large class of phenomena. This shows that the mathematical language has more to commend it than being the only language which we can speak; it shows that it is, in a very real sense, the correct language. Let us consider a few examples.

The first example is the oft quoted one of planetary motion. The laws of falling bodies became rather well established as a result of experiments carried out principally in Italy. These experiments could not be very accurate in the sense in which we understand accuracy today partly because of the effect of air resistance and partly because of the impossibility, at that time, to measure short time intervals. Nevertheless, it is not surprising that as a result of their studies, the Italian natural scientists acquired a familiarity with the ways in which objects travel through the atmosphere. It was Newton who then brought the law of freely falling objects into relation with the motion of the moon, noted that the parabola of the thrown rock's path on the earth, and the circle of the moon's path in the sky, are particular cases of the same mathematical object of an ellipse and postulated the universal law of gravitation, on the basis of a single, and at that time very approximate, numerical coincidence. Philosophically, the law of gravitation as formulated by Newton was repugnant to his time and to himself. Empirically, it was based on very scanty observations. The mathematical language in which it was formulated contained the concept of a second derivative and those of us who have tried to draw an osculating circle to a curve know that the second derivative is not a very immediate concept. The law of gravity which Newton reluctantly estab-

lished and which he could verify with an accuracy of about 4 percent has proved to be accurate to less than a ten thousandth of a percent and became so closely associated with the idea of absolute accuracy that only recently did physicists become again bold enough to inquire into the limitations of its accuracy.[10] Certainly, the example of Newton's law, quoted over and over again, must be mentioned first as a monumental example of a law, formulated in terms which appear simple to the mathematician, which has proved accurate beyond all reasonable expectation. Let us just recapitulate our thesis on this example: first, the law, particularly since a second derivative appears in it, is simple only to the mathematician, not to common sense or to non-mathematically-minded freshmen; second, it is a conditional law of very limited scope. It explains nothing about the earth which attracts Galileo's rocks, or about the circular form of the moon's orbit, or about the planets of the sun. The explanation of these initial conditions is left to the geologist and the astronomer, and they have a hard time with them.

The second example is that of ordinary, elementary quantum mechanics. This originated when Max Born noticed that some rules of computation, given by Heisenberg, were formally identical with the rules of computation with matrices, established a long time before by mathematicians. Born, Jordan and Heisenberg then proposed to replace by matrices the position and momentum variables of the equations of classical mechanics (1925, 1926). They applied the rules of matrix mechanics to a few highly idealized problems and the results were quite satisfactory. However, there was, at that time, no rational evidence that their matrix mechanics would prove correct under more realistic conditions. Indeed, they say "if the mechanics as here proposed should already be correct in its essential traits." As a matter of fact, the first application of their mechanics to a realistic problem, that of the hydrogen atom, was given several months later, by Pauli. This application gave results in agreement with experience. This was satisfactory but still understandable because Heisenberg's rules of calculation were abstracted from problems which included the old theory of the hydrogen atom. The miracle occurred only when matrix mechanics, or a mathematically equivalent theory, was applied to problems for which Heisenberg's calculating rules were meaningless. Heisenberg's rules presupposed that the classical equations of motion had solutions with certain periodicity properties; and the equations of motion of the two electrons of the helium atom, or of the even greater number of electrons of heavier atoms, simply do not have these properties, so that Heisenberg's rules cannot be applied to these cases. Nevertheless, the calculation of the lowest energy level of helium, as carried out a few months ago by Kinoshita at Cornell and by Bazley at the Bureau of Standards, agree with the experimental data within the accuracy of the observations, which is one part in ten millions. Surely in this case we "got something out" of the equations that we did not put in.

The same is true of the qualitative characteristics of the "complex spectra," that is the spectra of heavier atoms. I wish to recall a conversation with Jordan who told me, when the qualitative features of the spectra were derived, that a disagreement of the rules derived from quantum mechanical theory, and the rules established by empirical research, would have provided the last opportunity to make a change in the framework of matrix mechanics. In other words, Jordan felt that we would have been, at least temporarily, helpless had an unexpected disagreement occurred in the theory of the helium atom. This was, at that time, developed by Kellner and by Hilleraas. The mathematical formalism was too clear and unchangeable so that, had the miracle of helium which was mentioned before not occurred, a true crisis would have arisen. Surely, physics would have overcome that crisis in one way or another. It is true, on the other hand, that physics as we know it today would not be possible without a constant recurrence of miracles similar to the one of the helium atom which is perhaps the most striking miracle that has occurred in the course of the development of elementary quantum mechanics, but by far not the only one. In fact, the number of analogous miracles is limited, in our view, only by our willingness to go after more similar ones. Quantum mechanics had, nevertheless, many almost equally striking successes which gave us the firm conviction that it is, what we call, correct.

The last example is that of quantum electrodynamics, or the theory of the Lamb shift. Whereas Newton's theory of gravitation still had obvious connections with experience, experience entered the formulation of matrix mechanics only in the refined or sublimated form of Heisenberg's prescriptions. The quantum theory of the Lamb shift, as conceived by Bethe and established by Schwinger, is a purely mathematical theory and the only direct contribution of experiment was to show the existence of a measurable effect. The agreement with calculation is better than one part in a thousand.

The preceding three examples, which could be multiplied almost indefinitely, should illustrate the appropriateness and accuracy of the mathematical formulation of the laws of nature in terms of concepts chosen for their manipulability, the "laws of nature" being of almost fantastic accuracy but of strictly limited scope. I propose to refer to the observation which these examples illustrate as the empirical law of epistemology. Together with the laws of invariance of physical theories, it is an indispensable foundation of these theories. Without the laws of invariance the physical theories could have been given no foundation of fact; if the empirical law of epistemology were not correct, we would lack the encouragement and reassurance which are emotional necessities without which the "laws of nature" could not have been successfully explored. Dr. R. G. Sachs, with whom I discussed the empirical law of epistemology, called it an article of faith of the theoretical physicist, and it is surely that. However, what he called our article of faith can be well supported by actual examples—many examples in addition to the three which have been mentioned.

The Uniqueness of the Theories of Physics

The empirical nature of the preceding observation seems to me to be self-evident. It surely is not a "necessity of thought" and it should not be necessary, in order to prove this, to point to the fact that it applies only to a very small part of our knowledge of the inanimate world. It is absurd to believe that the existence of mathematically simple expressions for the second derivative of the position is self-evident, when no similar expressions for the position itself or for the velocity exist. It is therefore surprising how readily the wonderful gift contained in the empirical law of epistemology was taken for granted. The ability of the human mind to form a string of 1000 conclusions and still remain "right," which was mentioned before, is a similar gift.

Every empirical law has the disquieting quality that one does not know its limitations. We have seen that there are regularities in the events in the world around us which can be formulated in terms of mathematical concepts with an uncanny accuracy. There are, on the other hand, aspects of the world concerning which we do not believe in the existence of any accurate regularities. We call these initial conditions. The question which presents itself is whether the different regularities, that is the various laws of nature which will be discovered, will fuse into a single consistent unit, or at least asymptotically approach such a fusion. Alternately, it is possible that there always will be some laws of nature which have nothing in common with each other. At present, this is true, for instance, of the laws of heredity and of physics. It is even possible that some of the laws of nature will be in conflict with each other in their implications, but each convincing enough in its own domain so that we may not be willing to abandon any of them. We may resign ourselves to such a state of affairs or our interest in clearing up the conflict between the various theories may fade out. We may lose interest in the "ultimate truth," that is in a picture which is a consistent fusion into a single unit of the little pictures, formed on the various aspects of nature.

It may be useful to illustrate the alternatives by an example. We now have, in physics, two theories of great power and interest: the theory of quantum phenomena and the theory of relativity. These two theories have their roots in mutually exclusive groups of phenomena. Relativity theory applies to macroscopic bodies, such as stars. The event of coincidence, that is in ultimate analysis of collision, is the primitive event in the theory of relativity and defines a point in space-time, or at least would define a point if the colliding particles were infinitely small. Quantum theory has its roots in the microscopic world and, from its point of view, the event of coincidence, or of collision, even if it takes place between particles of no spatial extent, is not primitive and not at all sharply isolated in space-time. The two theories operate with different mathematical concepts—the four dimensional Riemann space and the infinite dimensional Hilbert space, respectively. So far, the two theories could not be united, that is, no mathematical formulation exists to which both of these theories are approximations. All physicists believe that a union of the two theories is inherently possible and that we shall find it. Nevertheless, it is possible also to imagine that no union of the two theories can be found. This example illustrates the two possibilities, of union and of conflict, mentioned before, both of which are conceivable.

In order to obtain an indication as to which alternative to expect ultimately, we can pretend to be a little more ignorant than we are and place ourselves at a lower level of knowledge than we actually possess. If we can find a fusion of our theories on this lower level of intelligence, we can confidently expect that we will find a fusion of our theories also at our real level of intelligence. On the other hand, if we would arrive at mutually contradictory theories at a somewhat lower level of knowledge, the possibility of the permanence of conflicting theories cannot be excluded for ourselves either. The level of knowledge and ingenuity is a continuous variable and it is unlikely that a relatively small variation of this continuous variable changes the attainable picture of the world from inconsistent to consistent.[11]

Considered from this point of view, the fact that some of the theories which we know to be false give such amazingly accurate results, is an adverse factor. Had we somewhat less knowledge, the group of phenomena which these "false" theories explain, would appear to us to be large enough to "prove" these theories. However, these theories are considered to be "false" by us just for the reason that they are, in ultimate analysis, incompatible with more encompassing pictures and, if sufficiently many such false theories are discovered, they are bound to prove also to be in conflict with each other. Similarly, it is possible that the theories, which we consider to be "proved" by a number of numerical agreements which appears to be large enough for us, are false because they are in conflict with a possible more encompassing theory which is beyond our means of discovery. If this were true, we would have to expect conflicts between our theories as soon as their number grows beyond a certain point and as soon as they cover a sufficiently large number of groups of phenomena. In contrast to the article of faith of the theoretical physicist mentioned before, this is the nightmare of the theorist.

Let us consider a few examples of "false" theories which give, in view of their falseness, alarmingly accurate descriptions of groups of phenomena. With some goodwill, one can dismiss some of the evidence which these examples provide. The success of Bohr's early and pioneering ideas on the atom was always a rather narrow one and the same applies to Ptolemy's epicycles. Our present vantage point gives an accurate description of all phenomena which these more primitive theories can describe. The same is not true any more of the so-called free-electron theory which gives a marvelously accurate picture of many, if not most, properties of metals, semiconductors and insulators. In particular, it explains the fact, never properly understood on the basis of the "real theory," that insulators show a specific resistance to electricity which may be 10^{26} times greater than that of metals. In fact, there is no experimental evidence to show that the resistance is not infinite under the conditions under which the free-electron theory would lead us to expect an infinite resistance. Nevertheless, we are convinced that the free-electron theory is a crude approximation which should be replaced, in the description of all phenomena concerning solids, by a more accurate picture.

If viewed from our real vantage point, the situation presented by the free-electron theory is irritating but is not likely to forebode any inconsistencies which are unsurmountable for us. The free-electron theory raises doubts as to how much we should trust numerical agreement between theory and experiment as evidence for the correctness of the theory. We are used to such doubts.

A much more difficult and confusing situation would arise if we could, some day, establish a theory of the phenomena of consciousness, or of biology, which would be as coherent and convincing as our present theories of the inanimate world. Mendel's laws of inheritance and the subsequent work on genes may well form the beginning of such a theory as far as biology is concerned. Furthermore, it is quite possible that an abstract argument can be found which shows that there is a conflict between such a theory and the accepted principles of physics. The argument could be of such abstract nature that it might not be possible to resolve the conflict, in favor of one or of the other theory, by an experiment. Such a situation would put a heavy strain on our faith in our theories and on our belief in the reality of the concepts which we form. It would give us a deep sense of frustration in our search for what I called the "ultimate truth." The reason that such a situation is conceivable is that, fundamentally, we do not know why our theories work so well. Hence their accuracy may not prove their truth and consistency. Indeed, it is this writer's belief that something rather akin to the situation which was described above exists if the present laws of heredity and of physics are confronted.

Let me end on a more cheerful note. The miracle of the appropriateness of the language of mathematics for the formulation of the laws of physics is a wonderful gift which we neither understand nor deserve. We should be grateful for it and hope that it will remain valid in future research and that it will extend, for better or for worse, to our pleasure even though perhaps also to our bafflement, to wide branches of learning.

The writer wishes to record here his indebtedness to Dr. M. Polanyi who, many years ago, deeply influenced his thinking on problems of epistemology, and to V. Bargmann whose friendly criticism was material in achieving whatever clarity was achieved. He is also greatly indebted to A. Shimony for reviewing the present article and calling his attention to C. S. Peirce's papers.

References

1. Born, M., and Jordan P., *On quantum mechanics,* Zeits. f. Physik, No. 34, 1925, pp. 858–

888. Born, M., Heisenberg, W., and Jordan, P., *On quantum mechanics, Part II*, Zeits. f. Physik, No. 35, 1926, pp. 557–615. (The quoted sentence occurs in the latter article, page 558.)

2. Dirac, P. A. M., *Quantum Mechanics*, 3rd Edit., Clarendon Press, Oxford, 1947.

3. Schrödinger, E., *Über Indeterminismus in der Physik*, J. A. Barth, Leipzig, 1932; also Dubislav, W., *Naturphilosophie*, Junker und Dünnhaupt, Berlin, 1933, Chap. 4.

4. von Neumann, J., *Mathematische Grundlagen der Quantenmechanik*, Springer, Berlin, 1932. English translation, Princeton Univ. Press, 1955.

5. Wigner, E. P., *Invariance in physical theory*, Proc. Amer. Philos. Soc., Vol. 93, 1949, pp. 521–526.

6. Wigner, E. P., *The limits of science*, Proc. Amer. Philos. Soc., Vol. 94, 1950, pp. 422 also Margenau, H., *The Nature of Physical Reality*, McGraw-Hill, New York, 1950, Chap. 8.

Notes

1. The remark to be quoted was made by F. Werner when he was a student in Princeton.

2. This statement is quoted here from W. Dubislav's *Die Philosophie der Mathematik in der Gegenwart*. Junker und Dunnhaupt Verlag, Berlin, 1932, p. 1.

3. M. Polanyi, in his *Personal Knowledge*, University of Chicago Press, 1958 says: "All these difficulties are but consequences of our refusal to see that mathematics cannot be defined without acknowledging its most obvious feature: namely, that it is interesting," (page 188).

4. The reader may be interested, in this connection, in Hilbert's rather testy remarks about intuitionism which "seeks to break up and to disfigure mathematics," Abh. Math. Sem. Univ. Hamburg, Vol. 157, 1922, or Gesammelte Werke, Springer, Berlin, 1935, page 188.

5. See, in this connection, the graphic essay of M. Deutsch, Daedalus, Vol. 87, 1958, page 86. A. Shimony has called my attention to a similar passage in C. S. Peirce's *Essays in the Philosophy of Science*, The Liberal Arts Press, New York, 1957 (page 237).

6. E. Schrödinger, in his *What Is Life*, Cambridge University Press, 1945, says that this second miracle may well be beyond human understanding (page 31).

7. The writer feels sure that it is unnecessary to mention that Galileo's theorem, as given in the text, does not exhaust the content of Galileo's observations in connection with the laws of freely falling bodies.

8. See, for instance, E. Schrödinger (1932, 1933).

9. It is attributed to Galileo.

10. See, for instance, R. H. Dicke, *American Scientist*, Vol. 25, 1959.

11. This passage was written after a great deal of hesitation. The writer is convinced that it is useful, in epistemological discussions, to abandon the idealization that the level of human intelligence has a singular position on an absolute scale. In some cases it may even be useful to consider the attainment which is possible at the level of the intelligence of some other species. However, the writer also realizes that his thinking along the lines indicated in the text was too brief and not subject to sufficient critical appraisal to be reliable.

Nonanalytic Aspects of Mathematics and Their Implication for Research and Education

Philip J. Davis and James A. Anderson

Philip J. Davis obtained his Ph.D. from Harvard in 1950 in applied mathematics. He was chief of the numerical analysis section of the National Bureau of Standards in Washington, D.C., from 1951 to 1963 during which time he was named as a Guggenheim fellow. He has been professor of applied mathematics at Brown University since 1963. Davis received the Washington Academy of Science award in 1960 and the Chauvenet prize in 1963.

James A. Anderson was associated with the neural sciences and department of psychology, Brown University, Providence, Rhode Island, at the time of the publication of this article.

While some of the titles in this anthology may have evoked a few anticipatory smiles, it is absolutely certain that no one is planning on belly laughs from an essay whose title begins "Nonanalytic Aspects of Mathematics. . . ." Indeed the reader may well feel that rubber boots and a large shovel are essential for safely approaching any such work. But again, titles can be very misleading. This article has been written in a most sprightly style and explains in essentially nontechnical terms what the authors mean by nonanalytic mathematics. It would be pointless to repeat the author's thesis here since that is the purpose of the essay, and the authors do a better job than the editors ever could. This introduction thus ends by simply asking the reader to give this essay a chance; it really is worth the effort.

Conscious and Unconscious Mathematics

When the average person gazes up at the heavens, it is perfectly clear that he does not see differential equations nor when he peers into a cloud chamber does he see the abstract symbols of quantum physics. These symbolic structures have emerged as the end product of millennia of experience and thought, but their physical visibility is on a par with that of the Great Bear who was depicted as residing in the constellation Ursa Major.

If we are inclined to the Platonic view, then we are to understand that the universe and all that is within is perpetually mathematizing. If we like, we can anthropomorphize this understanding by thinking of each particle or each aggregate as the residence of a mathematical demon whose function it is to ride herd and say: "mind the inverse square law. Mind the differential equations." Such a demon also resides in human beings for they, too, are constantly mathematizing. They do it, like breathing, without conscious thought or effort. They are mathematizing when they cross the street in fierce traffic, thereby solving mechanistic-probabilistic extremal problems of the utmost complexity. They are mathematizing when their bodies constantly react to transient conditions and seek regulatory equilibrium. The de-

Source: Philip J. Davis and James A. Anderson, "Nonanalytic Aspects of Mathematics and Their Implication for Research and Education," *SIAM Review* 21 (1979): 112–127. Reprinted by permission of the Society for Industrial and Applied Mathematics.

mon resides in a flower seed when it tells it to produce petals with six-fold symmetry.

Let us call the Platonic mathematizing that is inherent in the universe "unconscious" mathematics. Unconscious mathematizing goes on despite what anyone thinks: it cannot be prevented or shut off. It is natural, it is automatic. It does not require a brain or special computing devices. In a sense, the body, or the flower, or the planet is its own computer. It requires no intellectual force or effort to do, and in this sense it is done easily.

In opposition to unconscious mathematics we may also distinguish "conscious" mathematics. This would seem to be limited to humans and possibly to some of the higher animals. Conscious mathematics is what one normally thinks of as mathematics. It is acquired largely by special training. It seems to take place in the brain. One has special awareness of its going on or not going on. It is often tied to a symbolic and abstract language. If often occurs with an external assist from pencil and paper, mathematical instruments, or reference books.

But conscious mathematics does not always proceed through abstract symbols. It may operate through a "number sense" or a "space sense" or a "kinaesthetic sense." For example, the problem "will this object fit into that box?" is answerable with high reliability on the basis of a mere glance. What lies behind these special "senses" is often not clear. Whether they represent stored experiences, analog-type solutions performed on the spot, inspired by partly random guesses, nonetheless the fact remains that this type of judgement can often be arrived at quickly and consistently. Although one is conscious of the problem as posed, one is only partly conscious of the means by which the solution is brought about. Reflection after the fact often reveals a mixture of independent and overlapping operations. There is therefore no sharp dividing line between conscious and unconscious mathematizing.

Analog and Analytical Mathematics

It is convenient to divide conscious mathematics into two categories. The first, possibly more primitive, will be called "analog-experimental" or analog, for short. The second category will be called "analytic." Analog mathematizing is sometimes easy, and can be accomplished rapidly, and may make use of none, or very few, of the abstract symbolic structures of "school" mathematics. It can be done to some extent by almost everyone who operates in a world of spatial relationships and everyday technology. Although sometimes it can be easy and almost effortless, sometimes it can be very difficult, as, for example, trying to understand the arrangement and relationships of the parts of a machine, or trying to get an intuitive feeling for a complex system. Results rarely are expressed in words but in "understanding," "intuition," or "feeling."

In analytic mathematics, the symbolic material predominates. It is almost always hard to do. It is time consuming. It is fatiguing. It requires special training. It may require constant verification by the whole mathematical culture to assure reliability. Analytic mathematics is performed only by very few people. Analytic mathematics is elitist and self-critical. The practitioners of its higher manifestations form a "talentocracy." The great virtue of analytic mathematics arises from this, that while it is hard to verify another's intuitions, it is possible, though often difficult, to verify his proofs.

Insofar as the words "analog" and "analytic" are commonplace words that are used in many specific contexts in science, and since we intend them to have a special meaning in the course of this essay, we shall illustrate our intent with a number of examples. We begin with a very ancient problem which had a religious basis.

Problem: When is the time of the summer solstice, or of the new moon, or of some other important astronomical event?

Analog solution:

i. Wait till it happens. Relay the happening to those concerned by messengers from the point of first detection.

ii. Build some kind of physical device to detect important astronomical measures. Numerous astronomical "computers" were used from prehistoric times in both the Old and New Worlds to detect the solstices and important lunar or stellar alignments, which are often of great importance for agricultural or religious reasons.

Analytic solution: Formulate a theory of astronomical periodicities and build it into a calendric structure.

Problem: How much liquid is in this beaker?

Analog solution: Pour the liquid into a graduated measure and read off the volume directly.

Analytic solution: Apply the formula for the volume of a conical frustrum. Measure the relevant linear dimensions and then compute.

Problem: What route should a bus take between downtown Providence and downtown Boston in order to maximize profits for the company?

Analog solution: Lay out a half dozen plausible routes. Collect time-cost-patronage data from the bus runs and adopt the maximizing solution.

Analytical solution: Make a model of the mileage, toll, and traffic conditions. Solve the model in closed form, if possible. If not, run it on a computer.

Analytical-existential solution: Demonstrate that on the basis of certain general assumptions, the calculus of variations assures us that a solution to the problem exists.

Problem: Given a function of two variables $f(x, y)$ defined over a square in the xy-plane. It is desired to formulate a computer strategy which will give a plot of the contour lines of the function ($f(x, y)$ = constant).

Analytic solution: Starting at some point (x_0, y_0) compute $c = f(x_0, y_0)$. By means of inverse interpolation, find nearby points (x_1, y_1), (x_2, y_2), $\cdots$ for which $f(x_i, y_i) = c$. Connect these points. Iterate.

Analog-like solution: Place a fine grid over the square and think of the final picture as produced in a raster-scan fashion. Compute the function on the grid points and divide the range of values with, say, 20 values: $v_1, \cdots$ v_{20}. Selecting a value v_i, draw in each small square either (a) nothing or (b) a straight line segment in the event that the four corner values are compatible with v_i. Iterate on i.

Contrasting Analog vs. Analytical Solutions

It should be observed that in some problems both analog and analytical solutions may be available. It may also happen that one is available and not the other, or that both are lacking. Neither type is to be preferred a priori over the other as regards accuracy or ease of performance. If both types of solutions are available, then the agreement of the two solutions is highly desirable. This may constitute the crucial experiment for a physical theory.

An attack on a problem is often a mixture of the two approaches. In the real world, an analytical solution, no matter how good, must always be "fine tuned" when a real system is to be modeled or constructed. Therefore, in engineering, the analytical solution is generally taken as a point of departure, and, hopefully, a good first approximation.

The analog solution appears to be closer to the unconscious mathematizing that goes on in the universe. Analog solutions probably predominate in the world of technology—but this is a pure conjecture.

The Hierarchy of Intellectual Values

When it comes however to the intellectual value that is set on these two modes, it is clear what the ordering is. At the very lowest level, there is the unconscious mathematizing of the universe. The fact that my body has brought forth ten fingers and ten toes and that it possesses a fair amount of axial symmetry is not regarded as much of a mathematical accomplishment for me.

At the next higher level is analog mathematics. At the highest level stands analytical mathematics. Although an analog solution may be clever, based on sophisticated and subtle instrumentation, it does not carry the accolade of the purely intellectual solution.

The intellect looks after its own. What is consciously more difficult is the more praiseworthy. The level of intellectual acclaim is proportional to the apparent complexity of the abstract symbolization. Up to a point, of course; for the house built by intellect may crash to the ground when confronted by experimental reality. Scientific education is often directed not to the explication or solution of specific problems, but toward the carrying on of a discourse at the highest possible intellectual level.

The hierarchy we have just described is that of the practicing mathematician. From the point of view of an engineer, say, an analytical solution is of little interest unless it leads to a functioning device, which corresponds to an analog solution to a problem. A well designed, highly developed device can show the economy of means and the elegance of thought that characterizes the best science and mathematics, but that is almost never recognized as such by theoretically oriented scientists. The ingenuity and artistry that go to make a functioning airplane, or a computer that works and is reliable and efficient is seldom appreciated until one tries to do something along these lines oneself (Ferguson[39]).

Similar Hierarchies Exist in the Nonscientific World

Nor is this tendency toward stressing the intellect limited to science. It occurs, for example, in the art world. At the very "lowest" level is the commercial artist. Somewhat higher is the artist who paints portraits on demand. At the highest level stands the "fine artist" who is supposed to respond to the abstract and unfettered promptings of the intellect and spirit. The work of art is often accompanied by an *explication de texte* whose abstraction often rivals the deepest productions of mathematics.

Mathematical Proof and Its Hierarchy of Values

The hegemony of the definition-theorem-proof approach to mathematics which has almost, it would seem, become the sole paradigm of mathematical research, instruction and experience, should be apparent to any serious student.

Of course, this is not the way mathematics is created, propagated, or even understood. How shall we view this inheritance from Euclid's elements which is at once so powerful, so fruitful and in a certain sense so false? What are its successes, its failures? What are its prospects? Is it really intrinsic to the subject or is it true, as one perceptive scholar has written (Prof. R. Hersh, University of New Mexico), that

> . . . the logical analysis of mathematics, which reduces a proof to an (in principle) mechanizable procedure, is a fiction. Mathematics is a human activity, and the formal-logical account of mathematics is only a fiction; mathematics itself is to be found in the actual practice of mathematicians.

> If there is a discrepancy between what mathematicians really do and what some legend purports that they do, then the accuracy of the legend falls into question, not the reality of mathematical life and practice. If the legend is taken as a commandment of what mathematics *should* be, then the burden falls on the preacher to show that this commandment is obligatory and possible. I maintain that to reduce mathematical proof to "modus ponens" is neither obligatory, possible, nor even desirable.[14]

An interesting phenomenon should be noted in connection with difficulties of proof comprehension. A mathematical theorem is popularly called "deep" if its proof is hard. Some of the elements that contribute to deepness are nonintuitiveness of statement or of argument, novelty of ideas, complexity or length of proof material measured from some origin which itself is not deep.

The opposite of "deep" is "trivial" and this word is often used in the sense of a put-down. Some synonyms for "trivial" might be "transparent," "intuitive," "short." It should be noted that although what is trivial is not considered to be on the same intellectual level as what is deep, it does not follow that what is trivial is uninteresting, unuseful, or unimportant.

Now despite this hierarchical ordering, what is deep is frequently suspect and undesirable, so that there is a constant effort on the part of the profession towards simplification, towards the finding of alternative ways at looking at the matter which trivializes what is deep. Thus, we all feel better when we have moved from the analytic toward the analog portion of the experiential spectrum.

Cognitive Style

An obvious statement about human thought is that people vary dramatically in what might be called their "cognitive style," that is, their primary mode of thinking.

This was well known to 19th century psychologists. Galton, in 1880, asked a wide range of people to "describe the image in their mind's eye of their breakfast table on a given morning." He found that some subjects could form vivid and precise pictures while others could form only blurry images or, in some cases, no image at all. William James[16] (Chap. 19) noted that people varied greatly in the sense modality they primarily used to think in, most being auditory or visual. There was a smaller number, however, who were powerfully influenced by the sense of touch or of kinesthesis (movement), even in what is usually called abstract thought.

We might expect that such a wide range of ways of thinking should cause no problems. Indeed, we might regard with pleasure the diversity of methods of thinking about the world our species shows, and value all of them highly as giving us a number of valid ways of approaching problems.

Unfortunately, tolerance is a rare virtue, and a common response to different ways of thinking is to deny, first, that they are possible, and, second, that they are valuable.

William James remarked, "A person whose visual imagination is strong finds it hard to understand how those who are without the faculty can think at all."[16] (p. 311). Conversely, those who think mostly in words are literally incapable of imagining nonlinguistic thought. W. V. O. Quine commented that ". . . memories mostly are traces not of past sensations but of past conceptualizations or verbalizations." Max Muller wrote, "How do we know that there is a sky and that it

is blue? Should we know of a sky if we had no name for it?" He then argued that thought without language is impossible. Abelard said, "Language is generated by the intellect and generates intellect." (Some of the preceding examples are from Chapter VI of Hadamard.[13]) Chomsky said that "One would expect that human language should directly reflect the characteristics of human intellectual capacities, that language should be a direct 'mirror of mind' in ways which other systems of knowledge and belief cannot." The Chandogya Upanishad: "The essence of man is speech." The Gospel of John starts, "In the beginning was the word. . . ." In the Greek philosophical tradition of this time, this meant exactly what it said.

However, many have held somewhat opposing views. Aristotle said we often think and remember with images. Bishop Berkeley held that words are an impediment to thought. Many philosophers and theologians view concepts and words as dangerously misleading "word play." The Lankavatara Sutra is typical: "Disciples should be on their guard against the seductions of words and sentences and their illusive meanings, for by them, the ignorant and dullwitted become entangled and helpless as an elephant floundering around in deep mud. Words and sentences . . . cannot express highest reality. . . . The ignorant and simple minded declare that meaning is not otherwise than words, that as words are, so is meaning. . . . Truth is beyond letters and words and books." The Tao Te Ching (LXXXI) says, "True words are not fine sounding; fine sounding words are not true. The good man does not prove by argument and he who proves by argument is not good. . . ." A Biblical quotation in this tradition says, "The letter killeth, but the spirit giveth life. . . ."

Cognitive Style in Mathematics

Hadamard, as described in his well-known book[13] *The Psychology of Invention in the Mathematical Field*, tried to find out how famous mathematicians and scientists actually thought while doing their work. Of those he contacted in an informal survey, he wrote "Practically all of them . . .

avoid not only the use of mental words, but also
. . . the mental use of algebraic or precise signs
. . . they use vague images" (p. 84) and ". . .
the mental pictures of the mathematicians whose
answers I have received are most frequently visual, but they may also be of another kind—for
example kinetic" (p. 85).

Albert Einstein wrote to Hadamard that "the
words or the language, as they are written or spoken, do not seem to play any role in my mechanism of thought. . . . The physical entities
which seem to serve as elements in thought are
certain signs and more or less clear images which
can be 'voluntarily' reproduced and combined. . . . The above mentioned elements are,
in my case, of visual and some of muscular type.
Conventional words or other signs have to be
sought for laboriously only in a secondary state
. . ." (p. 142).

Several recent studies on the way in which nonmathematical adults perform simple arithmetic
seem to suggest the same is true for nonmathe-
maticians as well. Moyer and Landauer[21,22] tried
to see if numerical inequality judgments are performed in the same way as judgments as to which
of two physical quantities is larger. Large differences in physical magnitude (weight, size, and so
on) give quick judgments of difference, small inequalities are more difficult and take longer.
Numbers might not be expected to act this way
since they are "abstract," but Landauer and
Moyer found they did. Restle[30] performed a similar study on addition, with a similar conclusion.
The wide use of analog teaching aids used in the
teaching of elementary arithmetic (Cuisenaire
rods, for example) is practical acknowledgement
of this fact about human thought.

An Example of Cognitive Style in Combinatorial Geometry

We have already described and contrasted analog
solutions and analytical solutions. Insofar as
mathematical discovery may have large components of one or the other, we are dealing here
with differences in cognitive style.

Here is a striking example where an analytic
solution might be very difficult while an analog-

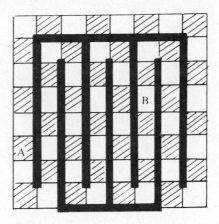

Figure 1

like solution makes the whole business transparent.

GOMORY'S THEOREM.   *Remove one white and
one black square from an ordinary checkerboard. The
reduced board can always be covered with 31 dominoes of size 2 × 1.*

Analog solution. Convert the checkerboard into
a labyrinth as in the accompanying figure. No
matter which black square "A" and which white
square "B" are deleted, the board can be covered
by threading it through the labyrinth with a caterpillar tractor chain of dominoes which break off
at "A" and "B." (Ref. 15, p. 66.)

The imagery of a moving caterpillar tread is
sufficient to enable one to grasp the solution at a
glance. Note the powerful kinesthetic and action
oriented mode of proof. It would be difficult for
the normal (i.e., somewhat visual) reader to work
through this proof and not feel a sense of movement.

We are not aware of an analytical solution to
the problem. Of course one should "tighten up"
the above solution by counting blacks and whites
to provide a more formal proof.

Here is a geometrical problem where both types
of solutions are available.

THEOREM.   *It is impossible to fill up a circle C
with a finite number of nonoverlapping smaller circles
contained in C.*

Analog solution. This is visually obvious.

Analytical solution. For a neat proof based on

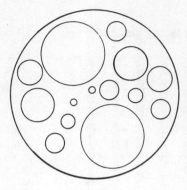

Figure 2

notions of linear independence, see Davis.[5] The
analog solution is so apparent that to insist on
more is a piece of mathematical pedantry.
This leads us to the nortorious

JORDAN CURVE THEOREM. *A simple closed
curve in the plane separates the plane into two regions, one finite and one infinite.*

Analog solution. This is visually obvious.

Analytical solution. Very difficult, the difficulty
deriving from the fact that an excessive degree of
analytical generality has been introduced into the
problem.

Mathematical Imagery

Reference has been made to Hadamard's description of the semi-conscious stream of thought
which may accompany the process of conscious
mathematizing. This kind of thing surely exists
although it is very difficult to describe and document.

A few more words along this line describing the
experiences of one of the authors (P. J. Davis)
might therefore be appropriate.

The semi-conscious stream of thought—which
might be referred to as mathematical imagery—
does not seem to relate directly to the analytical
work attempted. It feels to be more analog, almost visual, sometimes even musical. It accompanies and occasionally helps the dominant
stream of thought. It frequently seems irrelevant,
a mere hovering background presence.

Some years ago Davis spent considerable time
working in the theory of functions of a complex
variable. This theory, as is well known, has a considerable geometric underlay. In fact, it can be
developed independently from a geometric (Riemannian) or from an analytic (Weierstrassian)
point of view. The geometrical illustrations in
textbooks often feature spheres, maps, surfaces of
an unusual kind, configurations with circles,
overlapping chains of circles, etc. As he was

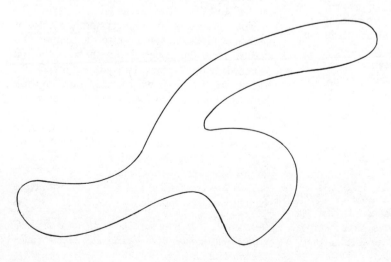

Figure 3

working along with the analytic material, he found it was accompanied by the recollection of the mixed debris of dozens of pictures of this type that he had seen in various books, together with inchoate but repetitious nonmathematical thoughts and musical themes.

He worked out, more or less, a body of material which he set down in abbreviated form. Something then came up in his calendar which prevented him from pursuing this material for several years. He hardly looked at it in the interval. At the end of this period, time again became available, and he decided to go back to the material and see whether he could work it into a book.

At the beginning he was completely cold. It required several weeks of work and review to warm up the material. After that time he found surprisingly that what appeared to be the original mathematical imagery and the melody returned, and he pursued the task to a successful completion.

The Proper Goal of Mathematical Applications Is for the Mathematics to Become Suppressed

Analytical mathematics is hard to do and is inaccurately performed if done quickly. We do not expect that an astronaut landing on the moon will be laying out his actions as the result of computing with a table of logarithms and trigonometric functions in real time. Although there is a considerable mathematical underlay to the landing manoeuvre, we expect that the astronaut will re- spond to instrument or computer readouts or verbal instructions which are surrogate readouts. The analytical mathematics must be suppressed or bypassed and replaced by analog mathematics which is lower down on the intellectual scale, but higher on the kinesthetic scale. Ideally, as in the unmanned flight, the whole system might be automated with even the analog mathematics being replaced by a hardware system.

One sees this over and over again in applied mathematics. The more complete and successful is an application, the more automatic, programmed, rote, it must become. A contracting engineer does not normally build a City Civic Center with vast amounts of axiomatic work on whether 3×3 matrices commute or not. Ultimately, even computer software gets replaced by printed circuits, chips, etc. and at this stage the whole business stands at the level of the nonconscious mathematizing of the universe.

The most complete and the most successful applications of mathematics operate finally at the lowest possible intellectual level. It is somewhat different with the goals of "pure" mathematics. There, one of the goals appears to be to "be fruitful and multiply." It might be thought, for example, that the program of generalization and abstraction which is inherent in the subject acts to eliminate redundant information. Perhaps it does, somewhat, but the great historical experiences of abstraction have probably created a thousand times the information than that which originally led to the abstraction. In this way, pure mathematics maintains itself at the highest analytical level.

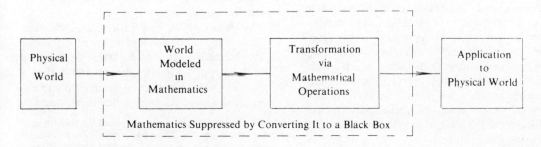

Figure 4

An Example from Computer Graphics

A striking example of the suppression of the mathematical underlay occurred in the last 10–15 years in the area of computer art and animation.

Computer art can be traced back to mechanical instruments that produced cyclic motions of various sorts, hypocycloids, Lissajous's figures, "spirographic" figures etc. These were easily produced on CRT's by oscillators or analog circuitry. The idea was to draw figures which were visually pleasing or exciting. There was a constant identification of the figure with the mathematical equation.

In the first decade or so of computer art, the mathematical presence was quite noticeable. In addition to having artistic sensibilities, practitioners had to know computer programming, graphical programming, a certain amount of basic mathematics, such as analytic geometry, elementary transformations, interpolation schemes. Gradually, higher and higher level languages were written for computer art. The mode of operation became less analytic, more linguistic and more analog. As this occurred the mathematical substructure was either built in, suppressed, or bypassed.

An excellent instance of this suppression is the PAINT program developed at the University of Utah and New York Institute of Technology (Catmull[4]). As a response to a desire to do commercial animation by computer, a very high level language was developed which could be learned easily and used by commercial animators *without a knowledge of mathematics*. Working in color, the artist is able to select a palette and create brushes of various widths and splatter characteristics. He creates shapes working with a stylus on a computer sketchpad. Numerous menu items allow him to fill with color, to exchange colors continuously in real time, to replicate, to transform (zoom), to "phantom," to animate via linear and nonlinear interpolation. This feature which is valuable for creating human limb articulation works in a mode which is an interesting interplay between an input which is mathematics at the graphical level and a visual output which carries a humanistic interpretation.

Thus the artist inputs to the computer his own muscle movements of wrist and arm and shoulder as well as a set of verbalized menu options representing a grammatical or linguistic aspect of the painting process. Since these options are also controlled by the stylus, the whole process proceeds in imitation of the manner of painting in conventional media.

The Degradation of the Geometric Consciousness

It has been remarked by numerous authorities that over the past century and a half there has been a steady and progressive degradation of the geometric and kinesthetic elements of mathematical instruction and research. During this period the formal, the symbolic, the verbal, the analytic elements have prospered greatly.

What are some of the reasons for this decline? The following come to mind immediately.

1. The tremendous impact of Descartes' *La Géométrie* wherein geometry was reduced to algebra.
2. The impact in the late 19th century of Felix Klein's *Erlanger Programm* wherein the medium (algebra) became the message.★
3. The collapse, in the early 19th century, of the view, derived largely from limited sense experience, that the geometry of Euclid, has a priori truth for the universe; that it is *the* model for physical space.
4. The incompleteness of the logical structure of classical Euclidean geometry as discovered in the 19th century and as corrected by Hilbert and others.
5. The limitations of two or three physical dimensions which form the natural backdrop for visual geometry.
6. The discovery of non-Euclidean geometries. This is related to the limitations of the visual ground field over which visual geometry is built as opposed to the great generality that is possible when geometry is algebraized and abstracted (non-Euclidean geometries, complex

---

★Klein himself must not be blamed for this. In conversations with O. Neugebauer who knew him, it emerged that Klein had a tremendous competence and intuition in visual geometry. It was a question of the successive generations being "plus royaliste que le roi."

geometries, finite geometries, linear algebra, metric spaces, etc.).

7. The limitations of the eye in its perception of mathematical "truths" (continuous, nondifferentiable functions; optical illusions, low velocity living; suggestive, but misleading special cases).

An excellent and intriguing exposition of the counter-intuitive nature of analytical mathematics when it attempts to extend the visual field can be found in the article by Hahn in Vol. III of Newman's Anthology.[24] It has become traditional to regard these "pathological examples" as pointing to failures of the "visual intuition." But they can equally well be interpreted as examples of the inadequacies of the analytical modeling of the visual process.

Right Hemisphere and Left Hemisphere

There is an intriguing, but speculative similarity between the two approaches to mathematics we suggest exist and current work on the functions of the two cerebral hemispheres. Although this work is still in its beginnings, it seems clear that the right and left hemispheres are designed to do somewhat different tasks. For a review of this rapidly growing field, see Part One, of Schmitt and Worden,[31] and for an informal discussion, see Gardner, *The Shattered Mind*.[11]

It has been known for over a hundred years that in virtually all right-handed humans and in about half of the left-handed, the parts of the brain associated with speech are primarily located in the left cerebral hemisphere. This appears to be an innate biological specialization, and a slight anatomical asymmetry has been shown to exist between the hemispheres in both newborn infants and in adults. Damage to certain areas of the left hemisphere will cause characteristic types of difficulties with speech, while damage to the right hemisphere in the same location will not. To oversimplify a complex issue, the left hemisphere in most humans is primarily concerned with language based behavior and with the cognitive skills we might crudely characterize as "analytical" or "logical." It has become apparent recently, that the right hemisphere is far superior to the left in

most visual and spatial abilities, discriminations by touch, and in some nonverbal aspects of hearing: for example, music.

A great deal of information about hemispheric specialization has come from careful study of a small number of neurosurgical patients who had to have the two hemispheres disconnected as a last resort against life-threatening epilepsy. Sperry[32] has summarized many of the results of research on these patients:

Repeated examinations during the past 20 years has consistently confirmed the strong lateralization and dominance for speech, writing, and calculation in the disconnected left hemisphere in these right handed patients. . . . Though predominately mute . . . the minor hemisphere is nevertheless clearly the superior cerebral member for certain types of tasks. . . . Largely they involve the apprehension and processing of spatial patterns, relations, and transformations. They seem to be holistic and unitary rather than analytic and fragmentary, . . . and to involve concrete perceptual insight rather than abstract, symbolic, sequential reasoning (p. 11).

We should always remember, that the two hemispheres combine to give a whole brain. Even in the left hemisphere function of speech, the right hemisphere plays an important role, and the hemispheres work in harmony in a normal individual.

The melodic aspects of speech—rhythm, pitch, and intonation—seem related to the right hemisphere. Gardner provides an apt description of other functions:

With individuals who have disease of the right hemisphere, the abilities to express oneself in language and to understand . . . others are deceptively normal . . . (however) these patients are strangely cut off from all but the verbal messages of others. . . . They are reminiscent of language machines . . . appreciative of neither the subtle nuances or non-linguistic contexts in which the message was issued . . . (p. 434).

Somewhat unflatteringly to the public image of mathematicians, Gardner then goes on,

Here the patient (with right hemisphere damage) exemplifies the behavior . . . associated with the brilliant young mathematician or computer scientist. This highly rational individual is ever alert to an inconsistency in what is being said, always seeking to formulate ideas in the most airtight way; but in neither case does he display any humor about his own situation, nor . . . the many subtle intuitive interpersonal facets which form so central a part of human intercourse. One feels rather that the answers are being typed out at high speed on computer printout paper (p. 435).

The anecdotes we have given earlier, and our own experiences, indicate that mathematics makes use of the talents that are found in both hemispheres, rather than being restricted to the linguistic, analytic specialties of the left hemisphere. The nonverbal, spatial, and holistic aspects of thought are prominent in what most good mathematicians actually do though perhaps not so much in what they *say* they do when they speak for public consumption.

It is a reasonable conclusion that a mathematical culture that specifically excludes the spatial, visual, kinesthetic, and nonverbal aspects of thought does not fully use all the capacities of the brain.

The deemphasis of the analog elements of mathematics represents the closing off of one channel of mathematical consciousness and experience. Surely, it would be better to develop and use and be able to apply all the special talents and abilities of our brains, rather than to suppress some by education and professional prejudice. We suggest that in mathematics, it would be better for the contributions of the two halves of the brain to cooperate, complement, and enhance each other, rather than for them to conflict and interfere.

On the Creation of a Receptive Milieu for Nonanalytic Mathematics

There are obvious reasons for the success of the linguistically based mathematics. The *communication* of visual material has always been much more difficult than the *communication* of verbal mate-

rial. It often requires special skills. Formerly it was more difficult to generate and manipulate visual material than to generate linguistic material of comparable richness and complexity.

We suggest that current developments in technology may make it possible to change this state of affairs. Contemporary developments in computer graphics make it possible for very complex mathematical structures to be developed, inspected, and manipulated on line. We suggest that deep insights into mathematics may be developed by use of this capacity as a research tool. For example, we know that there are purely visual theorems and proofs (Davis[7]).

Little is known about their nature and their relation with conventional mathematical material. The production of visual theorems should be encouraged.

Conversely, one should supplement this by producing conventional proofs of mathematical features which are primarily visual. To what extent do visual intricacies of features correspond to levels of mathematical complexity? What is the tie-in here with linguistic theories of pattern recognition?

Simulation and interpretation of kinesthetic experiences via person-computer interaction can be carried out in a number of ways. For example, the exploration of 4-dimensional objects as has been done by Banchoff and Strauss[3] can be pursued extensively. In another direction, one might display solutions of (say) four sets of coupled differential equations, linear or with some simple nonlinearities. One would then set up the specific goal of communicating some of the elementary qualitative properties of coupled sets of equations. Since the parameters could be easily varied by the experimenter, the kinesthetic component as well as the visual component of the intuition could be developed.

Again, a very suggestive guidebook to the intuitive discovery of the differential geometry of surfaces via "the Turtle" has been prepared (di Sessa[10]). Similar guides exist for planetary motions under central force fields, etc. Interesting problems in architecture and "mathematical sculpture" have been solved by people with strong analog orientations; these problems have in turn suggested difficult questions of conventional mathematics.[29]

At the level of informal exploration and research therefore and at the level of instruction, much can be done which would be both useful and intriguing.

All of this depends upon the creation of a milieu which is receptive to nonanalytic mathematics. This, in turn requires a certain reordering of the hierarchical values of analog vs. analytic mathematics.

Applications to Mathematical Education

There is a striking tendency on the part of research people who have worked intensely in a certain area to thread innovations in education through the eye of their own private needle. Enthusiasts for set theory, for logic, for algebra, for nonstandard analysis, for computer languages, for computer-aided instruction, abound and each sees his fraction of the universe as Truth.

To some extent the program known as "The New Math" had this as a fault. Though notable for its modernity and its enthusiasm, the New Math represented only a partial mathematical experience and apparently was unsuitable to the widespread needs of our culture. Luckily, as the saying has it: It is harder to change a curriculum than to move a graveyard. Thus, we are provided with a sheltering stability that smooths out the highs of temporary euphoria. Ultimately, though, in our grinding and uncertain way, our curricula must confront innovation, discovery, and changes in the condition of life.

It seems to us that the major impetus to curriculum change in the next decade will come from computer science and technology. We shall therefore discuss several aspects of this in the light of our thesis. This thesis, applied to curricula, calls for a *balance; the use of all the capacities of the brain.*

High Level Analytic Languages and College Curricula

High level algebraic or analytical manipulation languages such as SKETCHPAD or MACSYMA, enable the user to do formal manipulations within algebra, calculus, differential equations, infinite series, etc. They are tremendously versatile and are being improved from day to day. They are also becoming increasingly available. They, therefore, pose an important question as to how they should be accommodated within a mathematical curriculum.

To some extent these languages are backward looking in that they focus strong attention on mathematical problems and procedures that were of great concern in the mid-19th century (e.g., the possibility of formal integration in closed form). They redirect attention to the topic of "Special Function Theory" which has not been very popular within the mathematics community in the past generation. On the other hand, they show much promise as a research tool and there is no doubt that exposure to them is of great potential benefit to the student.

One of the intellectual games that can be played is to speculate on how the development of mathematics would have been altered if, say, at the time of Newton, electronic computers were available. It is clear that certain subsets of mathematics grew up as a response to the tediousness of algebraic or numerical computation and the impossibility of obtaining solutions within special function theory. It learned, out of necessity, to make do with partial substitutes such as qualitative analysis. These substitutes became goals of their own, replacing previous goals. The long range goals of mathematical training are therefore in a turmoil and have been inadequately examined in the light of computing potential. The very way in which one studies the subject has been called into question by the possibility of writing interactive computer tutors.[20]

High Level Geometric and Kinesthetic Languages

Insofar as algebraic manipulative languages emphasize essentially the analytic portions of mathematics, it is of importance to restore the balance by developing and making available high level geometric and kinesthetic languages. One sees the beginnings of such languages in such diverse places as computer art and animation, computer aided geometrical and architectural design, artificial intelligence, and in ad hoc attempts to bring computer graphics to illustrate dynamically various mathematical principles.

Conformal mapping and partial differential equations, four dimensional geometry, kinematics of orbital motion all come to mind. At the elementary school level, kinesthetic intuition and programmatic skills have been simultaneously developed by using "turtle geometry."[27]

Mathematics in Crisis

Despite the marvellous accomplishments over the past century of an essentially analytic type of mathematics, despite the high level of current mathematical activity, there is a considerable feeling of malaise in the profession. As is usual in human affairs, the threads of disgruntlement are tangled and contradictory. Too much activity and information, too few jobs, too few ideas, too many ideas, too much specialization, too much scholasticism, idle generalization, idle abstraction, overproduction of products that no one wants, not enough great men.

In physics, too, there is malaise. The Nobel Laureate H. Yukawa has devoted considerable thought to the question of why, with a plethora of interesting problems, the physics of the current generation should be suffering from a lack of inspiration. His answer[38] (p. 13), in a nutshell is excessive "digitality" and an abhorrence and consequent poverty of metaphysics.

Our answer to the corresponding question for mathematics lies along parallel lines. It can be formulated on the doctrine of the whole man.

The Doctrine of the Whole Man

Mathematics has elements that are spatial, kinesthetic, elements that are arithmetic or algebraic, elements that are verbal, programmatic. It has elements that are logical, didactic and elements that are intuitive, or even counter-intuitive. It has elements that are related to the exterior world and elements that seem to be self generated. It has elements that are rational and elements that are irrational or mystical. These may be compared to different modes of consciousness.

To place undue emphasis on one element or group of elements upsets a balance. It results in an impoverishment of the science and represents an unfulfilled potential. The doctrine of the whole man says that we must bring everything we have to bear on our subject. We must not block off arbitrarily any mode of experience or thought. "There is a Nemesis," says Whitehead, "which waits upon those who deliberately avoid avenues of knowledge."

We must realize that the future of the subject depends only in part on the contribution of those who have rigid establishment interest or training in the subject. As regards this training and our own teaching we must

Restore geometry.

Restore kinesthetics and mechanics.

Restore combinatorics.

Restore intuitive and experimental mathematics.

Deemphasize somewhat the theorem-proof type of lecturing.

Give a proper place to computing and programmatics.

Make full use of computer graphics.

Eliminate the fear of metaphysics, recognizing that in such principles may lie seeds of future growth.

What we want to do is to create as rich and diverse a brew of thought and action as we can. This is the kind of culture which has fostered mathematics in the past and should be our very present hope for the future.

References

1. R. Arnheim, *Art and Visual Perception*, University of Calif. Press, Berkeley, CA, 1957.
2. ———, *Visual thinking*, University of Calif. Press, Berkeley, CA, 1969.
3. T. Banchoff and C. M. Strauss, *On folding algebraic singularities in complex 2-space*, talk

and movie presented at the AMS Meeting (Dallas, Texas, January 1973).

4. Edwin Catmull, personal communication.

5. P. J. Davis, *Simple quadratures in the complex plane*, Pacific J. Math., 15 (1965), p. 816.

6. ———, *Fidelity in mathematical discourse: Is one and one really two?*, Amer. Math. Monthly, 79 (1972), pp. 252–263.

7. ———, *Visual geometry, computer graphics, and theorems of perceived type*, Proceedings of Symposia in Applied Mathematics, vol. 20, American Mathematical Society, Providence, RI, 1974.

8. ———, *Mathematics by fiat?*, Applied Math. Division, Brown University, Providence, RI, October, 1976.

9. ———, *Towards a Jamesian history of mathematics*, Div. of Appl. Math., Brown University, Providence, RI, 1976.

10. A. di Sessa, *Turtle escapes the plane: Some advanced turtle geometry*. A. I. memo 348, Artificial Intelligence Lab., M.I.T., Boston, MA, Dec. 1975.

11. H. Gardner, *The Shattered Mind*, Knopf, New York, 1975.

12. Ira Goldstein and Seymour Papert, *Artificial intelligence language and the study of knowledge*, M.I.T. Artificial Intelligence Lab., memo 337, Boston, MA, March 1976.

13. Jacques Hadamard, *The Psychology of Invention in the Mathematical Field*, Princeton, N.J., 1945.

14. R. Hersh, *Some proposals for reviving the philosophy of mathematics*, TR 315, Dept. of Math., Univ. of New Mexico, Albuquerque, Feb. 1976.

15. R. Honsberger, *Mathematical gems, II*, Mathematics Association of America, Washington, D.C., 1973.

16. William James, *Psychology (Briefer Course)*, Reprint: Collier, New York, 1962.

17. M. Kline, *Logic versus pedagogy*, Amer. Math. Monthly, 77 (1970), pp. 264–282.

18. ———, *Mathematical thought from ancient to modern times*, Oxford University Press, London, 1972.

19. K. Knowlton, *The use of FORTRAN-coded EXPLOR for teaching computer graphics and computer art*, Proc. ACM SIGPLAN Sympos,

on Two-Dimensional Man-Machine Communication, Los Alamos, NM, October 5–6, 1972.

20. Edwina R. Michener, *Epistemology, representation, understanding, and interactive exploration of mathematical theories*, Doctoral thesis, Dept. of Mathematics, M.I.T., Boston, MA, 1977.

21. R. S. Moyer and T. K. Landauer, *Time required for judgments of numerical inequality*, Nature, 215 (1967), pp. 1519–20.

22. ———, *Determinants of reaction time for digit inequality judgments*, Bull. Psychonomic Society, 1 (1973), pp. 167–168.

23. O. Neugebauer, personal communication.

24. J. Newman, ed., *The World of Mathematics*, Simon and Schuster, New York, 1956.

25. N. J. Nilsson, *Problem-solving methods in artificial intelligence*, McGraw-Hill, New York, 1971.

26. R. E. Ornstein, *The Psychology of Consciousness*, W. H. Freeman, San Francisco, 1972.

27. S. Papert, *Teaching children to be mathematicians vs. teaching about mathematics*, memo no. 249, Artificial Intelligence Lab. M.I.T., Boston, MA, July 1971.

28. M. Polanyi, *Personal knowledge*, University of Chicago Press, Chicago, IL, 1958.

29. R. D. Resch, *The topological design of sculptural and architectural systems*. AFIPS-Conference Proceedings, vol. 42, 1973, pp. 643–650.

30. F. Restle, *Speed of adding and comparing numbers*, J. Experimental Psychology, 83 (1970), pp. 274–278.

31. F. O. Schmitt and F. G. Worden, Eds., *The Neurosciences: Third Study Program*, MIT Press, Cambridge, MA, 1975.

32. R. W. Sperry, *Lateral specialization in the surgically separated hemispheres*, The Neurosciences: Third Study Program, F. O. Schmitt and F. G. Worden, eds., MIT Press, Cambridge, MA, 1975.

33. C. M. Strauss, *Computer-encouraged serendipity in pure mathematics*, Proc. IEEE, 62 (1974).

34. René Thom, *Modern mathematics: An educational and philosophic error?*, American Scientist, Nov.–Dec. (1971), pp. 695–699.

35. Paul S. Wang, *Implication of symbolic compu-*

tation for the teaching of mathematics, Dept. of Math., M.I.T., Boston, MA, 1975.

36. Peter Wegner, *Three computer cultures: Computer technology, computer mathematics, and computer science,* Advances in Computers, vol. 10, Academic Press, New York, 1970.

37. A. N. Whitehead, *Science and the Modern World,* Macmillan, New York, 1925.

38. Hideki Yukawa, *Creativity and Intuition,* Kodansha International, Tokyo, New York, San Francisco, 1973.

39. E. S. Ferguson, *The mind's eye: Nonverbal thought in technology,* Science, 197 (1977), pp. 827–836.

Mathematics and Population

Nathan Keyfitz

Nathan Keyfitz was born in Quebec in 1913. He received his Ph.D. in sociology in 1952 from the University of Chicago. He has been a professor of sociology at Harvard since 1972 and is a member of the American Academy of Arts and Science.

When pressed for a practical example of a discrete random variable, a well-known statistician suggested the set of predictions of economic growth for the next six months of any group of economists. Such is the intractability of the questions which the dismal science of economics must grapple with. It is no wonder that observations on the inaccuracy of its practitioners' predictions have become trite. But they, the economists, are much more to be pitied than scorned. The problems they face render nuclear physics a sandbox amusement by comparison. Subatomic particles, so far as we know, are not influenced by the rise in skirt lengths or the fate of the Dodgers, while humans are.

The task undertaken by Keyfitz in this essay is that of devising a valid mathematical model of population growth. But almost all of the forces that influence population change are directed, as is the economy, by the myriad individual decisions of the people of childbearing age. The introduction of a new method of contraception or a change in public attitude can radically alter the most carefully devised projections. Keyfitz quite candidly admits the essentially insurmountable difficulties inherent in his undertaking but nevertheless defends the effort as important if only as an exercise in exploring the options available.

Population Dilemmas

We are told that our rapid population growth threatens the future of the human race: we are growing so fast that we will soon crowd ourselves to death. Our technology, which is man's ability to control the environment in his own interest, has become so effective that the environment is being destroyed. The economy is booming, but many of the services we took for granted yesterday when we were poorer—good schools, good hospitals, clean cities and safe streets—have now become too expensive for most of us to afford. Each of these three propositions, by no means original with me but widely heard in one form or

another, seems self-contradictory, and we may well ask whether current writers who discuss population and its related problems have abandoned logic in favor of some other form of discourse.

The same statements can be made in a less surrealistic manner. The more there are of us the more likely we are to destroy the support base of human life on the planet, and this could make life impossible even for a small population. The threat of self-destruction through excessive numbers is used by those who would have us treat the planet like permanent farmers rather than like slash-and-burn primitives. But the mechanisms by which increased human population would provoke a crash like that which affects a lynx popu-

Source: Nathan Keyfitz, "Mathematics and Population," *SIAM Review* 15 (1973): 370–375. Reprinted by permission of the Society for Industrial and Applied Mathematics. (Some references omitted.)

lation are by no means understood, and the analogy is often presented in an incoherent way.

The illogic is not confined to rich countries. Many of the poor countries of the world, especially those that have empty spaces, are told by their governments that they need more people; they must fill those empty spaces just as the United States filled its spaces in the 19th century. But no one is moving towards the empty spaces of Mexico, and not many to the outer islands of Indonesia. Far from setting out to clear their jungles, peasants are leaving well-settled and relatively comfortable countrysides and moving into cities. Brazilians dream of settling their interior as did the heroes of the American west, but most do not imitate the action; rather they strive to find an apartment in Sao Paulo or Rio de Janeiro, where they can watch western stories on their television sets.

One apparent paradox that needs explaining is that a poor country ambitious for large population ought to start using birth control as soon as possible. If it continues to increase rapidly it will be burdened with children whose upbringing and schooling will drain away resources and so hinder the accumulation of industrial capital. If births are initially fewer, saving can increase and thus increase industry, and industrial power can be applied to improve agriculture and otherwise build the means for supporting population. At that point births can rise again, though people may not want more children; we can nonetheless assert that a poor country can have a larger ultimate population if it begins by reducing its births.

The suspicion that logic has been abandoned is confirmed when we see some of the mechanisms that are proposed to analyze environmental constraints. Air pollution can raise the death rate; when the death rate gets high enough and remains high enough for a long enough period, population density will decrease; with fewer people there will be fewer automobiles and other sources of pollution; the diminution of the sources of pollution will lower the death rate and allow population to rise again; ultimately an equilibrium level of population will be reached, determined by the amount of usable air. This unattractive picture is presented in the good cause of persuading us to do something about population and pollution, but

no one so far knows enough about the effect of pollution on mortality to establish such a mechanism.

To self-contradictory statements of the population problem and mechanisms that go far beyond known empirical relations are added some unilluminating forms of statistical description of the economy. Accounting systems for individual businesses are scrupulous in allowing for the depreciation of the firm's assets; an airline that failed to depreciate its planes before declaring a dividend would find itself bankrupt the moment the planes had to be replaced. Even a corner grocery store keeps books that financially protect those assets that will be physically wasted.

But no such elementary precautions are taken for the human enterprise as a whole. No world accounting system reckons the oil in the ground as an asset that will be needed for lubrication for the next million years. This invaluable resource is burned on the highways in an inefficient means of transportation; it pollutes the air; it kills 55,000 persons every year in the United States alone; it makes quiet and pleasant streets barbarously noisy and dangerous. Extracting the oil from the ground and burning it is added into the wrong column in the national accounts; it is taken as income rather than as loss. The principles of accounting that ensure a degree of permanence in the operation of an airline are not applied to ensure the permanence of the human habitat. The global affairs of mankind are not run with the caution and foresight applied by a grocery store.

The Large Problem

Underlying all the dilemmas and paradoxes of population are difficulties of housekeeping on the planet Earth, the only home man is ever likely to have. After being one species competing with many others in approximate equilibrium for most of a million years, man has taken over; his present four billion compares with possibly as few as four million only 10,000 years ago. He changes the course of evolution of plants, extracts fossil fuels, flies through the stratosphere. His technical triumphs are so recent that there has not yet been time to adjust them to ensure the long-term stability of the environment. The question is how much time he has to bring his techniques into balance with the environment.

This phrasing of the problem applies especially to the rich populations. They are increasing at about one-half percent per year and may not take long to drop to stationarity. For the poor countries rates of increase are as high as three and one-half percent per year, and their crisis is not due to improving technology and rising incomes, but to more people with distressingly low incomes. They both crowd their environments and hinder capital accumulation. Their question is how long it will be until they have only our problems to cope with. Like the question of the preceding paragraph this is not an easy one to answer.

The few things that can be said about the big problems of mankind and its environment without gross violation of the rules of logic are negative. Human population growth cannot continue indefinitely in a finite world. On the average of the long-term future, the number of births cannot be much larger than the number of deaths. With present low death rates, an average of three children per couple leads quickly to population explosion; two children per couple to population extinction.

One of the large problems, that crucially affects what line of action is appropriate, is whether population or income is responsible for environmental troubles. Is it our numbers or the way we live that makes the air unbreathable in an increasing number of places and threatens the supplies of essential materials? The answer must be both: more people living the way we live would make things worse, and expansion along the lines of our present incomes with the same number of people would likewise make things worse. Just as production is the joint outcome of the action of capital and labor, so pollution and exhaustion of materials are the joint outcome of the action of population and affluence, possibly representable by a function like $P^a \overline{Y}^b$, where P is population and $\overline{Y}$ average income. The task is to find the values of a and b and to lower them by suitably oriented changes in technology and the pattern of life. Among other changes, our throwaway economy may give place to one in which houses, automobiles and clothing are meant to last. We know some of the technical means for attaining durability, but they are not valued sufficiently in the market, and the economic means to implement them in a free society are elusive.

These examples are enough to show that the major problems of population cannot in the present state of our knowledge be clearly formulated, let alone solved. Certainly I am in no position to state the population question in a sharp enough way that the techniques of mathematics can be brought to bear on it. This lack of incisiveness, if not actual self-contradiction, with which we tend to confront the major issues effectively prevents for the moment a scientific attack on them.

Formulation of Smaller Problems

But I can show that the case is not hopeless by dropping down to some smaller problems and showing how these can be sharply formulated and precisely solved. Their solution ought to encourage us to try for the larger problems, and may even provide some hints as to the methods to use.

The most fully developed model of formal demography deals with one species (man) and one sex only, and is deterministic in supposing that the probability of an event occurring to an individual gives also the fraction of individuals in the population to whom the event will occur. Usually ages are recognized, and at each age the fraction dying and the fraction bearing a child are obtained from data on a real population; the fractions are called age-specific rates, and they are taken as fixed and given. This stable population theory can hardly be called realistic, but it nonetheless gives useful answers to many questions: what is the effect on age distribution of a fall in births as against a fall in deaths? what is the effect on the rate of increase of a population of a stream of emigration at specified ages? how are age distribution and rate of increase affected by a drop in the death rate at one given age? Sensitivity analysis (for example, finding the effect on certain output parameters of varying a birth or death input) is carried out with any complete mathematical model and is indeed a main object of constructing such models; it is especially convenient with the stable model.

Population theory has gone beyond the stable model in a number of directions. Present-day writings in the mathematics of population often recognize two sexes and two or more species, as well as age-specific rates of birth and death that vary through time. The theory is often stochastic in allowing to each individual member of the population his own separate risk, rather than deterministic in supposing that whatever probability applies to each individual is also the fraction of the population that succumbs to the risk.

Applied Mathematical Demography

What may be called the pure mathematics of population, that is, the formal demography described above, is population analysis in separation from other disciplines. Applied mathematical demography overlaps with substantive fields of natural and social science: biology, sociology, economics, actuarial science, and many others. A few examples of the nature of the overlap can be given here.

A demographic-sociological model may be constructed for social mobility to show in what degree the increase of a population accelerates the upward movement of its individual members, for example, their promotion within an office or factory. Population increase favors mobility more than does mortality (even for those who survive). This is true whether the population consists of a firm, a government agency, a nation, or other organization. For the stable model, the relation of promotion to rate of increase can be expressed as a simple equation, and a set of age specific rates of birth and death suffices to calculate average or expected rank as a function of population increase. An extension can be worked out for an irregularly increasing population, in which the amount of advantage for a person born in a valley of births, who through his life stays in a valley of the age distribution, is calculated, as well as the disadvantage for a person born at the peak of a baby boom. The point can be discussed in terms of the size of the cohorts, which is to say groups

of individuals born in given years, each such cohort being followed through its work-career and childbearing.

But the relatively advantaged cohort, as Easterlin (1961) has suggested, is then likely to have more children, and the disadvantaged fewer. This phenomenon may be shown to produce waves in births of length twice the generation. As the large number of births proceeds through the life of a cohort, it will continue to be larger than that for the cohorts born just before or just after, who will be accordingly disadvantaged in promotion and have fewer children. We have here a chain of causation that proceeds from the demographic to the social-economic and then feeds back into the demographic again.

The relation of population to insurance, and in particular to social insurance, has been studied by actuaries, but they have not fully explored the overlap with demography. For a fixed rate of increase of the population, consider the premium for old-age pensions in a no-reserve system, i.e., a system where current pensions are paid out of current premiums. Contrast this with the premium in a reserve system with given rate of interest. It can be shown that the two are identical if the rate of increase of the population in the no-reserve system is the same as the rate of interest in the reserve system. In the reserve system each cohort looks after itself, in the no-reserve system each cross section of time looks after itself, but no difference arises except at the point where the scheme is initiated or terminated.

If the population growth rate changes, then gross inequities arise in the period or no-reserve system. Those belonging to small cohorts will have higher premiums if the pension is fixed, and higher pensions than they have paid for if the premium is fixed. The amount of these inequities can be established by a demographic-actuarial analysis.

The educational system is especially sensitive to demographic changes. Until a few years ago it seemed that college enrollments were steadily growing, existing graduate schools were increasing in size, and new schools were being initiated; indefinite expansion at all levels was projected. We now know that such extrapolations give nonsensical results—they show that ultimately the entire population goes to graduate school and finds jobs as college teachers. A demographic-educational model in which two or more levels of schooling are provided for avoids such absurdities. It shows how fluctuations in the population input to the educational system result in greatly amplified fluctuations in jobs for the output of graduate schools.

The area common to anthropology and demography centers on the study of kinship. We know that expected numbers of all kin are implied by a given set of age-specific rates of birth and death, and explicit formulas for these have been established. Formulas for the variances of numbers of kin are not yet discovered, and work requiring them has had to be carried out by simulation. Further research is required for the inverse problem: given the various mean numbers of kin, taken from a genealogical table, to find age-specific rates of birth and death. Some results on this are now available; it is hoped they can be made more precise. The study is important both for historical demography and for the present-day populations in which birth and death registrations are not to be had; it can be shown that any two observations of kin—average number of aunts along with the fraction of grandmothers alive, for instance—will in principle give the regimen of mortality and fertility, if these regimes can each be represented as a one-dimensional set of model tables. Different combinations of kin will select the appropriate model table with different degrees of precision.

Demography overlaps with economics on an especially wide front. Since the work of Coale and Hoover we have known that economic and social development will take place more rapidly with slower population increase, a fact shown by alternative demographic-economic projections. One further task is to extend this by setting up a variety of economic-demographic models, each containing at least a production function and a savings function, and see in what degree the

drawback of increasing population is a consequence of the functions assumed.

Within biology demographers are interested in genetics, and human population genetics is a well developed field. Demography also overlaps with reproductive biology. Given the probability of conception per month for individual couples, what is the birth rate in the population as a whole? How does frequency of intercourse affect the birth rate? How does modification of the probability of conception—which is the immediate object of contraception—lower the number of births, which is its ultimate object? We know that abortion reduces the births, but does it do so in a number equal to the number of abortions? Such questions are answerable by looking at conception and birth as a stochastic process.

Many more examples of this detailed reasoning are to be found in the writings of Ansley J. Coale, Louis Henry, Robert G. Potter, Norman B. Ryder, Mindel C. Sheps, and other workers in the mathematics of population. It is no depreciation of their results to say that they have not tackled the larger problems of population. In contrasting the precise work that they have done with the self-contradictory statements on the larger issues, I express the hope that precise methods that have worked well in the small will ultimately prove applicable in the large.

References

R. A. Easterlin, *The baby boom in perspective*, American Economic Review, 51 (1961), pp. 869–911.

Nathan Keyfitz, *Introduction to the Mathematics of Population*, Addison-Wesley, Reading, Mass., 1968.

———, *On the momentum of population growth*, Demography, 8 (1971), pp. 71–80.

part three

Counting, Guessing, Using

TO HELP THE reader understand the dangers of inappropriate use of applied mathematics we recount a well-known story that emerged from some attempts at operations research during World War II.

As the American bombing of Japan intensified during the summer of 1944, Japanese air defense efforts began to exact a very heavy toll of American aircraft and crews. The U.S. generals tried everything they could devise to stem the losses but without much effect. In desperation they turned to an operations research analysis of American air tactics and Japanese defense capabilities. A number of suggestions emerged from this analysis, among which was a proposal to reduce the altitude of approach by 5,000 feet. This suggestion defied conventional wisdom, which held that the highest possible approach altitude was the safest. In desperation, however, the military forces tried this seemingly irrational suggestion, and to the generals' amazement it worked. The incidence of aircraft losses decreased and bombing accuracy improved. Then the inevitable happened. Some dolt at headquarters concluded that if going in 5,000 feet lower reduced losses and improved accuracy, why, then going in 10,000 feet lower should save even more aircraft and achieve even better results. Naturally the new reduction resulted in a disaster; the price of such guesswork was paid in the lives of the air crews involved.

The foregoing incident is of a type that has occurred in the history of mathematical applications with a regularity both tiresome and depressing. Those ignorant of the power and limitations of mathematics have frequently performed a curious kind of bipolar oscillation. First, they ridicule the notion that the esoteric ramblings of some bearded scholar can affect the real world of action. Then, on seeing mathematics used to surmount an apparently insurmountable obstacle, they assume that any difficulty can be similarly resolved by a feat of mathematical legerdemain if only the right wizard can be summoned. This is probably the worst possible approach to the application of mathematics.

The rather simple fact is that at any given time mathematics can solve exactly that set of problems which it can solve, no more and no less. It does not matter that a problem ought to be solvable by mathematical methods; until someone has in fact found the solution, it is still unsolved. History suggests that it is very difficult to predict progress in the applications of mathematics. Questions that Greek mathematicians felt should be answerable 2,500 years ago are still open. Tasks that seemed impossible twenty-five years ago are now routinely accomplished. Our ability to effectively predict what will and what will not work is just not very good. So what should we do? A reasonable strategy would be to be generous and eclectic in support of mathematics and its applications and to maintain an informed skepticism about all the results.

Statistics, Sports, and Some Other Things

Robert Hooke

Robert Hooke received his Ph.D. in mathematics in 1942 from Princeton. He served as a staff member of the Operations Evaluation Group for the U.S. Navy at M.I.T. from 1951 to 1952. In 1954 he joined Westinghouse Corporation. At Westinghouse he has been a research mathematician, the manager of the statistical section, and since 1963, the manager of the entire mathematics department.

Most baseball fans know perfectly well what is meant by the term baseball statistics. *The dedicated fan reads the box scores of yesterday's games with the same regularity and attention stockbrokers devote to market reports. The superfan knows the batting averages of all the starters of the '37 Yankees and can tell you what Sandy Koufax's E.R.A. was in 1963. There is probably no other sport that amasses and reports such a variety of facts about various aspects of play. The "stats" are an integral part of the game. This article deals with baseball and with statistics, but the statistics are of a type not at all familiar to the average baseball fan.*

The statistics so often recited by baseball fans and announcers are really more facts or data than statistics as that term is used by statisticians. The exception to this is the use of "average" such as in a batting average or an earned run average. Although these two averages are a rather crude type of statistic, they can provide helpful insight if properly used. This essay is, however, concerned with a much more sophisticated statistical analysis of one aspect of baseball. The purpose of this analysis is to suggest a general strategy for playing that will, over time, maximize a team's chance of scoring. This kind of statistical analysis has long been a trademark of American business and industry—it is one of the factors that accounts for the ascendency of U.S. industry during the first half of this century. The fact that baseball is amenable to the same kind of analysis makes it, one could assert, truly the American national pastime.

SPECTATOR SPORTS PROVIDE more than just observation of athletes who perform with admirable skill. There is, for example, the drama of a young quarterback trying to lead a professional football team for the first time in front of 70,000 onlookers or that of a veteran pitcher calling on his experience to augment his dwindling physical resources in a crucial game of a close pennant race. Because these dramas are truly "live" and unpredictable, they are much more fascinating to some people than the well-rehearsed performances of the stage.

Not every moment in sports is dramatic, of course, but throughout any contest between professionals, the spectator is privileged to watch a group of people carrying out their jobs almost in full public view, to see how they meet their problems, and to see how they react to their own

Source: Robert Hooke, "Statistics, Sports, and Some Other Things," in J. M. Tanur et al., *Statistics: A Guide to the Unknown* (San Francisco: Holden-Day, 1978), pp. 297–306. (Problem section and references omitted.)

successes and failures. Baseball and football provide especially good opportunities for such observation because each of these games consists of a sequence of plays, as opposed to the fairly continuous action of basketball, hockey, soccer, and racing sports. The spectator sees more than strikeouts and home runs, completed passes and interceptions. He sees a manager gambling on a hit-and-run play, or a quarterback deciding whether to run or pass for the first down that he desperately needs. The fan has opinions on what his team should do in various situations, and he comes to decide that its manager or coach is a good strategist or a poor one.

Management in professional sports has many similarities to management in business and industry. Some managers and coaches are smarter than others, and some make use of more advanced methods than others do. This is true in sports, as it is in business, in spite of the folk wisdom of the sports pages that often maintains that all managers and coaches are pros and about equally good. Some can get a great deal out of inferior personnel, but none can overcome more than a certain amount of incompetence among the people who work for them. Some are natural gamblers, some are always conservative, and only a few are intelligent enough to be one or the other depending on what the circumstances call for. Sports managers are different from business managers mainly in that their actions are so much more visible. Because of this visibility we should all be able to learn by watching them as they make their various moves in the goldfish bowl of professional sports.

Statistics and Management

What does all this have to do with statistics? The real concern of statistics is to obtain usable quantitative information, especially about complex situations that involve many variables and uncertainties. "Usable" means that its purpose is to help us to improve our behavior in the future, that is, to help us learn how to extract from these situations more of whatever it is that we're trying

to get. Some managers make good use of statistics and some don't; this is true whether they manage factories or baseball teams.

Suppose, for example, that we are manufacturing rubber tires. An expert will no doubt be able to detect from the example that I know nothing about the tire business; in fact, I chose this example because I've never been in the tire business and hence it will not implicate real people. At some point in the process, let's suppose that we have a mass of liquid rubber that will ultimately be turned into tires. Being aware that this batch may possibly have been improperly prepared, we would like to test it in some way so that, if it is defective, we can throw it away without wasting money processing it into defective tires. Unfortunately, the true test of a tire is a road test, and we can't road test a batch of liquid, so we must perform some test that we think is relevant, such as a viscosity measurement. This measurement will take time and cost money, and sooner or later someone will raise the question "Is it worth the money we're spending on it?" This is always a good question, and it usually leads to much heated debate. The debate will include arguments based on intuition, experience, laboratory tests, and scientific theory; each has its place in the process of seeking after the truth, but they are basically predictors, and the only way to be sure of what will happen in the field is to see what actually happens in the field. This means that we should collect statistics. After measuring a batch, we should follow it through the manufacturing process and see what is the quality of a sample of tires made from this batch. We repeat this on another batch, and so on. After a while we can establish the relationship between tire quality and viscosity, and we can use this to determine whether to continue with the test, taking into account the testing costs, the cost of the manufacturing process that follows the test, the value of a good finished tire, and so on. Now you may say, of course, that this method isn't infallible because it involves sampling and, hence, sampling error and because the process may change unexpectedly, and so on. But this method gets us as close to the truth as we can come, and this final objection merely says that you never have it made, even if you use statistics.

The Strategy of Bunting

The student of management behavior can find many instances of this type of problem in sports, and if he is smart, he can profit from the mistakes that are made visibly on the diamond or the grid-iron. Take, for example, the sacrifice bunt in baseball. There are those who swear by it and there are those who seldom use it. They engage in passionate arguments as to whether it is a good strategy. As we shall see, statistics can't settle the issue once and for all, but it can shed a great deal of light on the problem, and most of the argument could be eliminated if people would look at some of the facts.

The sacrifice bunt is a play that is used to advance a base runner from first base to second, or from second to third, normally sacrificing the batter, who is thrown out at first. Many managers use the sacrifice bunt routinely, and they refer to their behavior as "percentage baseball," as if they knew the percentages, which, apparently, most of them do not. The routine is that you bunt if there is a man on first or second, nobody out, and your team is only slightly ahead, tied, or not "too far" behind. One or more runs behind is considered too far for the visiting team, and two or more runs behind too far for the home team, the difference coming from the fact that the home team bats last and can afford to "play for a tie."

Why does the manager decide to bunt? Ultimately, of course, he does it to win more games. At the moment of doing it, he is trying to increase his chance of getting one additional run while giving up some of his opportunity to get several. The theory is simple. It takes at least two singles or a double to score a man from first, while a single alone will usually score him from second; if he is already on second, we note that if we could get him to third with only one out, he could score on any hit, error, wild pitch, passed ball, long fly, balk, or slow grounder. Proponents of bunting are fond of quoting this list, but it contains some fairly rare events, and this raises the real questions: when we use the bunt, by *how much* is our chance of scoring one run increased, and *how much* do we sacrifice in terms of possible additional runs? Again, the only way to get an answer to this question that is relevant to real major

league players playing under pressure of real games is to take statistics from actual games. There is no way to provide realistic conditions for an experiment, and theory (see Refs. 1 and 2) is of dubious value.

Although records of games played exist in the archives of organized baseball, turning these into usable data is a major task which, if it has been done, has not been made public to my knowledge, except in Lindsey (1963).* Lindsey discussed records of several hundred major league games played in 1959 and 1960, and he produced some very interesting statistics, some of which are shown in Table 1.

To see how we, as armchair managers, would use this table to decide about bunting, let's look at the first two lines. (For the moment, we'll think only of average cases, but no good statistician dwells on averages alone, so we'll discuss special situations later.) We start, say, with a man on first and no outs. The table says that this situation was observed 1728 times (occasionally, perhaps more than once in the same inning). In a proportion of these cases equal to 0.604, no runs were scored during the remainder of the inning; that is, in 1044 cases no runs scored, and 1044/1728 = 0.604. This means also that the proportion of times at least one run scored from this situation is $1 - 0.604$, or 0.396. We use these proportions as estimated probabilities of the various events; thus near the end of a tight game, the number 0.396 measures the average "value" of having the situation of a man on first and no outs. For earlier parts of the game, the value is more closely related to the number of runs that are scored in an inning, on the average, starting from this situation; this is given in the fourth column as 0.813 for the situation in question.

Now if we make a sacrifice bunt that succeeds in the normal way, the runner on first will move to second and there will be one out. Is this a better situation than we had? In the sense of average number of runs scored, it is decidedly worse; the first and second line of Table 1 show that the average number of runs scored from the man-on-first-no-out situation is 813 per thousand, but

*G. R. Lindsey, 1963, "An Investigation of Strategies in Baseball." *Operations Research* 11:477–501.

Table 1   Relation of Runs Scored to Base(s) Occupied and Number of Outs

Base(s) Occupied	Number of Outs	Proportion of Cases with No Runs Scored in Inning	Proportion of Cases of at Least One Run Scored in Inning	Average Number of Runs in Inning	Number of Cases
1st	0	0.604	0.396	0.813	1728
2nd	1	0.610	0.390	0.671	657
2nd	0	0.381	0.619	1.194	294
3rd	1	0.307	0.693	0.980	202
1st, 2nd	0	0.395	0.605	1.471	367
2nd, 3rd	1	0.27	0.73	1.56	176

Source: Lindsey (1963).

from the man-on-second-one-out situation, it is only 671 per thousand. On the average, then, a normally successful bunt loses 142 runs per 1000 times it is tried. But what about the last inning of a tight game when we only care what has happened to the probability that at least one run will be scored? This figure has dropped from 0.396 to 0.390; these numbers are so close that their difference is readily explained by chance fluctuation from the sample. So we conclude that although the probability of scoring at least one run is increased by moving the runner to second with no additional outs incurred the increase is almost exactly canceled when an additional out occurs, as usually happens in a bunt play.

Conclusion.   On the average, bunting with a man on first loses a lot of runs. On the average, it doesn't increase the probability of scoring at least one run in the inning. Here we've assumed that the batter is always out at first, but, of course, he is sometimes safe, thereby increasing the efficacy of bunting. It is probably more often true, however, that the front runner is thrown out at second, a disaster to the team that chose to bunt. It would appear that bunting with a man on first early in the game should be done only when it so takes the defense by surprise that the chance of the batter's being safe is substantial. Even late in a tight game there is no visible advantage to such bunting unless special circumstances prevail.

Now let's think of the problem of the man on second with nobody out. The table tells us that he will score (or at least somebody will score) in

all but 381 cases out of 1000, that is, in 619 cases out of 1000. *If* we can move him to third by sacrificing the batter, we can raise the 619 to 693. (Note that we lose 214 runs per 1000 tries doing this, but let's again consider the case where it is late in the game and we need only one run.) Here there is indeed something to be gained by a successful bunt play, but it's time to face reality: the bunt play doesn't always work. How often it works depends on a lot of things, and we don't have statistics for an average result, but let's see how we would use them if we did.

If the batter bunts the ball a little too hard, the defending team happily fires the ball to third base and the lead runner is put out, leaving the offensive team with a man on first and one out, their probability of scoring at least one run having gone from 0.619 to 0.266, the latter figure coming from the complete table in Lindsey's paper. The typical manager does not admit the possibility of such an event. After it happens he dismisses it with the remark "These young fellows don't know how to bunt like we used to." I know this remark was being made before any of today's managers were making their first appearance as professional players, and it was probably originated in the nineteenth century by the first nonplaying manager. The remark is merely an excuse for not studying the problem, but let's not be too hard on the baseball managers; we have pointed out already that the moves they make in plain sight are duplicated by other kinds of supervisors in less visible circumstances.

As we said above, we don't have statistics for the results of a bunt try with a man on second, so we'll make up some, trying to be as realistic as possible from unrecorded personal observations over the years. Here they are:

1. 65% of the time the runner moves to third and the batter is out (normal case).
2. 12% of the time the runner is put out at third, and the batter is safe at first.
3. 10% of the time the runner must stay at second and the batter is out, for example when the batter bunts a pop fly, or strikes out.
4. 8% of the time the batter gets on first safely, that is he gets a hit, and the runner also advances.
5. 5% of the time the bunter hits into a double play, that is, he and the runner are both thrown out.

Now to compute the overall probability of scoring at least one run, we simply multiply and add according to the rules of probability. The reader who doesn't know these rules can do it this way: start with 1000 cases. In 650 (i.e., 65%) of these we have result (1), namely a man on third and one out. The table says that he will score 69.3% of the time, so we take 69.3% of 650, and get 450. That is, in 450 cases the bunt succeeds as in (1), and a run ultimately scores. Now in 120 cases the outcome is as in (2), and Lindsey's complete table says that a score then occurs 26.6% of the time. So we take 26.6% of 120 and get 32. Add this to the 450 and keep going. What we get for all five cases, using Lindsey's complete table where necessary, is

$$0.693(650) + 0.266(120) + 0.390(100)$$
$$+ 0.87(80) + 0.067(50)$$
$$= 450 + 32 + 39 + 70 + 3$$
$$= 594.$$

In other words, we will get at least one run in only 594 cases out of 1000. Before the bunt our chances were 619 out of 1000, so we have shot ourselves down. Of course, if our hypothetical data in (1) to (5) above are too pessimistic, the correct result will be a little more favorable to bunting, but it would appear that any realistic estimates will lead to the conclusion that bunting is not profitable on the average.

The intelligent use of statistics requires more than just a look at the averages. The above data

and accompanying arguments show that bunting, used indiscriminately as many managers do, is not a winning strategy. This doesn't mean that one should never bunt, however. The man at bat may be a weak hitter who is an excellent bunter, and the man following him may be a good hitter; the batter may be a pitcher whose hitting ability is nil, but who can occasionally put down a good bunt; or the other team may clearly not be expecting a bunt, so that the element of surprise is on our side to help the bunt become a base hit. In any of these cases the bunt can be a profitable action. The role of statistics is to show us what our average behavior should be. In general, if the average result of a strategy is very good, we should use it pretty often. If the average result is poor, we should use it sparingly, that is, the special circumstances that lead to it should be very, very special. There are those who say that statistics are irrelevant and that they treat every case as a special case. This is probably impossible, and if such people would examine their behavior over a long period of time, they would probably find it quite statistically predictable. Incidentally, if one takes the point of view that surprise is the whole thing, that is, that the objective is to be unpredictable, then a randomized strategy is indicated; this is elaborated in any book on mathematical game theory.

The Strategy of the Intentional Pass

Another strategic move in baseball is the intentional base on balls. The opposing team has a man on second, say, with one out, and we decide to put a man on first intentionally, either to try to get a double play or to have a force play available at all three bases. Is it worth it? Lindsey's table shows that before the intentional walk the probability of scoring at least one run is 0.390, but afterward it is 0.429. Clearly, on the average, the intentional pass is a losing move; followed by a double play it's great, but followed by an unintentional walk it can lead to a calamity, and the latter possibility is part of the reason for the numerical results just quoted. Widespread use of the intentional pass seems to be based on sheer optimism, as the statistics appear to show that the bad effects, from the point of view of the team in the field, definitely outweigh the good ones, on the average. What about special cases? If the batter is a good one, to be followed by a poor one, the data don't necessarily apply, and the intentional pass may be a good thing. It probably should seldom be used early in the game, though, unless the following batter is a weak-hitting pitcher because it causes the average number of runs to go up from 671 per 1000 to 939 per 1000 owing to the additional base runner, and it is doubtful that there are many special cases that are so special as to outweigh this fact.

Collection and Use of Data

Figures such as those in Table 1 are obviously of little value unless they are based on a rather large number of cases. It isn't at all obvious, though, how large the number of cases should be. Mathematical statistics answers questions about how large sample sizes should be, but the questions must be specific. We can't, as we are sometimes asked to do, say that 100 (or 1000 or 2000) is a good all-around sample size. If, however, we are asked to find the probability of at least one run resulting from a man on first with no outs, we can, with certain reasonable simplifying assumptions, determine how large the sample must be so that we can be 90% sure, for example, of being within 0.005 of the correct answer. Table 1 shows in the last column the sample size that was used to produce the data of the earlier columns. For an individual keeping records as a pastime, this represents a major effort. We would think that baseball people, engaged in a competition in which a few extra victories can make a difference of a great deal of money, would go to the trouble to collect even larger samples. They wouldn't want to go too far in this direction, however, because information tends to become obsolete. Changing rules, playing fields, and personnel cause the game to change slightly from year to year. Sometimes scoring is relatively low for a few years, and then it increases for a few years. Data gathered in one of these periods of time may not be altogether valid as a basis for decisions in another.

Data of the sort we have been talking about here are sometimes called *historical* as opposed to *experimental*, or *controlled*. The distinction is important in many areas. For example, if statistics are produced showing that smokers have lung cancer with much higher frequency than non-smokers, this *historical* fact *in itself* does not demonstrate that smoking increases the lung cancer rate. (After all, children drink more milk than adults, but this is not why they are children.) The problem is that there may be other variables that, for example, help cause lung cancer and also influence people to become smokers. Nevertheless, the historical statistics on cancer were very suggestive and led to various experiments in laboratories which have strengthened most people's belief in a causal relationship. We can make good use of historical data, in other words, but we must be careful about inferring cause-and-effect relationships from them.

No doubt because of frustrations in trying to draw conclusions from historical data, statisticians developed the science and art called the *design of experiments*. If we can do a properly designed experiment, we are in a much better position to draw valid conclusions about what causes what, but the possibility of a designed experiment is not always open to us. When we can't experiment, we must do what we can with available data, but this doesn't mean that we shouldn't keep our eyes open to the faults that such data have.

Conclusions

So what have we learned from our look at sports statistics? We have learned these do's and don'ts:

1. Don't waste time arguing about the merits or demerits of something if you can gather some statistics that will answer the question realistically.
2. If you're trying to establish cause-and-effect relationships, do try to do so with a properly designed experiment.
3. If you can't have an experiment, do the best you can with whatever data you can gather, but do be very skeptical of historical data and subject them to all the logical tests you can think of.

4. Do remember that your experience is merely a hodgepodge of statistics, consisting of those cases that you happen to remember. Because these are necessarily small in number and because your memory may be biased toward one result or another, your experience may be far less dependable than a good set of statistics. (The bias mentioned here can come, for instance, from the fact that people who believe in the bunt tend to remember the cases when it works, and vice versa.)

5. Do keep in mind, though, that the statistics of the kind discussed here are averages, and special cases may demand special action. This is not an excuse for following your hunches at all times, but it does mean that 100% application of what is best on the average may not be a productive strategy. The good manager has a policy, perhaps based on statistics, that takes care of most decisions. The excellent manager has learned to recognize occasional situations in which the policy needs to be varied for maximum effectiveness.

References

1. E. Cook. 1966. *Percentage Baseball*. Cambridge, Mass.: MIT Press.
2. R. Hooke. 1967. Review of Cook (1966). *Journal of the American Statistical Association* 62:688–690.

Statistics, Molière, and Henry Adams

William Kruskal

William Henry Kruskal did his undergraduate work at Harvard and in 1955 he obtained his Ph.D. from Columbia University in mathematical statistics. He worked at the U.S. Naval proving grounds during World War II. From 1949 to 1973 he was with Columbia University and was chairman of their department of statistics from 1966 to 1973. He is presently a distinguished professor at the University of Chicago. Kruskal has served on numerous national committees concerned with aspects of statistics.

The most famous description of statistics is surely the pejorative definition implied by the phrase "lies, damned lies, and statistics." The implication that statistics are to be found in the purgatory of error on a circle lower than damned lies suggests that a great deal of frustration and anger is generated by the use and misuse of statistics. Much of this discomfort could be avoided if the users simply understood the nature of statistics a little better. It is really amazing that so many frequent users of rather involved and sophisticated statistical analyses are totally ignorant of the nature of the subject, its mathematical foundations, and most importantly, its limitations. It is hardly fair, for example, to blame automobile manufacturers for the deadly rise of traffic fatalities if the cars are increasingly being driven by irresponsible, ignorant, or drunken drivers. A more reasonable approach would be to demand that licensed drivers be able to control a car, know the driving laws, and be sober when driving. The same standards should apply to users of statistics. Those who don't have the time or the inclination to gain an understanding of the subject shouldn't use it.

William Kruskal wrote this article with the hope that its readers might gain a better insight into this much misunderstood subject. He takes some effort to point out the inherent limitations of statistical methods. This information should be especially useful for believers in the "damned lies" description. Much of the unhappiness with the use of statistics stems from a lack of understanding of exactly what statistics can and can't do. A man standing with one foot in a bucket of boiling water and the other in a bucket of freezing water would be a ridiculous fool to summarize his experience by saying, "On the average I feel fine."

I

AN OCCUPATIONAL HAZARD to which we statisticians are exposed occurs in the context of a social occasion, perhaps a dinner party. I am, let us say, seated next to a charming lady whom I have just met, and, as an initial conversational ice-breaking, she turns to me with a winning smile and says: "Now tell me what it is you do?"

We must tell the truth, of course, so I reply that I am a statistician. That usually ruins a fine conversation, for in 8.6 cases out of 10 the lady's smile disappears, she turns to my rival on her other side, and I attack the fried chicken in lonely, misunderstood dignity.

There are those in the statistical world who have worked out more effective, if less truthful, devices for this problem. For example, some fel-

Source: William Kruskal, "Statistics, Molière, and Henry Adams," *American Scientist* 55 (1967): 416–428.

low statisticians, when asked what they do, reply that they are mathematicians; this is often only a slightly better piece of conversationmanship, but it has the merit of not being a downright lie. Some cowards completely evade the issue by saying: "Oh, I don't do anything interesting; tell me about yourself." The first part of that statement is a whopping fib, and I hope today to explain something of what statistics is, why we statisticians find it fascinating, and why many more well-trained statisticians are badly needed.

The dinner table contretemps just described never happens to my acquaintances who are poets, physicists, African explorers, or salesmen of used cars. What is there about the word "statistics" that so often provokes strained silence?

To some minds the word conjures up a picture of wizened clerks on high stools, each with his green eye-shade, all forever adding long columns of figures. How could anyone be interested in such activity?

In other minds, the statistician is pictured as a fanatic about numerical facts. He will tell you, without any encouragement, the length of the Amazon river, the population of Vienna in 1892, the average number of children in the American family down to a hundredth of a child, and so on.

To still others, a statistician is a stock market analyst, someone who studies balance sheets and profit statements to produce analyses that are probably not looked at by one investor in fifty.

People of all these kinds exist, they are useful citizens, and their work often relates to statistical problems, but they are usually *not* statisticians in the sense that I use the term.

Sharp, concise definitions of a discipline are exceedingly difficult: they are typically either aphorisms that leave us amused but not informed,[1] or else they are woolly statements of vague generalities. But one must try: statistics, as I see it, is the study and informed application of methods for reaching conclusions about the world from fallible observations. This is too encompassing and it needs to be cut down in various ways, but it will do for a start. The key words are "methods" and "fallible." In statistics, we are concerned about methods, their characteristics, how to choose among alternative ones, concepts of optimality. We are also professionally concerned with the fallibility of observational data, and such fallibility

is pervasive. For this reason, most modern statistical study is in terms of probability models for the generation of data; that is, we study methods for reaching conclusions on the basis of a variety of assumptions about how data might have arisen from a random process.

Theoretical statistics is the abstract study of such methods; applied statistics is the application of the methods in the light of theory.

Many of you will remember that famous character, Monsieur Jordain, in a play by Molière. Monsieur Jordain was a great believer in cultural education; he was so naïve and ignorant a believer that his attempts to educate himself are ludicrous, yet touched with common humanity. One of the nicest parts of Molière's play for me is that in which Monsieur Jordain finds with tremendous delight that he has been speaking prose all his life.

Just so, each of us has been doing statistics all his life, in the sense that each of us has been busily reaching conclusions based on empirical observations ever since his birth. There are important differences, however, between the statistical inferences we make all our lives and the practice of professional statistics that I am attempting to describe in this lecture. Perhaps the most important difference lies in the use by professional statisticians of methods that are explicit, that have been theoretically analyzed, and whose properties are understood.

The prose that we speak naturally is professionally practiced by novelists, poets, and actors; it is professionally analyzed by linguists and grammarians. Just so, the statistical thinking we do continually is professionally practiced by applied statisticians—who may be called psychometricians, public health analysts, econometricians, and the like—while the professional analysis and advancement of statistics is carried on by theoretical statisticians. All of these kinds of people are important, and, at least in the case of statistics, there are not nearly enough of them.

II

This lecture is organized about two examples, the first representing a generic experimental situation and the second about an official government survey. In both examples, I shall point out some ways in which the data are fallible, and discuss something of methods for reaching conclusions from those fallible data.

Suppose, for our first example, that we are comparing two medical treatments, that we have carried out an experiment, and that the results are summarized as follows:

Treatment 1. Cure rate: 70%

Treatment 2. Cure rate: 90%

The ostensible conclusion is that Treatment 2 is appreciably better than Treatment 1. But how confident can we be of this? What sorts of fallibility are the above rates subject to, and what sorts of inferences may safely be drawn? Perhaps Treatment 2, which seems much better than Treatment 1, really has the same underlying cure rate; perhaps not.

It is clear, to begin with, that the cure rate percentages themselves are inadequate. We must at least know in addition the numbers of patients, the so-called sample sizes. Perhaps there were ten patients given each treatment, and of those given Treatment 1, 7 were cured, while of those given Treatment 2, 9 were cured. Or perhaps there were 100 patients per treatment, or 1000. Perhaps there were 1000 patients for Treatment 1 and 100 for Treatment 2. In order to be quite specific, suppose that there were 20 patients per treatment, so that the numerical results of the experiment may be expressed by the following table:

	Number Cured	Number not Cured	Total
Treatment 1	14	6	20
Treatment 2	18	2	20

We note in passing that the scheme of this table is applicable to many other phenomena besides cure rates for medical treatments. We might be working with germination rates for two kinds of seeds, or we might be considering numbers of students who pass an examination, with an interest in comparing pass rates for men and women. It will, however, be helpful to think concretely in terms of the medical situation.

The statistician typically classifies errors and sources of variability into two kinds. First there are the systematic errors, or errors of bias; these are factors that do not depend primarily on sample size but introduce distortion of the results

whether we take 20, 200, or 2000 patients per treatment. Second, there are random errors, whose effect may be reduced by taking larger samples and thus averaging out the effects of random variability.

What are some possible systematic errors in our generic medical example? One important kind of systematic error stems from *definitions*. For example, what does the word "cured" mean in this context? The most important problem here is that of the subjective opinion of the person who evaluates a patient as cured or not cured. Suppose, for example, that Treatment 1 is a conventional, standard treatment, while Treatment 2 is a novel, experimental one proposed by the scientist who carries out the experiment. Further, suppose that this scientist himself decides whether or not a patient is cured. A first level of resultant bias comes from the all too human tendency to classify a marginal case as cured if it is a Treatment 2 case, and uncured if Treatment 1. Such a practice sounds silly when so flatly described, but I assure you that it often happens. The problem is especially difficult in particular fields, for example in the evaluation of psychological therapy. A second level of bias occurs when the experimenter realizes the possibility of over-enthusiasm for his own treatment, and leans over backwards, so to speak, in evaluating results, thus penalizing his treatment. In either case we get distorted results.

The only way I know of escaping this problem of evaluation bias is that of *blind evaluation:* arranging matters so that the evaluator is completely ignorant of which treatment each patient has been exposed to. Sometimes this is difficult to arrange, but it is essential for scientific validity.

A closely related systematic error is that of *assignment to treatment*. How were the forty patients assigned to the two treatments? Again, it is clear that the experimenter could easily—presumably unconsciously—bias the results by assigning to the treatment he subjectively favors those patients who are healthier, younger, more cooperative, etc. I have heard of cases in which treatment assignment was carried out by a nurse or secretary, who was supposed to make the choice in an unbiased fashion, but who in fact knew which treatment was favored by her boss, and who consequently assigned to it those patients in better health. Again, at the next level, the assignment of patients to treatment might represent leaning over backwards to avoid bias in the subjectively favored direction, and thus create bias in the other direction.

The only way I know to avoid this problem is by *blind assignment,* that is, by assigning patients so that the assignment is completely independent of knowledge of which treatment is which. For reasons that we do not have time to explore, by far the best method of blind assignment is by the use of a random mechanism, akin to careful coin flipping or card shuffling.

Another source of systematic error is the complete exclusion of the record of a patient because he appears to be an aberrant case. This is a particularly insidious problem, because, when the scientific record contains no mention of a discarded case, the reader usually has no way of allowing for the omission.

Medical literature is replete with new treatments claimed to be marvelous discoveries. Many of these turned out later *not* to be effective cures, and the reasons have often been connected with sources of bias, as with those above.

There are various other sources of systematic error. For example, one might ask whether the treatments differ only in the supposed medical difference. If the two treatments are applied in two different hospitals there may be other aspects of the regimens in the hospitals—quite aside from the treatment differences—that affect the results. But let us resist the temptation to try to give a full listing of systematic errors. We turn to *random errors*.

Sources of bias do not as a rule depend on the numbers of patients: they are present whether we have 20 patients or 20,000 patients per treatment, they do not "average out" when there are large numbers of cases. In fact, experimenters are sometimes lulled into a false sense of security when analyzing large experiments just because of the many trials. In contrast, random errors do depend strongly on the number of trials.

Random errors arise in two major ways, although the first is probably minor in our medical context. First, we have measurement and computational error . . . there may simply be slips in deciding whether a patient is or is not cured, or clerical and computational errors in transmission of this information through files and tabulations.

It is easy to forget these, but every statistician knows that they must be watched for incessantly. Just the other day, a public announcement by a group of eminent physicians drew attention to dangers in the widespread use of a drug (Enovid) by women of certain ages. Naturally this caused quite a stir, and it was with mixed chagrin and relief that the physicians announced a bit later that their warning had erroneously been based upon what amounted to a simple miscalculation.

Second, we turn to *sampling error.* Suppose that we have satisfied ourselves that systematic errors, measurement errors, and computational errors are negligible for our two treatments. Nonetheless, if we could repeat the experiment, we would probably not obtain exactly the same results. Instead of 14 and 18 cured, respectively, we might get 13 and 19, or 16 and 16, or even 17 and 15, the last case completely reversing the apparent difference. How can we cope with sampling error, perhaps better termed sampling fluctuation?

One important method of statistical analysis is based on calculations of the probabilities or chances of obtaining various results, especially under the hypothesis that there is in fact no difference between the treatments. Recall that our observed results were:

	Cured	Not Cured
Treatment 1	14	6
Treatment 2	18	2

Now it may be computed by a standard statistical technique that the probability, or chance, of observing this result, if in fact the two treatments do not differ at all in cure rate, is about 1 out of ten; more exactly, it is .0958.

Similarly, we may compute the probabilities of other possible results, again under the hypothesis that the treatments have the same underlying cure rate. For example, we might have observed the slightly different table:

	Cured	Not Cured
Treatment 1	13	7
Treatment 2	19	1

giving observed cure rates of 65 and 95%. This observed table, under the hypothesis of equal underlying cure rates, would be observed about 1 time out of 50; more exactly, the probability is .0202.

The general approach I am describing is to base statistical inference upon computations of the probabilities of a variety of possible observed tables under a variety of hypotheses about what the true, underlying cure rates are. These true, but unknown, rates may be thought of as those we would observe if we could try the treatments on a tremendously large sample of patients, say one million, under the same circumstances as in the actual experiment.

It is traditional, and often useful, to concentrate attention on the hypothesis mentioned earlier, that the two treatments have exactly the same cure rates. Let us think of lining up all possible observed tables so that tables to the right show extreme observed differences between the cure rates, while tables at the left show no differences, or small ones. Thus at the left end, we might have tables like:

$$
\begin{array}{cccccc}
0 & 20 & 8 & 12 & 17 & 3 \\
0 & 20 & 8 & 12 & 17 & 3
\end{array}
$$

and so on. At the right end we would have the extreme cases:

$$
\begin{array}{cccc}
0 & 20 & 20 & 0 \\
20 & 0 & 0 & 20
\end{array}
$$

Imagine then these many possible tables lined up, and let us represent each table by a dot:

ments in fact have the same underlying cure rates. Now *if* the probability is small, then either (1) we have observed something quite surprising under the hypothesis, or (2) the hypothesis is false. On the other hand, if the computed probability is moderate or large, then we have observed a result that is quite consistent with the hypothesis of no difference. Thus a small computed probability throws doubt on the hypothesis of no difference, while a moderate or large computed probability does not throw doubt on the hypothesis.

In our particular case, we find that the probability of our observed table, or a more extreme one, under the hypothesis of no difference (symmetrical, two-sided Fisher "exact test" sample significance level), turns out to be 24 out of 100; more exactly, 0.2352. That is, in 24 out of 100 repetitions of the experiment, we would find a difference of cure rates like the one we found or a greater difference, although the true, underlying cure rates are identical.

Now a result that can happen 24 times out of 100 under a hypothesis would ordinarily not be viewed as discrediting that hypothesis seriously, and so we conclude that our 70% and 90% observed cure rates might very well represent the results of sampling randomness acting on patients treated by two equally effective treatments. This

Somewhere among these dots will be the actual table that we observed; I have indicated it by an arrow. (A full treatment of this topic would include a precise description of this lining up of possible observed results, and would clarify several points that are slurred over in our condensed treatment, for example, the distinction between a test conditional on all the marginals and a test conditional on row marginals only.)

One important statistical method goes as follows: let us compute the probability of observing what we actually observed, *or more extreme cases;* the cases whose total probability we compute are bracketed in the diagram. We compute the probability under the hypothesis that the two treat-

does not, of course, say that the treatments are equally effective, only that equivalence is quite consistent with the observed sample.

Next let us suppose that the samples are no longer of size 20, but of size 40, while the observed cure rates remain the same. The result would then be:

	Cured	Not Cured	Totals
Treatment 1	28	12	40
Treatment 2	36	4	40

If we go through computations similar to the prior ones, we find that, if the treatments really do not differ in cure rate, then the probability of such a deviation in observed cure rate—or greater—changes from the prior 24 out of 100 to only about 5 out of 100. That is, the observed results are rather surprising, and would often be taken as good evidence that the treatments are really different.

Continuing in this way, if the samples were increased to 100 each, a multiple of 5 from the original ones, and if the observed cure rates were the same, the crucial probability would go down to less than 1 in 1000, and a difference between the treatments would be nearly unquestionable.

Notice how the interpretation of the same observed cure rates changes sharply as we go from sample sizes of 20 to 40, and then to 100. If we considered still larger sample sizes, the crucial probability would decrease still further.

One important area of statistics is that of helping to plan or design experiments, and, in the present context, a major part of design *before the experiment is carried out* would be to decide on sample size. Should we look at 20 patients, 40 patients, or 100 patients for each treatment? Monetary costs may play an important role in such decisions; in addition, the statistician can make a contribution by computing how likely it is that a real difference, of some given magnitude, between the treatments will evince itself by giving rise to a small probability of surprise based on the results to be observed.

We have now seen, in one simple context, how several different kinds of errors arise and how one method of reaching conclusions works out. We have hardly made a beginning at a complete analysis of the method, and we have not discussed at all other methods of statistical analysis that might be used.

III

The second example I want to discuss arises in a completely different area, that of official government statistics. As an introduction, I want to cite a quotation from a classic American autobiography, *The Education of Henry Adams*. I shall then make a few digressive remarks suggested by the quotation, and then we shall turn to the second example proper.

Henry Adams, at one point of his endless, fu-tile search for ultimate truth, decided that he might find it by studying statistics, statistics in the plural sense of columns of figures. Adams says, speaking of himself in the third person:

Taking for granted that the alternative to art was arithmetic, he plunged deep into statistics, fancying that education would find the surest bottom there; and the study proved the easiest he had ever approached. Even the Government volunteered unlimited statistics, endless columns of figures, bottomless averages merely for the asking. At the Statistical Bureau [in Washington, D.C.], Worthington Ford supplied any material that curiosity could imagine for filling the vast gaps of ignorance, and methods for applying the plasters of fact. One seemed for a while to be winning ground, and one's averages projected themselves as laws into the future. Perhaps the most perplexing part of the study lay in the attitude of the statisticians, who showed no enthusiastic confidence in their own figures. They should have reached certainty, but they talked like other men who knew less. The method did not result in faith. Indeed, every increase of mass— of volume and velocity—seemed to bring in new elements, and, at last, a scholar, fresh in arithmetic and ignorant of algebra, fell into a superstitious terror of complexity at the sink of facts. (Chapter 23, Houghton Mifflin Co., 1918)

This passage has several aspects that are well worth discussion. First, consider the key phrase "ignorant of algebra." Adams realizes that the numbers alone usually mean little. They must be reworked and condensed—in short, analyzed. But analysis is inevitably in terms of abstract concepts, and abstract concepts about numbers are usually expressed mathematically. Statistical thinking requires a measure of mathematical ability and training, the proper amount depending on the kind of statistics one does. Some mathematics is necessary for statistics; on the other hand, fine statistical work, both theoretical and applied, can be done without becoming a Ph.D. in mathematics.

A second interesting aspect of the Henry Adams statement is his complaint that the statisticians showed no "enthusiastic confidence," that their method "did not result in faith." One sometimes hears it said that statisticians are professionally cynical and destructive. A variant is the complaint that statistics is fine for the routine analysis of data, but that the creative construction of theories in science has little to gain from statistics. I think that these complaints reflect something real, but that they are also gross caricatures. If statisticians tend to be professionally cynical it is because they so often see the results of undue optimism, of scientific credulity, and of childish faith in numbers written on a piece of paper. As for the construction of grand theories about nature, statistics, properly interpreted, has a real and positive role in this activity.

We turn now to a specific example of government statistics. A few years ago, a colleague—an economist—and I became interested in the Consumer Price Index of the Bureau of Labor Statistics, a respected agency of the federal government. This Index is an official government number, published periodically, to the accompaniment of newspaper publicity. The index number is expressed to an impressive apparent level of accuracy, and we consumers cheer or groan as it decreases or increases a few tenths of a point. Its economic effects are considerable, through labor contracts that are tied to it and through business decisions that are based upon it. In addition, the Index and its detailed components—by city of region, and by kind of commodity—are used widely by economists for a great variety of analyses.

When we began to study the Consumer Price Index, my colleague and I were interested primarily in its error structure: what sorts of errors affected it, and what sort of accuracy did the Index have? We soon learned that one quality of government statisticians had changed since the days of Henry Adams. The Washington statisticians he knew, some seventy years ago, may have shown a lack of confidence, but those currently writing about the Consumer Price Index showed a surprising amount of confidence. The written material we found expressed great faith in the accuracy of the Index and said that the errors were generally small and negligible. It would be fascinating to speculate about this change in the culture of government statistics—for example, we might imagine that the increase in confidence stemmed from a growing sensitivity in government to public relations and the image presented—but I leave that investigation to sociologists and political scientists.

We found, to our surprise, that there was little evidence available about the error structure of the Index. We studied what evidence we could find, and we published a paper[2] about the problem. That paper was one small part of a general movement toward further research into the error structure of the Index, and I understand that the Bureau of Labor Statistics is now carrying out its own detailed studies of error, as indeed it should.

What do we mean by error structure? Let me try to give some idea of it by considering only the price of food, an important component of the Index. This food price part of the Index is itself a sub-index made up of prices of many quite specific foods. Let us suppose that we are concerned now with the price per pound of a well-defined cut and grade of beef in Chicago on a certain day. On that day, in the city of Chicago, there are doubtless thousands of retail sales, at various prices, of the cut and grade of beef we have selected; clearly all of these sales cannot be observed, and a sample must somehow be chosen. Current practice is to work with a relatively fixed sample of food stores, to send representatives of the Bureau of Labor Statistics to the manager of each store in the store sample, and to ask each manager for his current price of beef (as well, of course, as his prices for many other foods). In Chicago the large chains and about 90 independent food stores were asked for prices in 1960. This whole sampling procedure is subject to a variety of errors, many doubtless negligible but others perhaps large.[3]

As in the case of our two medical treatments, it is convenient to classify errors into systematic and random ones. Let us first consider one possible systematic error, an error of bias, that is an error that tends to push in one direction by about the same amount and that is relatively insensitive to sample size. It is the case that some stores are unwilling to cooperate with the Bureau of Labor Statistics, in that these stores refuse to list prices systematically for the Bureau's representatives. (Of course the representatives could simply walk into a store and look at prices, but this is a much more time-consuming operation than simply taking down numbers from a list.) Now it might well be that the uncooperative stores tend to have a different pattern of prices and price changes than the stores with more public-spirited managers. For example, stores run on a shoe-string, newer stores, and stores in slum areas might be less likely to cooperate. Thus a bias or systematic error could easily arise from differentials between cooperating and non-cooperating stores. Of course you might think of many other sources of bias; one function of a statistician is to be alert for them and to suggest special experimental programs for evaluating their magnitudes. For example, a statistician might plan a special program for observing some prices in non-cooperating stores, with the aim of comparing those price movements with price movements of cooperating stores.

Now what about random errors in the present context? As before, we may subdivide these into measurement and computation errors, and sampling errors proper. Random measurement errors are easy to think about in the present context; a store manager may simply quote a wrong price, the agent of the Bureau of Labor Statistics may not hear the price correctly or may make a mistake in writing it down. There may be clerical errors in the further processing of the numbers. Such errors at first sound laughably trivial, but they are more frequent than you may think, especially in a large, complex operation. Many of you have checking accounts; how often do you have difficulty reconciling your monthly statement because of a silly arithmetic slip? One time in five, in ten, in twenty? Probably at least the last. Now think what can happen in a complex procedure requiring thousands of clerical and arithmetic steps.

We turn now to the second subdivision of random error: sampling error proper. Suppose that every single sale of our particular kind of beef in Chicago during our specific day could be accurately recorded. Then we might know without error the true average price for that day. If we only *sample* prices, and strike an average for the sample, we will in general obtain a different number than the true average. How much is the sample average likely to differ from the true average? One cent, two cents, five cents? It makes a difference. This is the sampling error.

The most important aspect of sampling error for our purposes is probably the sampling of food stores. Suppose that the Bureau of Labor Statistics' records about its Chicago food store sample suddenly disappeared, and that it became necessary to select a new sample in ignorance of the prior one, but by the same methods. The stores in the new sample would generally be different stores from those in the prior sample, and hence the store prices—and the average price for the sample—would be different. How much different? How can we discuss this kind of store sampling error?

Suppose that we know the average price for each possible sample that might be chosen. Let us suppose that these average prices range from 77 cents to 89 cents, with most average prices in the neighborhood of 83 cents, give or take about two cents. This distribution of prices would show the *variability of average price from sample to sample*, and from the distribution we could compute the probability that the average of a single randomly chosen sample deviates from the true average by one cent, by two cents, and so on.

Unfortunately, there is no practicable way of obtaining the average price for each possible sample, and thus finding the variability of average price from sample to sample. Here is where one fundamental discipline of statistics enters. If the sampling method is that of choosing stores by what is called *probability sampling*, that is by letting entry or non-entry of a store into the sample be determined by a known chance mechanism, we can usually tell quite well what the variability of average price from sample to sample would be by looking only at the price variability from store to store of the *actually selected* sample. The concept of probability sampling is of fundamental importance, and I wish that we had time to explore it further.

The basic notion of going from the *observable* within-sample variability to the *unobservable* between-sample variability is easily appreciated. Just as we can estimate the average price of all stores from the average of a properly chosen sample, so we can estimate the price variability among all stores from the store-to-store price variability within a properly chosen sample. Once we have an estimate of variability from store to store, we can modify it to take account of our interest in variability between sample averages.

Thus, assuming that our sample is chosen by probability methods, we can estimate the variability of average price from sample to sample, and hence make statements about how likely our sample average is to deviate by various amounts from the true, over-all average.

On the other hand, if the stores are selected by expert judgment (so-called), by asking for volunteers, or by other nonprobability methods, one cannot tell from the internal structure of the sample the sample-to-sample variability that is present. I might add that the Consumer Price Index stores are *not* chosen by probability sampling (at least they were not so chosen in 1960), and this considerably complicates the discussion.

So here again we have examples of two broad classes of errors: systematic and random errors. There are some kinds of errors that are not easily classified this way. In surveys that include questions about age, several interesting phenomena appear. Older ladies tend to decrease their ages, while quite young ladies tend to increase theirs. Another sort of error that does not strictly fall under our rubrics is a chance error that affects whole clumps of observations. Interviewer personality characteristics are known to influence responses in certain sample surveys, so that all responses obtained by a given interviewer will be subject to the same influence. Such an error may have a systematic component together with a chance component, stemming from randomness in the selection of interviewers. The effect of the chance component will decrease, not as the total number of observations increases, but as the number of interviewers increases.

IV

I have not been able, in this limited time, to describe the work of theoretical statisticians, who compare competing methods of inference in abstract terms, and who invent new methods. Almost all theoretical statisticians, however, draw renewed motivation and interest from continued association with problems of applied statistics. One of the charms of statistics is the almost unlimited variety of investigations that one comes in touch with. Let me mention a few from my own experience:

Weather modification by the seeding of clouds

Authorship of the disputed *Federalist Papers*

Patterns of book use in a university library

X-radiation as a cure for ulcers

Testing theories of breakage for brittle materials

I hope that I have given you some feeling for the kinds of thinking and work that statisticians do. Although we all do statistics in a sense, the professional practice of statistics requires disciplined study in the same way as do the professional practices of law or medicine; the statistics we have, with Molière, been talking all our lives is like the legal and medical discussions we have as laymen: often roughly serviceable, but requiring a visit to the expert when a real problem arises. Statistical experts are, as Henry Adams says, often profoundly skeptical, just as legal and medical experts are, but it is a skepticism that we hope leads to truth, by the analysis of error and study of methods of inference.

Notes

1. Examples: (1) Statistics is the art of stating in precise terms that which one does not know; (2) A statistician is a man who draws a mathematically precise line from an unwarranted assumption to a foregone conclusion.
2. William H. Kruskal and Lester G. Telser, "Food Prices and the Bureau of Labor Statistics," *J. Business*, Univ. Chicago, *33* (1960), 258–279; comment by Ewan Clague and rejoinder, 280–5.
3. A systematic discussion of sampling problems for index numbers is given by Philip J. McCarthy, under Index Numbers, article on "Sampling" in Volume 7 of the forthcoming *International Encyclopedia of the Social Sciences*, New York: The Macmillan Co. and the Free Press, 1968. (This footnote did not appear in prior publications of this essay.)

Deciding Authorship

Frederick Mosteller and David L. Wallace

C. Frederick Mosteller was born in West Virginia and received his doctorate in mathematics from Princeton in 1946. He has been associated with Harvard since 1946, serving as chairman of their statistics department from 1957 to 1969. He is a member of the National Academy of Science and has been a Guggenheim fellow.

David Lee Wallace received his Ph.D. in mathematics in 1953 from Princeton. He has been a professor of statistics at the University of Chicago since 1967 and is a fellow of the Royal Statistical Association, a fellow of the Center for Advanced Studies in Behavioral Science, and a fellow of the American Statistical Association.

An excellent and pointed example is surely worth volumes of stilted pedantry. This article presents just such an example; as a means for gaining insight into how mathematics may be used to solve actual problems it is excellent. The problem Mosteller and Wallace present is that of determining the authorship of a manuscript, a subject of more than passing interest to historians, lawyers, librarians, and a number of others. The account of this problem and its resolution is fascinating in three ways. First, it suggests the vast range of potential applications of mathematics. That a topic so remote from the usual areas of mathematical application can be illuminated by mathematical methods suggests that we have hardly begun to fully realize the potential of this powerful tool.

Second, an important aspect of this example is the fact that the resolution of the problem is probabilistic. Absolute certainty in matters of this kind can almost never be achieved. What mathematics can do is quite precisely quantify the likelihood of each candidate for authorship. While a deeper or more refined analysis may reduce the uncertainty it can never eliminate it. This is an aspect of many applications of mathematics and statistics and is a reality that the users must appreciate and be prepared to deal with. Unfortunately many users of mathematics simply refuse to learn enough mathematics to appreciate the strengths and the limitations of the application. In the case of deciding authorship, even the most determinedly ignorant must see that the analysis can only make authorship probable; certainty is possible only if there is an eyewitness who saw the person write the manuscript. In that case statistics are not needed.

Finally, this article is an excellent example of the mathematical problem solver at work. Notice how the problem is approached. The first step is to find some aspect of authorship amenable to treatment by the mathematics currently available. Indeed, the simpler the mathematical methods, the better. Notice that there is an almost organic development of the solution. It begins with some crude word-counting attempts. These are refined through statistical methods into comparative usage profiles that evolve into an author's "word print." A rather precise description of the probability that a given document meets a given "word print" emerges, and this leads to a general methodology for the determination of authorship. This is a most useful introduction into the "how" of mathematical application.

Source: Frederick Mosteller and David L. Wallace, "Deciding Authorship," in J. M. Tanur et al., *Statistics: A Guide to the Unknown* (San Francisco: Holden-Day, 1978), pp. 207–218. (Problem section omitted.)

ART, MUSIC, LITERATURE, the social, biological, and physical sciences share a common need to classify things: What artist painted the picture? Who composed the piece? Who wrote the document? If paroled, will the prisoner repeat his crime? What disease does the patient have? What trace chemical is damaging the process? In the field of statistics, we call these questions classification or discrimination problems.

Questions of authorship are frequent and sometimes important. Most people have heard of the Shakespeare-Bacon-Marlowe controversy over who wrote the great plays usually attributed to Shakespeare. A less well-known but carefully studied question deals with the authorship of a number of Christian religious writings called the Paulines, some being books in the New Testament: Which ones were written by Paul and which by others? In many authorship questions the solution is easy once we set about counting something systematically. But we treat here an especially difficult problem from American history, the controversy over the authorship of the 12 *Federalist* papers claimed by both Alexander Hamilton and James Madison, and we show how a statistical analysis can contribute to the resolution of historical questions.

The Federalist papers were published anonymously in 1787–88 by Alexander Hamilton, John Jay, and James Madison to persuade the citizens of the State of New York to ratify the Constitution. Seventy-seven papers appeared as letters in New York newspapers over the pseudonym "Publius." Together with eight more essays, they were published in book form in 1788 and have been republished repeatedly both in the U.S. and abroad. *The Federalist* remains today an important work in political philosophy. It is also the leading source of information for studying the intent of the framers of the Constitution, as, for example, in recent decisions on congressional reapportionment, since Madison had taken copious notes at the Constitutional Convention.

It was generally known who had written *The Federalist,* but no public assignment of specific papers to authors occurred until 1807, three years after Hamilton's death as a result of his duel with Aaron Burr. Madison made his listing of authors only in 1818 after he had retired from the Presidency. A variety of lists with conflicting claims have been disputed for a century and a half. There is general agreement on the authorship of 70 papers—5 by Jay, 14 by Madison, and 51 by Hamilton. Of the remaining 15, 12 are in dispute between Hamilton and Madison, and 3 are joint works to a disputed extent. No doubt the primary reason the dispute exists is that Madison and Hamilton did not hurry to enter their claims. Within a few years after writing the essays, they had become bitter political enemies and each occasionally took positions opposing some of his own *Federalist* writings.

The political content of the essays has never provided convincing evidence for authorship. Since Hamilton and Madison were writing a brief in favor of ratification, they were like lawyers working for a client; they did not need to believe or endorse every argument they put forward favoring the new Constitution. While this does not mean that they would go out of their way to misrepresent their personal political positions, it does mean that we cannot argue "Hamilton wouldn't have said that because he believed otherwise." And, as we have often seen, personal political positions change. Thus the political content of a disputed essay cannot give strong evidence in favor of Hamilton's or of Madison's having written it.

The acceptance of the various claims by historians has tended to change with political climate. Hamilton's claims were favored during the last half of the 19th century, Madison's since then. While the thorough historical studies of the historian Douglass Adair over the past several decades support the Madison claims, the total historical evidence is today not much different from that which historians like the elder Henry Cabot Lodge interpreted as favoring Hamilton. New evidence was needed to obtain definite attributions, and internal statistical stylistic evidence provides one possibility; developing that evidence and the methodology for interpreting it was the heart of our work.

The writings of Hamilton and Madison are difficult to tell apart because both authors were masters of the popular *Spectator* style of writing—complicated and oratorical. To illustrate the difficulty, in 1941 Frederick Williams and Frederick Mosteller counted sentence lengths for the undisputed papers and got averages of 34.5 and 34.6 words respectively for Hamilton and Madison. For sentence length, a measure used successfully to distinguish other authors, Hamilton and Madison are practically twins.

Marker Words

Although sentence length does measure complexity (and an average of 35 words shows that the material is very complex), sentence length is not sensitive enough to distinguish reliably between authors writing in similar styles. The variables used in several recent studies of disputed authorship are the rates of occurrence of specific individual words. Our study was stimulated by Adair's discovery—or rediscovery as it turned out—that Madison and Hamilton differ consistently in their choice between the alternative words *while* and *whilst*. In the 14 *Federalist* essays acknowledged to be written by Madison, *while* never occurs whereas *whilst* occurs in eight of them. *While* occurs in 15 of 48 Hamilton essays, but never a *whilst*. We have here an instance of what are called markers—items whose presence provides a strong indication of authorship for one of the men. Thus the presence of *whilst* in five of the disputed papers points toward Madison's authorship of those five.

Markers contribute a lot to discrimination when they can be found, but they also present difficulties. First, *while* or *whilst* occurs in less than half of the papers. They are absent from the other half, and hence give no evidence either way. We might hope to surmount this by finding enough different marker words or constructions so that one or more will always be present. A second and more serious difficulty is that from the evidence in 14 essays by Madison, we cannot be sure that he would never use *while*. Other writings of Madison were examined and, indeed, he did lapse on two occasions. The presence of *while* then is a good but not sure indication of Hamilton's authorship; the presence of *whilst* is a better, but still imperfect, indicator of Madison's authorship, for Hamilton too might lapse.

A central task of statistics is making inferences in the presence of uncertainty. Giving up the notion of perfect markers leads us to a statistical problem. We must find evidence, assess its strength, and combine it into a composite conclusion. Although the theoretical and practical problems may be difficult, the opportunity exists to assemble far more compelling evidence than even a few nearly perfect markers could provide.

Rates of Word Use

Instead of thinking of a word as a marker whose presence or absence settles the authorship of an essay, we can take the rate of relative frequency of use of each word as a measure pointing toward one or the other author. Of course, most words won't help because they were used at about the same rate by both authors. But since we have thousands of words available, some may help. Words form a huge pool of possible discriminators. From a systematic exploration of this pool of words, we found no more pairs like *while-whilst*, but we did find single words used by one author regularly but rarely by the other.

Table 1 shows the behavior of three words: *commonly, innovation, war*. The table summarizes data from 48 political essays known to be written by Hamilton and 50 known to be by Madison. (Some political essays from outside the *The Federalist*, but known to be by Hamilton or Madison, have been included in this study to give a broader base for the inference. Not all Hamilton's later *Federalist* papers have been included. We gathered more papers from outside *The Federalist* for Madison.)

Neither Hamilton nor Madison used *commonly* much, but Hamilton's use is much more frequent than Madison's. The table shows that in 31 of 48 Hamilton papers, the word *commonly* never occurred, but that in the other 17 it occurred one or more times. Madison used it only once in the 50 papers in our study. The papers vary in length from 900 to 3500 words, with 2000 about average. Even one occurrence in 900 words is a heavier usage than two occurrences in 3500 words, so in-

Table 1   Frequency Distributions of Rate per 1000 Words in 48 Hamilton and 50 Madison Papers for *Commonly*, *Innovation*, and *War*

Commonly			Innovation			War		
Rate per 1000 Words	H	M	Rate per 1000 Words	H	M	Rate per 1000 Words	H	M
0 (exactly)*	31	49	0 (exactly)*	47	34	0 (exactly)*	23	15
0+–0.2	cannot occur†		0+–0.2	cannot occur†		0+–2	16	13
0.2–0.4	3	1	0.2–0.4		6	2– 4	4	5
0.4–0.6	6		0.4–0.6	1	6	4– 6	2	4
0.6–0.8	3		0.6–0.8		1	6– 8	1	3
0.8–1.0	2		0.8–1.0		2	8–10	1	3
1.0–1.2	2		1.0–1.2		1	10–12		3
1.2–1.4	1					12–14		2
						14–16	1	2
Totals	48	50	Totals	48	50	Totals	48	50

Source: Mosteller and Wallace (1964).

*Each interval, except 0 (exactly), excludes its upper end point. Thus a 2000-word paper in which *commonly* appears twice gives rise to a rate of 1.0 per 1000 exactly, and the paper appears in the count for the 1.0–1.2 interval.

†With the given lengths of the papers used, it accidentally happens that a rate in this interval cannot occur. For example, if a paper has 2000 words, a rate of 1 per 1000 means 2 words, and a single occurrence means a rate of 0.5 per 1000. Hence a 2000-word paper cannot lead to a rate per thousand greater than 0 and less than 0.5

stead of working with the number of occurrences in a paper, we use the rate of occurrence, with 1000 words as a convenient base. Thus, for example, the paper with the highest rate (1.33 per 1000 words) for *commonly* is a paper of 1500 words with 2 occurrences. *Innovation* behaves similarly, but it is a marker for Madison. For each of these two words, the highest rates are a little over 1 per 1000.

The word *war* has a spectacularly different behavior. Although absent from half of Hamilton's papers, when present it is used frequently—in one paper at a rate of 14 per 1000 words. *The Federalist* papers deal with specific topics in the Constitution and huge variations in the rates of such words as *war*, *law*, *executive*, *liberty*, and *trade* can be expected according to the context of the paper. Even though Madison uses *war* considerably more often than Hamilton in the undisputed papers, we explain this more by the division of tasks than by predilections of Madison for using *war*. Data from a word like *war* would give the same troublesome sort of evidence that historians have disagreed about over the last 100 years. Indeed, the dispute has continued because evidence from subject and content has been hopelessly inconclusive.

Use of Non-contextual Words

For the statistical arguments to be valid, information from meaningful, contextual words must be largely discarded. Such a study of authorship will not then contribute directly to any understanding of the greatness of the papers, but the evidence of authorship can be both strengthened and made independent of evidence provided by historical analysis.

Avoidance of judgments about meaningfulness or importance is common in classification and identification procedures. When art critics try to authenticate a picture, in addition to the historical record, they consider little things: how fingernails and ears are painted, what kind of paint and canvas were used. Relatively little of the final judgment is based upon the painting's artistic excellence. In the same way, police often identify people by their fingerprints, dental records, and scars, without reference to their personality, occupation, or position in society. For literary identification, we need not necessarily be clever about the appraisal of literary style, although it helps in some problems. To identify an object, we need not appreciate its full value or meaning.

What non-contextual words are good candidates for discriminating between authors? Most attractive are the filler words of the language: prepositions, conjunctions, articles. Many other more meaningful words also seem relatively free from context: adverbs such as *commonly, consequently, particularly,* or even abstract nouns like *vigor* or *innovation.* We want words whose use is unrelated to the topic and may be regarded as reflecting minor or perhaps unconscious preferences of the author.

Consider what can be done with filler words. Some of these are the most used words in the language: *the, and, of, to,* and so on. No one writes without them, but we may find that their rates of use differ from author to author. Table 2 shows the distribution of rates for three prepositions—*by, from,* and *to.* First, note the variation from paper to paper. Madison uses *by* typically about 12 times per 1000 words, but sometimes has rates as high as 18 or as low as 6. Even on inspection though, the variation does not obscure Madison's systematic tendency to use *by* more often than Hamilton. Thus low rates for *by* suggest Hamilton's authorship, and high rates Madison's. Rates

for *to* run in the opposite direction. Very high rates for *from* point to Madison but low rates give practically no information. The more widely the distributions are separated, the stronger the discriminating power of the word. Here, *by* discriminates better than *to,* which in turn is better than *from.*

Probability Models

To apply any of the theory of statistical inference to evidence from word rates, we must construct an acceptable probability model to represent the variability in word rate from paper to paper. Setting up a complete model for the occurrence of even a single word would be a hopeless task, for the fine structure within a sentence is determined in large measure by nonrandom elements of grammar, meaning, and style. But if our interest is restricted to the rates of use of one or more words in blocks of text of at least 100 or 200 words, we expect that detailed structure of phrases and sentences ought not to be very important. The simplest model can be described in the language of balls in an urn, so common in classical probability. To represent Madison's usage of the word *by,* we suppose there is a typical Madison rate, which would be somewhere near 12 per 1000, and we imagine an urn filled with many thousands of red and black balls, with the red occurring in the proportion 12 per 1000.

Table 2   Frequency Distribution of Rate per Thousand Words in 48 Hamilton and 50 Madison Papers for *By, From,* and *To*

By			From			To		
Rate per 1000 Words	H	M	Rate per 1000 Words	H	M	Rate per 1000 Words	H	M
1– 3*	2		1– 3*	3	3	20–25*		3
3– 5	7		3– 5	15	19	25–30	2	5
5– 7	12	5	5– 7	21	17	30–35	6	19
7– 9	18	7	7– 9	9	6	35–40	14	12
9–11	4	8	9–11		1	40–45	15	9
11–13	5	16	11–13		3	45–50	8	2
13–15		6	13–15		1	50–55	2	
15–17		5				55–66	1	
17–19		3						
Totals	48	50	Totals	48	50	Totals	48	50

Source: Mosteller and Wallace (1964).
*Each interval excludes its upper end point. Thus a paper with a rate of exactly 3 per 1000 words would appear in the count for the 3–5 interval.

Our probability model for the occurrence of *by* is the same as the probability model for successive draws from the urn, with a red ball corresponding to *by*, a black ball corresponding to all other words. To extend the model to simultaneous study of two or more words, we would need balls of three or more colors. No grammatical structure or meaning is a part of this model, and it is not intended to represent behavior within sentences. What is desired is that it explain the variation in rates—in counts of occurrences in long blocks of words, corresponding to the essays.

We tested the model by comparing its predictions with actual counts of word frequencies in the papers. We found that while this urn scheme reproduced variability well for many words, for other words additional variability was required. The random variation of the urn scheme represented most of the variation in counts from one essay to another, but in some essays authors change their basic rates a bit. We had to complicate the theoretical model to allow for this, and the model we used is called the negative binomial distribution.

The test showed also that pronouns like *his* and *her* are exceedingly unreliable authorship indicators, worse even than words like *war*.

Inference and Results

Each possible route from construction of models to quantitative assessment of, say, Madison's authorship of some disputed paper, required solutions of serious theoretical statistical problems, and new mathematics had to be developed. A chief motivation for us was to use the *Federalist* problem as a case study for comparing several different statistical approaches, with special attention to one, called the Bayesian method, that expresses its final results in terms of probabilities, or odds, of authorship.

By whatever methods are used, the results are the same: overwhelming evidence for Madison's authorship of the disputed papers. For only one paper is the evidence more modest, and even there the most thorough study leads to odds of 80 to 1 in favor of Madison.

Figures 1 and 2 illustrate how the 12 disputed papers fit the distributions of Hamilton's and Madison's rates for two of the words finally chosen as discriminators. In Figure 1 the top two histograms portray the data for *by* that was given earlier in Table 2. Madison's rate runs higher on the average. Compare the bottom histogram for the disputed papers first with the top histogram for Hamilton papers, then with the second one for Madison papers. The rates in the disputed papers are, taken as a whole, very Madisonian, though 3 of 12 papers by themselves are slightly on the Hamilton side of the typical rates. Figure 2 shows the corresponding facts for *to*. Here again the disputed papers are consistent with Madison's distribution, but further away from the Hamilton behavior than are the known Madison papers.

Table 3 shows 30 words used in the final inference, along with the estimated mean rates per thousand in Hamilton's and Madison's writings. The groups are based upon the degree of contex-

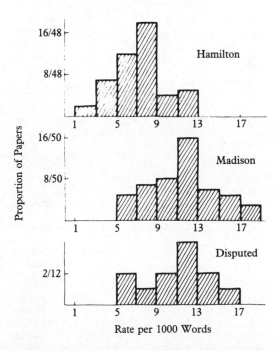

Figure 1   Distribution of rates of occurrence of *by* in 48 Hamilton papers, 50 Madison papers, 12 disputed papers.

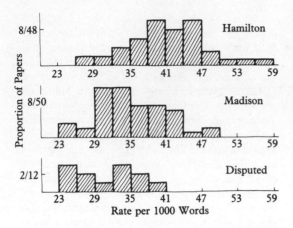

Figure 2 Distribution of rates of occurrence of *to* in 48 Hamilton papers, 50 Madison papers, 12 disputed papers.

tuality anticipated by Mosteller and Wallace prior to the analysis.

The combined evidence from nine common filler words shown as group B was huge—much more important than the combined evidence from

20 low-frequency marker words like *while-whilst* and shown as groups C, D, and E.

There remains one word that showed up early as a powerful discriminator, sufficient almost by itself. When should one write *upon* instead of *on?* Even authoritative books on English usage don't provide good rules. Hamilton and Madison differ tremendously. Hamilton writes *on* and *upon* almost equally, about 3 times per 1000 words. Madison, on the other hand, rarely uses *upon*. Table 4 shows the distributions for *upon*. In 48 papers Hamilton never failed to use *upon;* indeed, he never used it less than twice. Madison only used it in 9 of 50 papers, and then only with low rates. The disputed papers are clearly Madisonian with *upon* occurring in only one paper. That paper, fortunately, is strongly classified by other words. It is not the paper with modest overall odds.

Of course, combining and assessing the total evidence is a large statistical and computational task. High speed computers were employed for many hours in making the calculations, both mathematical calculations for the theory, and empirical ones for the data.

Table 3   Words Used in Final Discrimination and Adjusted Rates of Use in Text by Madison and Hamilton

Word	Rate per 1000 Words		Word	Rate per 1000 Words	
	Hamilton	Madison		Hamilton	Madison
Group A			**Group D**		
Upon	3.24	0.23	Commonly	0.17	0.05
			Consequently	0.10	0.42
Group B			Considerable(ly)	0.37	0.17
Also	0.32	0.67	According	0.17	0.54
An	5.95	4.58	Apt	0.27	0.08
By	7.32	11.43			
Of	64.51	57.89	**Group E**		
On	3.38	7.75	Direction	0.17	0.08
There	3.20	1.33	Innovation(s)	0.06	0.15
This	7.77	6.00	Language	0.08	0.18
To	40.79	35.21	Vigor(ous)	0.18	0.08
			Kind	0.69	0.17
Group C			Matter(s)	0.36	0.09
Although	0.06	0.17	Particularly	0.15	0.37
Both	0.52	1.04	Probability	0.27	0.09
Enough	0.25	0.10	Work(s)	0.13	0.27
While	0.21	0.07			
Whilst	0.08	0.42			
Always	0.58	0.20			
Though	0.91	0.51			

Source: Mosteller and Wallace (1964).

Table 4   Frequency Distribution of Rate per Thousand Words in 48 Hamilton, 50 Madison, and 12 Disputed Papers for *Upon*

Rate per 1000 Words	Hamilton	Madison	Disputed
0 (exactly)*		41	11
0+–0.4		2	
0.4–0.8		4	
0.8–1.2	2	1	1
1.2–1.6	3	2	
1.6–2.0	6		
2.0–3.0	11		
3.0–4.0	11		
4.0–5.0	10		
5.0–6.0	3		
6.0–7.0	1		
7.0–8.0	1		
Totals	48	50	12

Source: Mosteller and Wallace (1964).
*Each interval, except 0 (exactly), excludes its upper endpoint. Thus a paper with a rate of exactly 3 per 1000 words would appear in the count for the 3.0–4.0 interval.

You may have wondered about John Jay. Might he not have taken a hand in the disputed papers? Table 5 shows the rates per thousand for nine words of highest frequency in the English language measured in the writings of Hamilton, Madison, Jay, and, for a change of pace, in James Joyce's *Ulysses*. The table supported the repeated assertion that Madison and Hamilton are similar. Joyce is much different, but so is John Jay. The words *of* and *to* with rate comparisons 65/58 and 41/35 were among the final discriminators between Hamilton and Madison. See how much more easily Jay could be discriminated from either Hamilton or Madison by using *the, of, and, a,* and *that.* The disputed papers are not at all consistent with Jay's rates, and there is no reason to question his omission from the dispute.

Summary of Results

Our data independently supplement the evidence of historians. Madison is extremely likely, in the sense of degree of belief, to have written the disputed *Federalist* papers, with the possible exception of paper number 55; and there our evidence yields odds of 80 to 1 for Madison—strong, but not overwhelming. Paper 56, next weakest, is a very strong 800 to 1 for Madison. The data are

Table 5   Word Rates for High-Frequency Words (Rates per 1000 Words)

	Hamilton (94,000)*	Madison (114,000)*	Jay (5000)*	Joyce (Ulysses) (260,000)*
The	91	94	67	57
Of	65	58	44	30
To	41	35	36	18
And	25	28	45	28
In	24	23	21	19
A	23	20	14	25
Be	20	16	19	3
That	15	14	20	12
It	14	13	17	9

Sources: Hanley (1937), Mosteller and Wallace (1964).
*The number of words of text counted to determine rates.

overwhelming for all the rest, including the two papers historians feel weakest about, papers 62 and 63.

For a more extensive discussion of this problem, including historical details, discussion of actual techniques, and a variety of alternative analyses, see Mosteller and Wallace (1964).

References

1. Miles L. Hanley. 1937. *Word Index to James Joyce's Ulysses*. Madison, Wis.: University of Wisconsin.
2. F. Mosteller and D. L. Wallace. 1964. *Inference and Disputed Authorship: The Federalist*. Reading, Mass.: Addison-Wesley.

The Sizes of Things

Herbert A. Simon

Herbert Alexander Simon is a social scientist who did his graduate work at the University of Chicago, receiving a Ph.D. in 1943. From 1949 to 1965 he was a professor of psychology at Carnegie-Mellon University, and since 1965 he has been a professor of computer science and psychology at Carnegie-Mellon. He has been a special lecturer at Princeton, Harvard, Northwestern, M.I.T., Dartmouth, Michigan, Yale, and Berkeley. In 1975 he received the A.M. Turing Award from the Association for Computing Machinery. He is a member of the National Academy of Science. He was awarded the Nobel Prize in economics in 1981.

An English essayist once observed that "everything is the right size." In one sense this is a nearly empty tautology which simply observes that the size of anything is its size. In another and rather deeper sense the statement suggests that there are inherent and underlying reasons for the sizes of things and that we might understand the why of the size if we better understood the nature of the thing.

Ants, for example, are about the right size for ants. The material forming the external skeleton of an ant is simply not physically capable of supporting those creatures, so beloved of science fiction movies, that have the form of ants, but the size of locomotives. Even if the entire creature were solidly fashioned from such material, the legs would be crushed by the weight of the body. As we come to understand ants and how they are fashioned, we can understand that they are indeed the right size.

In this essay Simon investigates the sizes of a variety of social groupings. He shows that an understanding of the dynamics of a group will lead to the determination of what is an appropriate size for that group. In coming to understand the nature of the social processes that form the group, we can understand why groups are the sizes that they are. The groups, like ants, are just the right size.

ON FIGURE 1 ARE drawn four lines. The lowest one, a simple straight line inclined at a 45° angle, serves merely for purposes of comparison in describing the three slightly wavy lines. The three wavy lines—and particularly the two just above the straight line—depict some curious facts about the world. Whether they are significant facts as well as curious facts is a question we examine.

The lower broken line relates, on a logarithmic scale,[1] the 1965 populations of the twenty largest cities in the U.S. to the ranks by size of the cities, arranged with New York, ranked 1 down to Kansas City, ranked 20. The population of each metropolitan area was used, not just that within the city limits. The horizontal axis shows, also on a logarithmic scale, the city ranks, from 1 through 20; on the vertical scale are shown the corresponding logarithms of populations in millions of persons. Ignoring the two largest cities (New York and Chicago), we can see that the rest of the line is nearly straight and inclined nearly at a 45°

Source: Herbert A. Simon, "The Sizes of Things," in J. M. Tanur et al., *Statistics: A Guide to the Unknown* (San Francisco: Holden-Day, 1978), pp. 240–247.

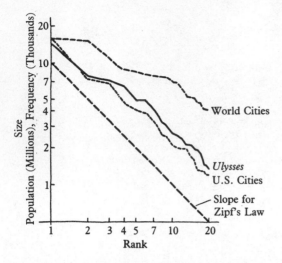

Figure 1   Logarithm of size plotted against logarithm of rank for frequencies of words and for populations of cities.

angle, parallel to the straight line below. Straightening out the left end of the curve would involve raising New York from about 16 million people to about 25 million and Chicago to 12 million (a heavy price to pay for a straight line), but the remaining 18 cities would require very little adjustment—generally less than 10% up or down.

The solid line, just above and very close to the line for cities, shows (again on logarithmic scales) the number of occurrences of each of the twenty words most frequently used in James Joyce's *Ulysses,* when the words are arranged in descending order of frequency of occurrence. For this line, the ordinates show the frequencies of occurrences in thousands. The most frequent word in *Ulysses, the,* occurred 14,887 times; the twentieth most frequent, *all,* occurred 1311 times. As with the city sizes, the word frequencies lie almost on a straight line, although straightening the line would again require adjustment of the first few words; *the* would have to be increased to about 26,000 occurrences, *of* to 13,000, and *and* to about 8700. The remaining seventeen frequencies are extremely close to a straight line inclined at 45°.

Observe that in these distributions the product of the rank of each item by its size remains con-

stant over the scale. If the first item (rank 1) has size 1,000,000, the tenth item will have size about 100,000 (10 × 100,000 = 1,000,000), and the twentieth item will have size 50,000 (20 × 50,000 = 1,000,000). The task before us is to explain why these regularities hold, why the product of number and rank in these distributions is almost constant, and—even more mysterious—why the size distribution of American cities should obey the same law as the frequency distribution of words in a stylistically unusual book like *Ulysses* (or in any book for that matter). Let's begin with the words.

Words: Common and Rare

In the late nineteenth century, several linguists (among them de Saussurre in France) discovered the surprising rank-frequency regularity in the relative contributions of different words to any body of text. Obviously, certain words, such as *of,* will occur rather frequently in almost any English text, while other words, such as *conundrum,* occur infrequently or not at all. The frequency of any specific word may vary widely from one text to another.

Whenever you arrange the various words occurring in a particular text in the order of their frequency of occurrence—first the word that occurred most often in that text, then the word that occurred next most often, and so on—the regularity depicted in Figure 1 will reappear. The twentieth word on your list will occur about one-half as often as the tenth word.[2] If you enjoy this kind of numerology, you will find equally startling regularities at the other end of the distribution among the rare words.

About one-half of the total number of *different* words in the text occur exactly once each, about one-sixth occur exactly twice each, and about one-twelfth occur three times each (see Table 1). The ratio $1/[n(n + 1)]$ gives the fraction of all the distinct words in the text that occur exactly n times each. This regularity in frequency of occurrence of the rare words is, of course, the same rank-size law we have been observing at the other end of the distribution, for the rank of a word is simply

Table 1   The Numbers of Rarely Occurring Words in James Joyce's *Ulysses*

Number of Occurrences (n)	Number of Words	
	Actual	Predicted*
1	16,432	14,949
2	4,776	4,983
3	2,194	2,491
4	1,285	1,495
5	906	997
6	637	712
7	483	534
8	371	415
9	298	332
10	222	272

*Predicted number $= K/[n(n+1)]$; $K = 29,899$, the total number of *different* words in *Ulysses*.

the cumulated number of different words that have occurred as frequently as it has, or more frequently. Suppose then, as the rank-size rule requires, that $K/(n+1)$ words occur $n+1$ or more times each, and K/n words occur n or more times each. Then the number of words occurring exactly n times will be $K/n - K/(n+1) = K/[n(n+1)]$.

The rank-size law, often called *Zipf's law* in honor of an American linguist who wrote a great deal about it, holds for just about all of the texts whose vocabularies have been counted, in a great range of languages, not excluding American Indian languages. Though it holds for *Ulysses*, it fails for James Joyce's *Finnegan's Wake*, and it fails for Chinese texts if individual Chinese ideograms are counted as words—which is as good an argument against the latter identification as it is against Zipf's law.[3]

Why does this regularity hold? Why should the balance between frequent and rare words be exactly the same in the daily newspaper as in James Joyce's *Ulysses*, the same in German books as in English books, or the same in most (not all) schizophrenic speech as in normal speech?

Several answers have been proposed, one of which is typical of the explanations that are provided by probability theory. Probability theory often explains the way things are arranged on average by conceding its inability to explain them in exact detail. To explain the laws of gasses it avoids tracing the path of each molecule.

To explain the word distribution, we make some assumptions that might be thought outrageous if applied in detail, but that might be plausible if only applied in the aggregate. We assume that a writer generates a text by drawing from the whole vast store of his memory, and by drawing from the even vaster store of the literature of his language. The former of these processes we might call *association*, the latter *imitation*. Specifically, we assume that the chance of any given word being chosen *next* is proportional to the number of times the word has previously been stored away—in memory or in the literature. Remember, these assumptions are intended to apply only in the large. To accept them, we need not believe that Shakespeare wrote sonnets by spinning a roulette wheel any more than we believe the individual molecules of a gas chart their courses by shaking dice.

If we accept the assumptions, then it becomes a straightforward mathematical matter but one beyond the scope of this paper to derive the probability distribution they imply. The derivation yields what is known as the *Yule distribution*. In the upper range, among frequently used words, the Yule distribution agrees with the rank-size law of Zipf; in the lower range, among rarely used words, it gives precisely the observed fractions $1/[n(n+1)]$.

Now we see why the *same* distribution can fit texts of diverse kinds drawn from the literatures of many languages. The same distribution can fit because it does not depend on any very specific properties of the process that generated the text. It only depends on the generator being, in a probabilistic sense, an associative and imitative process. We might even suspect that substantial departures from exact proportionality in association and imitation would not greatly change the character of the distribution. To the extent that the consequences of changing the assumptions have been explored, mathematically and by computer simulation, the distribution has indeed proved robust. We can give Shakespeare and Joyce a great deal of latitude in the way they write without altering visibly the gross size-rank relation of their vocabularies, but as *Finnegan's Wake* shows, we can't give them infinite latitude.

Megalopolis and Metropolis

Having stripped away some of the mystery of the vocabularies of literary texts, we are perhaps prepared to tackle the corresponding regularity in American city sizes. We have seen (Figure 1) that the city populations obey the same rank-size law, to a quite good approximation.[4] If two cities have ranks j and k, respectively, in the list, their populations ratio will approximate k/j.

The regularity is not just a happenstance of the 1960 Census. It holds quite well for all the Censuses back to 1780. It does *not* hold, however, for cities in arbitrarily defined geographical regions of the world, that are not relatively self-contained economic units. It does not hold, for example, for Austria, or for individual Central American countries, or for Australia. Nor does it hold if we put the cities of the whole world together (see the uppermost curve in Figure 1). In that case, the distribution is still relatively smooth and regular, but population does not drop off with rank as fast as Zipf's law demands. The distribution is flatter, and the largest metropolises are "too small," though, I hasten to add, this phrase should not be interpreted normatively.

In the case of city sizes, then, we must be prepared to explain *two* things: why Zipf's law has held for nearly two centuries for the cities of the U.S., and why it doesn't hold for many other aggregates of cities. Let's start with the former question and ask what the analogues might be to the association and imitation processes that explained the word distributions. More precisely, let's ask what processes would lead cities to grow at rates proportional, on average, to the sizes already achieved (sometimes called *Gibrat's principle*); for that is the main assumption the mathematical derivation requires.

Cities grow by the net balance of births over deaths, and they grow by the net balance of inward over outward migration. With respect to births and deaths, we need assume only that, on average, birth and death rates are uncorrelated with city size. With respect to migration, we assume that migration outward is proportional, on average, to city size (i.e., that per capita *rates* are independent of size), and migration inward (from rural areas, from other cities, or from abroad) is

also proportional to city size. The last assumption means that the cities in a given size group form a "target" for migration, which is larger, in total, as the total population already living in the cities of that group is larger. I leave to the reader the reasons why this might be a plausible assumption, at least as an approximation.

If we make these assumptions, we are again led by the mathematics of the matter to the rank-size law of Zipf. But now it is instructive to ask: under what circumstances would we expect a collection of cities to fit the assumptions? The answer is that the cities should form a "natural" region within which there is high and free mobility of population and industry, and which is not an arbitrary slice of a still larger region. The U.S. fits these requirements quite well, while an area playing a specialized role in a larger economic entity might not fit at all (for example, Austria after dissolution of the Empire, or a country specializing in agricultural exports and having a single large seaport).

If we put together a large number of distributions, each separately obeying the rank-size law, we get a new distribution of the same shape, simply displaced upward on the graph, but with the top few omitted. We would expect the totality of the world's cities to fit the rank-size distribution, except for a deficiency of extremely large metropolises at the very top, and so it does. If we take the published figures at their face value (the definitional problems are severe, and the census counts of varying accuracy), there are somewhat more than 50 urban aggregations in the world having over 2 million people each. Zipf's law would then call for a New York or a Tokyo of 100 million people, instead of the mere 16 million who now inhabit each of those cities. However, the deficiency of cities at the very top (mostly the top ten) is soon largely made up by the numerous cities over 5 million population each. Already, the tenth city on the list, Chicago, has a population of 7 million, only one-third fewer than the number demanded by Zipf's law.

The sizes of cities are of obvious importance to the people who live in them, but it is not obvious what practical conclusions we are to draw from the actual size distribution. One *possible* conclusion is that the distribution isn't going to be easy to change without strong governmental or economic controls over places of residence and work. Or to put the matter more palatably—because we generally wish to avoid such controls—the mathematical analysis that discloses the forces governing the phenomena teaches us that any attempt to alter the phenomena requires us to deal with those forces with sophistication and intelligence.

Big and Little Business

Economists have generally been more interested in the sizes of business firms than they have in the sizes of cities. Concentration of industry in the hands of a few large firms is generally thought to be inimical to competition and is generally also supposed to have proceeded at a rapid rate in the U.S. during the past half century.

It has long been known that business firms in the U.S., England, and other countries have size distributions that resemble Zipf's rank-size law, except that size decreases less rapidly with rank than in the situations described previously (that is, the ratio of the largest firm to the tenth largest is generally less than ten to one[5]). The slower the decrease in size with increase in rank, the less concentrated is business in the largest firms.

Economists have been puzzled by the fact that the rate of decrease in size with rank, which is one way of measuring industrial concentration, appears to be about the same for large American manufacturing firms at the present time as it was 25 years ago or even at the turn of the century. Even during periods of frequent mergers, the degree of industrial concentration, as measured by the rank-size relation, has changed slowly or not at all.

From our previous analyses, we should be ready to solve the puzzle. Indeed, it can be shown mathematically that under appropriate assumptions about the firms that disappear by merger, and those that grow by merger, mergers will have no effect on concentration. Moreover, the assumptions required for this mathematical derivation fit the American statistical data on mergers quite well. In analogy to the processes for words and cities, we can guess what those assumptions—and the data that support them—are like:

1. The probability of a firm "dying" by merger should be approximately independent of its size.
2. The average assets acquired by surviving firms through mergers should be roughly proportional to the size they have already attained.

And these are indeed true.

Thus, a line of scientific inquiry that began with a linguistic puzzle over word frequencies leads to an explanation of a paradox about industrial concentration in the U.S. That explanation opens new lines of research for understanding business growth and arriving at public policy for the maintenance of business competition.

Our fascination with rank-size distributions need not stop with the three examples we have examined here. We may expect the Zipf distribution to show up in other places as well, and each new occurrence challenges us to formulate plausible (and testable) assumptions from which the rank-size law can be derived and the occurrence explained. We will leave a final example as an exercise for the reader. List the authors who have contributed to a scientific journal over 20 years, or whose names have appeared in a comprehensive bibliography, such as *Chemical Abstracts*. Note the number of appearances for each author, and rank the authors by that number. Then about one-half of all the authors will have appeared exactly once, one-sixth will have appeared twice, and so on; the data will not stray far from the Yule distribution. What are the ways of authors that can provide a naturalistic explanation for that fact?

Notes

1. The common logarithm is familiar to many as a tricky device for multiplying numbers through a process of addition. Another way of looking at the logarithm is that taking the logarithm compresses the scale of numbers so as to create a new scale, one that makes multiplying the old number by 10 equivalent to adding one unit to the new number. For example, the logarithm of 10 is 1, of 100 is 2, of 1000 is 3, and so on. The logarithm of 2000 is about 3.300 and that of 20,000 is about 4.300. If a

city has a population of 5,000,000, then the logarithm of its population is about 6.70. The compression achieved by a logarithm scale increases as the numbers do.

2. In most cases, the first two or three frequencies are substantially lower than the rule predicts, as in Figure 1.

3. Most linguists would consider that more often pairs of ideograms than individual ideograms serve as the basic lexical units corresponding to words in Chinese. The entries in Chinese and Japanese dictionaries are mostly such pairs. It is less easy to say why *Finnegan's Wake* doesn't fit the rule, but the freedom Joyce exercises in creating all sorts of word fragments and variants of dictionary words undoubtedly has something to do with the matter.

4. We can take either the populations of cities as defined by their corporate boundaries, or populations within metropolitan areas as defined by the U.S. Census. The regularity shows up about as well in either case—perhaps it is a little more satisfactory if we use metropolitan areas.

5. Let m and n be the ranks of two members of a rank-size distribution, and let S_m and S_n be their respective sizes. Then the rank-size law, in this generalized form requires $S_m/S_n = (n/m)^k$, where the exponent k is a proper fraction. When k approaches unity as a limit, we get the special case of the Zipf distribution. The general distribution is usually called by economists the *Pareto distribution*. If we graph the logarithmic distribution, taking logarithms of both ranks and sizes, we again obtain a straight line with a slope equal to the fraction k. The steeper this straight line (the larger k), the larger are the first-ranking firms compared with the firms further down the list (i.e., the larger is k, the greater the concentration).

Mathematicians in Industry—the First 75 Years

Thornton C. Fry

Thornton Carl Fry was born in Ohio in 1892. He received a Ph.D. in mathematics, physics, and astronomy in 1913 from the University of Wisconsin. He has worked for Western Electric, Bell Labs, and Sperry Rand and has been an industrial consultant to both the Granville Phillips Company and Boeing Science Research Labs. Fry received the Presidential Certificate of Merit in 1948. In Bell Labs he has been a staff mathematician, director of research on switching, director of switching research and engineering, and assistant to the president.

In the years 1958 to 1968 the production of Ph.D.'s in mathematics was a growing industry in the United States. Shortly after the first Soviet Sputnik satellite was launched into orbit in 1957 a report was issued by an agency of the U.S. government which suggested that in the next twenty-five years there would be an exponentially increasing demand for mathematical doctorates. Inspired by this projected need and fertilized by generous governmental grants, many of which were provided by agencies of the military, there was a rapid growth in both the number of institutions offering a Ph.D. in mathematics and the number of graduates of such programs. For most of that decade any young person with a mathematics doctorate found that the world was truly his or her oyster. But, alas, nothing is forever, most especially good times.

By 1968 the climate in America and, by reflection, the climate in Washington, had changed. Technology, no matter how useful, was considered objectionable, criticized as the root of many social problems. It was fashionable to allow one's emotions to rule one's actions, to "go with the flow." The military was severely limited in funding scientific research, investing only in that which was immediately applicable to combat. And so the United States launched itself into the decade of "social relevance" and soon young Ph.D.'s in mathematics were most definitely a surplus item.

About this time a number of desperate young owners of newly tanned mathematical sheepskins discovered industrial applications of mathematics. There was, naturally, nothing really new about the use of mathematics and mathematicians in industry; it had been going on in a rather low-key way for some time. World War II provided abundant evidence of the kinds of dramatic technological change that dedicated, well-trained problem solvers could effect. But we seldom learn from history. With the end of World War II the mathematicians returned to their silent contemplations in the catacombs of the academies, and the industrialists reverted to the same production methods they had used for the last fifty years. Only after thirty years of relative industrial stagnation and some very painful historical lessons did mathematicians and industrialists get back together again.

Whether our current society genuinely recognizes the importance of having some of the best and most agile minds address themselves to social problems only the future can reveal. But a better appreciation of the kinds of contributions mathematics has made to practical problems may further such recognition. This essay is a brief but quite comprehensive tour of seventy-five years of interaction between industry and mathematics.

Source: Thornton C. Fry, "Mathematicians in Industry—the First 75 Years," *Science* 143 (1964): 934–938. Copyright 1964 by the American Association for the Advancement of Science. This article is adapted from a lecture delivered 7 August 1963, as one of the "Lectures in Science" series of the Boeing Scientific Research Laboratories.

IN 1888 A LOCAL group called the New York Mathematical Society was organized at Columbia University. Two years later it took on national character and became the American Mathematical Society. From this event we may quite reasonably date the beginning of mathematical research on this side of the Atlantic; for, prior to this time, there were not only no important centers of discussion and no important mathematical journals but there were essentially no creative mathematicians.

In the decade or so preceding 1890, however, it became quite usual for young men from the more affluent families to complete their education abroad. Those who were interested in mathematics, or in the broad analytical aspects of physical sciences which were then called "natural philosophy," came under the influence of the lively groups of mathematicians in England and Germany and returned with a new vision of scholarship and a determination to emulate it at home. It was one of these men, T. S. Fiske, who was the prime mover in organizing the group at Columbia, and he is generally recognized as the father of the American Mathematical Society. This, as I said, was in 1888, and the Society is now passing its 75th anniversary.

It was in 1888, also, that a young German student of mathematics was to take his doctor's degree at the University of Breslau. His dissertation had already been accepted, and only certain minor formalities remained to be completed. He never got the degree. He was a socialist agitator whom the police just then decided to close in upon, and, having been mysteriously forewarned, he fled in the best story-book fashion, in the middle of the night, to Switzerland. The following year he came to America, where he secured employment in what is now the General Electric Company. He was, so far as I know, the first mathematician in the modern sense of the word to be employed in industry. So 1963 comes within a year of being also the 75th anniversary of the first employment of mathematicians in industry.

The man in question was Charles Proteus Steinmetz, and the title of his thesis was, "On Involutory Self-Reciprocal Correspondences in Space which are Defined by a Three-Dimensional Linear System of Surfaces of the n-th Order." It has, for its time, a remarkably modern sound.

Steinmetz met Fiske very soon after his arrival, and the two became close friends. He became a charter member of the American Mathematical Society and participated actively in its affairs during those early years. He presented several original papers, which are referred to in volumes 1 and 2 of the *Bulletin*.

We may also date the beginning of industrial research from this same period. (Not the beginning of the institution now known to us as the "industrial research laboratory." That is an organizational concept which came later.) Prior to this time, American industry—in fact, the industry of the world—had been flourishing through inventive genius of the purely Edisonian type. But the problem of transmission in telephony, and the problems of transmission and generation in the power industry, raised questions of a more subtle and analytical type and required a more scientific approach. I know of no single event which heralded the birth of such research, but it certainly began within a very few years of 1890.

With only negligible errors of approximation, therefore, we can say that in America the year 1888 marked the beginning of mathematical research, the beginning of industrial research, and the first employment of mathematicians in industry.

The growth in all three areas has been phenomenal, but to the hardheaded businessman of that day, today's use of mathematicians in industry would no doubt be the most surprising of all.

Growth

In a study published in 1940[1] I made a serious attempt to estimate the number of professional mathematicians working in industry and came up with the figure 150.

This of course involved a matter of definition. In 1940, as today, many industrial physicists, chemists, and engineers had considerable mathematical training and ability and were using it in their work. It would have been foolish to count all these as mathematicians. I resolved the difficulty by counting the members of the American Mathematical Society who clearly had industrial or government employment. My thought in selecting this criterion was that those who had sufficient interest to belong to a society devoted exclusively to creative mathematical research could properly be defined as mathematicians.

This study was made in 1939, and the membership list on which it was based was probably that for 1938. There is a double coincidence in the fact that 1938 is just a quarter of a century ago and just a half century after 1888. So I thought it might be interesting to fill in the other quarter-century points.

The latest membership list is that for 1961–62, and from this, by a sampling process, I obtain a count of 1800. The closest list to 1913 available to me was that for 1915; from this, depending on whether or not some doubtful cases are included, I get 11 or 15.

Using these figures, and recording a "1" for Steinmetz opposite 1888 (which is within 1 year of the correct date), I arrive at the data of Table 1. The figures in column 3 are interesting. The actual count for 1963 is exactly 12 times that for 1938; that is, there was a 12-fold increase in the last quarter century. If we extrapolate backward at the same exponential rate, we get a figure of 12 for 1913 and of 1 for 1888—results which are both remarkably close to the actual counts. In other words, this exponential rate of growth has proceeded with amazing consistency for three-quarters of a century. If anyone is daring enough to infer from this that the same rate will continue for the next half century, he will conclude that there will be 22,000 mathematicians with nonacademic employment in 1988 and 270,000 in the year 2013.

I do not offer this as a serious prophecy. On the contrary, both numbers, and particularly the one for A.D. 2013, impress me as fantastic.[2] They do serve to indicate, however, the tremendous thrust of the social forces which have been injecting mathematicians in large numbers into industrial and government laboratories, an environment which only a few generations ago would have been judged inhospitable. I think they justify a closer examination of what these forces have been, and of the nature of the role mathematicians have played.

Science and Industry—1888–1913

If we examine the 25-year periods defined in Table 1, we can observe a very significant progression in the character of scientific thought as we pass from one to another. Not that there were abrupt transitions between them. The transitions were gradual and, to the men experiencing them, largely imperceptible. But the accumulated change over each quarter century is great enough to give character to the periods.

In industry the first period (1888–1913) can be characterized as one of Edisonian invention and handbook engineering. Looking back from the modern age, where science pervades almost every aspect of our lives, it is difficult for us to appreciate how primitive engineering was. Perhaps two anecdotes may bring this into focus.

The first concerns Steinmetz, and relates to the 1890's. One of the two principal things upon which his fame rests is his effort to awaken electrical engineers to the use of complex quantities in alternating-current theory. Mathematically, what he was teaching was not new. Mathematicians had been using the method for decades— perhaps for centuries. And in his *Theory of Sound*, which was published in 1877, Lord Rayleigh had used it extensively in discussing the sinusoidal oscillations of mechanical systems. Nor was the method difficult. It depended basically on two simple facts: that $e^{ix} = \cos x + i \sin x$, and that the sum of two solutions of a linear differential equation is also a solution. But the vast majority of electrical engineers found it incomprehensible, and were completely mystified that the square root of minus 1 should have anything to do with electric currents.

Table 1   Data on mathematicians in industry. X is the number of members of the American Mathematical Society with addresses in government or industry. X' is computed from the exponential growth function $X' = e^{(Y - 1888)/10}$, which gives a 12-fold increase every 25 years.

Year (Y)	X	X'
1888	1	1
1913	11–15	12
1938	150	150
1963	1,800	1,800
1988		22,000
2013		270,000

By 1913, when this quarter century ended, the idea was beginning to catch on. But the mathematics used by engineers, even in the universities, was still primitive, as my second anecdote will show.

In 1913 I was an instructor in mathematics at the University of Wisconsin. My classes were composed entirely of engineers, and the course material was selected and presented with the engineering student in mind. Yet no semester went by, either in my classes or in those of my fellow instructors, without someone's asking, "What is all this good for?" It revealed a hostile and foolish attitude, but an understandable one. For in the College of Engineering—which was reputed to be one of the most progressive in the country—the deflection of beams was still being taught with no reference whatever to the calculus, and most of alternating-current theory was also.

Viewed against the contemporary state of natural science, this primitive state of the world of industry is understandable. For, prior to 1900, physical science was entirely Newtonian and chemistry was entirely empirical. Scientifically speaking, engineering had had little to feed upon, and it is perhaps a little surprising that in 1915 there were even a dozen members of the American Mathematical Society with industrial or government addresses. But, with the new century, things began to happen in the more esoteric fringes of physics which would revolutionize first physics, then chemistry, and in the end engineering and society as well. The vast growth in employment of mathematicians in industry is one aspect of this revolution.

Let us note a few of these events. The quantum hypothesis was formulated in 1901. The vacuum tube[3] was invented in 1907. The special theory of relativity was published in 1908, and the general theory, in 1914. Millikan's measurement of the charge on the electron, which gave the first solid proof of the existence of a class of identical electric particles, was in 1912. Bohr's paper on the hydrogen atom appeared in 1913, and Mosley's on atomic numbers, in 1914. I believe these can properly be regarded as the beginnings of modern chemistry. Biochemistry began at about the same time; Fischer's discovery of the protein building blocks was also in 1913.

This is an exceedingly impressive list of discoveries. I think we can properly say that by 1913 atomic physics and atomic chemistry had been born. It was still true, of course, that the geometry of chemical bonds was inaccessible, but the diffraction of x-ray crystals would be observed by the Braggs shortly before 1915, and thus the mechanism for studying chemical geometry would be provided.

Science and Industry—1913–1938

The period from 1913 to 1938 was equally exciting, though in a quite different way.

In physics, I think it can best be described as a period of consolidation of the non-Newtonian concepts which had been so recently born, and exploitation of the great possibilities of electronic measurement. It was the period when quantum mechanics and electronic physics were the center of excitement.

Going on at the same time, of course, were the experimental studies of cosmic rays and the rather advanced thinking about atomic nuclei which we now know to have been the beginnings of particle physics, but these were somewhat out of the mainstream.

It was chemistry, rather than physics, which moved explosively ahead during this period under the impetus of the clear-cut structural ideas which grew out of the work of Bohr, Mosley, and the Braggs.

This was also a period of tremendous change in industry, which discovered that profits could be derived from scientific research, as distinguished from engineering development. Research laboratories sprang up by the hundreds, many in industries in which management was ill-equipped to direct them or even to understand the nature of their activities. If we call the preceding period in industry the age of the engineer, we may, not too inaccurately, call this the age of the scientist. Not that the engineer no longer had a function to perform; such an idea would be quite false. His function was, in fact, enlarged because of industrial scientific research, and his productivity was increased. This was the age of scientific research only in the restricted, but tremendously important, sense that scientific research was now being consciously organized and exploited by industry.

I had the good fortune in 1916 to be employed by one of the earliest and best of the industrial research laboratories, when it was almost new-born. I was, moreover, hired not as an engineer or physicist but as a mathematician. Thus I was in a favorable position to observe how the opportunities for mathematicians were affected by this awakening to the industrial value of scientific research.

For one thing, the presence of other scientists made the environment less awkward for the mathematician. More important, however, was the contrast between the attitude of the engineers on the job and that of my student engineers only a few years before. As the scientific method replaced Edisonian cut-and-try, the engineer's methods of design became more and more analytical. The practical engineer got his mathematics where he could—often through self-education, sometimes by seeking the help of his long-haired colleagues. But he did not question its value. Instead, a curious reverse situation arose in which the engineers, conscious of their own limitations, tended to give a high rating to anyone with mathematical training and interests who was reasonably articulate, regardless of his true mathematical ability.

Indeed, if my observation is sound, the industrial mathematician has seldom, if ever, been without honor in his own country. I have seen a weak scholar and a strong one honored equally because their associates were incapable of appraising their work critically. And I have seen a good mathematician and his associates equally frustrated when their working relations had not been properly defined. But I can recall no instance where a talented mathematician who attempted to cooperate with his engineering associates was not rewarded with their respect and appreciation.

Here again an anecdote from my own experience may illustrate the point. Between 1931 and 1933, the depression years, the professional staff of Bell Telephone Laboratories was reduced by about one-third. Each department head was required to select, on a pro-rata basis, the individuals to be separated from his department; then a conference of department heads was held in

which these selections were discussed and adjusted. The experience was a very grievous one for all concerned. But in the end, not a single member of the Mathematical Research Group was among those released; whenever the name of a mathematician was mentioned, the conference group decided that he could not be spared, and one of the other supervisors supplied a substitute.

The First Mathematical Research Department in Industry

The problem presented by the mathematician in industry was not then, and I do not think it ever has been, lack of appreciation. It was lack of understanding. Basically, it arose from the fact that the interests of mathematics and industry are almost antithetical. For the function of industry is to produce things and services and to make a profit in the process, while, in the whole spectrum of science, the discipline which is least concerned with things or profits and most dedicated to ideas for their own sake is mathematics.

Once this simple (one might say "obvious," except that it went for some years unnoticed) fact had been stated, certain consequences followed at once.

1. It became apparent that when a mathematician was practicing his trade—that is, so long as he was dealing only in ideas—he was working outside the mainstream of the industry's activities. A mathematician should not logically be responsible for any stage of the development process. Instead, he should function as a consultant to those who are.

2. Some men are by temperament interested exclusively in ideas and some in things, but there are many who are deeply interested in both. Hence a good mathematician may also be a good engineer. In an industrial environment there is a strong tendency to assign such a man the duties and responsibilities of an engineer, and when this is done his availability as a mathematician is reduced. This process, if allowed to continue, drains off the mathematicians who are interested in things as well as in

mathematics and leaves behind as consultants only those who are not, and who for that reason may be the least effective consultants.

With these ideas in mind, a Mathematical Research Department was created at Bell Telephone Laboratories in the late 1920's. I have described its organization and functions in some detail elsewhere. For the present discussion I need only say that it was explicitly understood that no project responsibility would be assigned to the men in this group, but that they would be consultants to the project engineers.

This concept was a wise one for its time, and though the department was not large, it was highly respected and performed a valuable service. Indeed, it was this group which, as I have said, the project supervisors preserved intact throughout the depression at the penalty of losing good men from their own staffs.

I am proud of the achievements of the men who were in it. Among these were John Carson and Sergei Schelkunoff, two outstanding experts in electromagnetic propagation and antenna theory; George Stibitz, whose early (1937) ideas regarding modern automatic computers have never been adequately recognized; Hendrik Bode, who contributed so much to the mathematical theory of feedback control, and who is now a vice president of the Laboratories; Claude Shannon, who originated information theory; and Walter Shewhart, the father of quality control.

Science and Industry—1938–1963

It is a little harder to tag the science of the final period, from 1938 to the present, because we are too close to it. We lack what my inimitable friend W. O. Baker calls "the exquisite acuity of hindsight." But some things of a very fundamental sort can be distinguished.

For one thing, I think it is safe to call it the era of particle physics. There have, of course, been important advances in other areas, notably solid-state physics, but none have the social impact of controlled and uncontrolled nuclear power.

Maybe we should also call it the biochemical

ical age, for the progress through chemistry toward an understanding of life processes and heredity has already been spectacular, and one has the feeling that tomorrow will be even more exciting.

There is also information theory, which in effect quantizes all intelligible thought and may lead to consequences not now foreseeable.

And, finally, there is something else which I find difficult to name. The electronic computer is the most ubiquitous example, but a somewhat special one. I refer to our emerging ability to control systems of all kinds, from the simplest machine to the most involved spacecraft, not through rigid procedures but through flexible processes akin to thought, where the only invariant is the underlying system of logic. Whatever this ability may be called, it is something new and important, and because of it the world will never be the same again. It may well be that 50 years from now particle physics, biochemistry, and this thing to which I have not given a name will stand out as the great scientific achievements of the period.

When we turn our attention to industrial research, the situation is not so confusing. Here I believe the most important evolution has been the team. Even today it is quite clear that without the team approach we could not have effectively exploited the better materials and better understanding which science has given us. With these materials we now make systems whose complexity exceeds that of the recent past by several orders of magnitude, but designing them often requires more skill and knowledge than a single man can give, and much more time than he is given. The team transcends these limitations by linking several or many brains into a single interacting agency—an agency which is as necessary for the final accomplishment as are the materials or the scientific theories.

The industrial research team has introduced problems of management from without, and of communication within, which are quite as revolutionary as were the problems accompanying the initial introduction of industrial research laboratories. I will not discuss these in detail. It is, however, important to note that, simultaneously with the emergence of the team and to some extent because of it, the place of the mathematician in industry has become more complex and sometimes more central. To understand why this is so, it will be helpful to digress for a moment and consider the nature of mathematics itself.

The Parts of Mathematics

The word *mathematics* does not connote a simple entity with a single facet. It relates to a useful art with at least four separate and important aspects. More specifically, mathematics is an art, a language, a tool, and a reckoning.

As an art, it deals with postulates and their logical consequences, the system of logic being a part of the postulates. In this aspect it is creative and has no necessary connection either with the physical world or with other parts of mathematics. As a simple example, two of the postulates of matrix algebra are

$$C = A \cdot B \quad \cdot \supset \cdot c_{ij} = \Sigma \, a_{ik} \, b_{kj},$$
$$C = A + B \cdot \supset \cdot c_{ij} = a_{ij} + b_{ij}.$$

A mathematical artist contemplating these postulates might wonder what the consequences would be if they were replaced by two other postulates,

$$C = A \cdot B \quad \cdot \supset \cdot c_{ij} = a_{ij} \, b_{ij},$$
$$C = A + B \cdot \supset \cdot c_{ij} = \Sigma \, (a_{ik} + b_{kj}),$$

which, in effect, interchange the rules for forming the elements of the sum and the product. The new mathematics thus created might or might not turn out to be interesting; as an entirely separate matter, it also might or might not turn out to be useful. But whether or not anything of permanent value results, the process is the *art* of mathematics.

One cannot, of course, practice the art of mathematics without using its *language*. The converse, however, is not true. Consider, for example, the pair of equations

$$l\frac{\partial i}{\partial t} + ri = \frac{\partial e}{\partial x},$$
$$k\frac{\partial e}{\partial t} + ge = \frac{\partial i}{\partial x}.$$

They express certain physical laws which define the propagation of electromagnetic disturbances in a one-dimensional medium. What they say is not mathematics; it is physics or engineering. They are either the speech of a physicist using the language of mathematics or the speech of a mathematician who is talking about physics.

When physical laws have been expressed in mathematical language, it becomes possible to make use of known mathematical facts and arrive at the physical consequences of the laws. To state it more simply, we could solve the foregoing differential equations and thereby derive formulas for the current and potential. In doing so, we would be using mathematics as a *tool*.

Finally, those procedures by which accounts and inventories are kept are also a part of mathematics, which I have called *reckoning*. It is a very important part, because, for one thing, without it no monetary system of trade could exist, and only primitive barter would be possible.

The order in which I have stated these aspects of mathematics is significant. From the point of view of the professional mathematician, they proceed from the most sophisticated, and therefore the most important, to the least. From the standpoint of industry, the order of importance would be reversed, for the art has no necessary connection with things and is therefore of little immediate value, whereas the language and the tool clearly have value, and, without reckoning, trade as we know it could not exist.

Mathematics may also be characterized by what we speak of as its method, and here there are three principal attributes. It is precise, concise, and rigorous—precise, because the discipline of mathematics requires that all terms be well defined; concise, because redundancy is recognized and avoided; rigorous, because logical principles are part of its clearly stated postulates, and are adhered to.

In industrial research, of course, the principal interest centers in the language and the tool. These are indispensable to science in general, and to industrial research in particular, precisely because they are precise, concise, and rigorous. This is why so many of today's scientists and engineers acquire such a high degree of skill in mathematics.

The Mathematician's Role in Industry Today

What role, then, does the mathematician play in today's industrial research, and how does it differ from his role in the past?

To begin with, his former role of consultant has not been eliminated because higher mathematical skills are now prevalent among project scientists. On the contrary, project scientists are now able to use his assistance more effectively. Organizationally this implies that mathematical research departments, such as the one I described earlier, are as logical now as they were some decades back.

In addition, two new functions have evolved from the scientific and organizational changes I have discussed.

The electronic computer has brought with it a greater need for experts on numerical analysis than existed a quarter- or a half-century ago. This is a rather specialized role, but nevertheless an important one.

Even more significant is the role which is growing out of the team concept. Clearly, such a team cannot function effectively without free and unambiguous communication between the experts of which it is composed. These may be from many disciplines, each with its own special language and special mode of thought. But today all, or almost all, have a fair training in mathematics, and many are highly skilled. Mathematics therefore provides the precise and unambiguous common language by means of which members of the team can communicate with each other and in terms of which they can formulate the problem with which they are concerned.

I am speaking particularly of the early phase in the evolution of a complex system which is often called "systems research." Here the exact definition of terms, and the rigorous formulation of questions and of logical answers to them, are necessary before the nature of the problem can be clearly understood and the requirements for its solution adequately formulated. The language of mathematics helps greatly in doing these things. Here also the mathematician, with his more severe schooling in the manipulation of abstract ideas, can be of very real service. Later, when the problem is thoroughly understood and requirements are set, and when the reduction of these requirements to "hardware" begins, his services are likely to be less needed. It is in the earlier phase, when general principles—sometimes unfamiliar ones—must be examined critically and without semantic or logical ambiguity, that he will be in greatest demand.

In this role the mathematician is no longer a consultant. He is a working member of the team, and if the problem is sufficiently analytical he may have a very central part indeed.

This is not a speculative suggestion. It has been repeatedly borne out by recent experience. For example, one of the leaders of the team which studied the ICBM interception problem and set the requirements for the Nike missile was H. W. Bode—one of the early members of the Mathematical Research Department at Bell Telephone Laboratories, who succeeded me as its director. And a leading member of the team which set the development requirements for nuclear warheads was Brockway MacMillan, a mathematician trained at M.I.T., who is now Undersecretary for Air.

To play this role well, however, it is not sufficient that the mathematician think straight and know the language of mathematics; for language alone does not suffice for intelligent conversation. Many English-speaking people cannot carry on an intelligent discussion of economic theory, though they know all the important words, and many mathematicians could not understand a discussion of atomic radiation, though they may be familiar with matrix algebra.

To be an effective member of the team, the mathematician must also understand the basic principles of the various disciplines which he is expected to discuss. He should be, in other words, the sort of man who a century ago was known as a natural philosopher—a man who had a keen analytical mind, adequate mathematical training, and a broad and sympathetic interest in a wide range of natural phenomena. There is already a clear need for such men, and, in my opinion, this may well become the most important role the industrial mathematician of the next generation will play.[4]

Educational Requirements

If this judgment is correct, we may well ask where these men are to come from.

Those I have known have often been physics or engineering undergraduates who developed a love for mathematics and majored in it for their doctor's degrees. This was true, for instance of Bode, MacMillan, Schelkunoff, and Shannon, among the men whose names I mentioned earlier. This is not hard to understand, since such men have interest both in ideas for their own sake and in things.

But while this is an effective pattern of education, the reverse—an undergraduate major in mathematics followed by a Ph.D. in science—does not have equivalent value. The reason is that the ingredient which the mathematician adds to the team is his greater emphasis on precise definition of terms and rigorous logical analysis, an emphasis seldom obtained outside the graduate mathematics curriculum.

There is, then, a legitimate need for graduate mathematical training which is both sound mathematically and sympathetic to the phenomena of the real world. Whether we call it applied mathematics or something else makes little difference. Its object is to train men who can be—in the sense I have explained—natural philosophers. This requirement runs exactly counter to the oft-stated view that "mathematics is concerned solely with symbols and the logical relations between them, and has no concern for their significance in the world of phenomena." That statement is true of the *art* of mathematics, but not of its other three parts. And it becomes both false and very dangerous when, as is sometimes done, the statement is made, not of "mathematics," but of "a mathematician."

We need, I think, in the universities and the Mathematical Society as well, a broader concept of the social value of mathematics. Not a de-emphasis of the art, for that would be a tragedy, but a greater pride in the full scope of the discipline and a stronger interest in its social values. Such a concept would greatly facilitate the training of the "natural philosophers" which industry will increasingly need in the foreseeable years ahead.

Notes

1. T. C. Fry, "Industrial Mathematics," a report for the National Resources Planning Board published as part of "Research—A National Resource," vol. 2, a House of Representatives document, 77th Congress.
2. I must add, however, that in 1940 I would have found a prophecy of 1800 for today almost equally fantastic. This is obvious from the grossly inadequate estimate of future growth which I included in the study.
3. The inclusion of a gadget, the vacuum tube, in this very impressive array of scientific advances may perhaps appear incongruous. But the vacuum tube is not only a valve and an oscillator, a modulator and a power amplifier; it is also a measuring instrument which profoundly broadened the scope of scientific experiments. I believe the social impact of the millions of tubes which have been used in scientific measurement greatly outweighs that of the billions which have been used in the communications and other industries.
4. Mathematicians of this kind will, of course, not be the most numerous.

Purity in Applications

Tim Poston

Tim Poston was born in England and received his first degree in mathematics from the University of Hull. He completed his doctorate at the University of Warwick in 1972. Since then he has been a peripatetic lecturer at Rio de Janeiro, Brazil; Rochester, New York; Porto, Portugal; Geneva, Switzerland; Bristol, England; Charleston, South Carolina; and Santa Cruz, California.

Pure versus applied is a distinction much fretted about in mathematical circles. In general, purity is honored and esteemed, and applications are allowed only in times of emergency, for example, to provide food, clothing, or an excuse to stay out of the army.

Historically a fairly good case can be made for the statement that there is little moral basis for drawing a distinction between the two aspects of mathematics. Many of the most famous and productive mathematicians were interested in solving practical problems. Indeed many took great delight in seeing their creations put to immediate use.

Yet it does seem to be true that what motivates the best minds is a good, devious puzzle. It is "the problem" that attracts and holds attention. Whether stated in terms as concrete as discovering whether the king's new crown is solid gold or just gold-plated lead or in terms as abstract as representing sheaves of germs of the almost everywhere ephemeral, problems and their solutions are what interest mathematicians.

In this essay Tim Poston suggests that in applying mathematics one ought to do, indeed, must do, mathematics. To concentrate excessively on the nonmathematical aspects of a particular real-world problem will frequently blind those who must solve the essential, the mathematical aspects of the problem. To be truly creative, the author suggests, demands purity in the process of application.

WHEN I WAS seventeen I regarded myself as a Pure Mathematician. There was perhaps arrogance in this—mathematically my academic record was not prodigious, and my purity was open to all sorts of doubt—but it is worth considering what I meant by it.

First, it did not mean that of the three courses I was by then taking in the early specialized British system—"Pure Maths," "Applied Maths," and "Physics"—I preferred the first. The "Pure" syllabus was an intellectual ragbag. Some series, some simple ordinary differential equations, some standard integrals which I could memorize for just over the time of an exam, a smattering of the axiomatics of three-dimensional Euclidean geometry . . . as coherent as the dates of kings. By contrast the "Applied" course centered on a few rich concepts (force, energy, velocity, mass, momentum . . .) and a few wild fictions (the inextensible or perfectly elastic string, the rigid rod, the smooth wire) whose function was to exclude everything *but* those concepts from the universe

Source: Tim Poston, "Purity in Applications," in Lynn Steen, ed., *Mathematics Tomorrow* (New York: Springer-Verlag, 1981), pp. 49–54.

of discourse. None of the messy irregularities of machines that might actually do something. More techniques relevant to the average user of mathematics were taught in the "Pure" course, but "Applied" had the majesty of a (small) bust of Newton through its coherence and sense of pattern. As a budding scientist I would have been disgusted by irrelevance: as a "Pure Mathematician" I basked in its beauty.

I fully expected this pattern to change at University, as it did. The Department of Pure Mathematics offered, at last, theories that combined the fine workmanship of rigorous argument with the noble unity of the great cathedrals. I know I was still in the lesser chapels (the books still had "Elementary" on their backs) but the style was unmistakable.

The other Department was a negative miracle. The clean intellectual dissection which could take apart one of those improbable smooth wire problems, argue the way to an equation whose solution demanded few messy sums, and present an elegant answer, was gone. There was no more realism than at school, but the extra dimensions involved in electromagnetism and gyroscopes meant that clear argument at an elementary level was no longer enough.

It was not replaced by coherent reasoning at a more advanced level.

It was replaced by the debauch of indices.

I cannot conceive that the idea of a function defined on triples of geometric vectors, giving the volume of the parallelepiped with vectors u, v, w for edges, is more abstruse and advanced than the mysterious symbol ϵ_{ijk} defined as "$+1$ for i, j, k a cyclic permutation of 1, 2, 3, -1 for a reversed permutation, and 0 if two of i, j, k coincide." Certainly ϵ_{ijk} represents the volume function, conveniently, in some coordinates. As an aid to calculation it is invaluable. But often a little clear thought can replace a great deal of calculation. Surely volume is an easier subject for clear thought than a set of 27 1's, 0's and (-1)'s which obscurely requires multiplication by a Jacobian determinant in some coordinate systems. (Again, this *need* not be obscure, if the idea of an operator A—represented by, but not consisting of, a matrix—has been made clear, so that det A can be

clearly introduced as the number A multiplies volumes by.)

It is good to quote Heaviside's defense, in 1893, of the use of mathematics in science:

Facts are not much use, considered as facts. They bewilder by their number and their apparent incoherency. Let them be digested into theory, however, and brought into mutual harmony, and it is another matter. Theory is of the essence of facts. Without theory scientific knowledge would be only worthy of the mad house.

Within mathematics, the facts are the formulae. They must be digested, brought into mutual, intellectual harmony or they are only worthy of a minor Applied Mathematics Department. This digestion, this bringing into harmony, is "pure" mathematics as a musical sound or a voice is pure: "Free from roughness, harshness or discordant quality; smooth, clear" (Oxford English Dictionary). It is also Pure Mathematics, in that it is not linked to any one particular application. The volume of a bucket, and the volume of a region in n-dimensional phase space, are both illuminated by thinking "in the abstract" about the concept of volume. The practical advantages of intellectual clarity can be enormous.

For example, in the very early (pre-electronic) days of computers, a computer group was given a large numerical matrix to invert by some aerodynamicists (Acton, 1970). The inverse that a major effort produced, to several significant figures, was . . . the transpose. A brief examination of the original, abstract matrix (with functions for entries, not the evaluated numbers the computer group was first given) showed it to be orthogonal. The inverse could have been known to be *precisely* the transpose, with no heavy calculation whatever. True, it is now so cheap to invert a matrix that some people will argue that studying it intellectually first is not cost-effective; but that way lies the mad house of the compulsive programmer "with sunken glowing eyes" who Weizenbaum (1976) says "has only technique, not knowledge." In a hurry, yes, press the button for an inverse. But if the habit of understanding is lost at an elementary level, or never learned, it will not reappear when the problems become more complicated.

Some years ago I became involved in numerical calculation of crystal spectra (Poston and Budgor, 1975), where vast and intricate routines, cunning in all their details, took hours to crunch their way. Since I had no training in this area I was not buried in technique, and could observe that the basic approach was as perverse as the numerical inversion of orthogonal matrices. If the "dispersion relation" between frequency v and wave number k was treated not as giving a "branched function" $v_i(k)$ but as a dependence of one component of k on v and the others, costly root searches could often be replaced by simple evaluation of functions. In any case a far more general, flexible and cheap approach resulted.

Conceptual thinking is the salt of mathematics. If the salt has lost its savor, with what shall applications be salted? In training users of mathematics, the question of what topics—viewed as techniques—from "Pure Mathematics" should be taught them is often a matter of fierce debate. But it is not fundamental. More important is the pure essence of mathematics, the understanding of structure, and intellectual harmony. If a student learns nothing of this, he or she has learned no mathematics; and the scientist, economist or engineer unconscious that mathematical understanding offers dollars-and-rubles rewards is half blind—even if the other eye sees grandly. Heaviside (1893), again:

> Unfortunately, in my opinion, Faraday was not a mathematician. It can scarcely be doubted that had he been one, he would have been greatly assisted in his researches, have saved himself much useless speculation, and would have anticipated much later work. . . . But it is perhaps too much to expect a man to be both the prince of experimentalists and a competent mathematician.

However, it should be reasonable to expect a man to be both an Applied Mathematics specialist and a competent mathematician in the sense developed above, with some skill in seeing the wood as well as the trees.

Sometimes, this expectation is justified.

Far too often, it is not. In Britain particularly, history has produced a whole tribe who are not mathematicians in this sense—and are not really working on applications either. Beads on wires have their higher analogues, largely drawn from 19th century continuum mechanics. General relativity, however, has found a place, perhaps because in classical notation it has so many indexed quantities—though not, usually, general relativity as expounded in the beautiful book of Misner, Thorne and Wheeler (1973). That book is addressed to people with a real interest in applications, like physicists and astronomers.

More representative of the bad pattern I am discussing (which is *not* universal, but is widespread) was a semester's work by a graduate student I knew, on whether one high-dimensional "spacetime" would embed in another. Calling the pseudo-Riemannian manifolds involved "spacetimes" made the work Applied, though not applied to the only universe in town. High-dimensional embedding problems are meat and drink to modern differential geometry, of course, which has developed a battery of powerful conceptual techniques for their study. Did he seek to learn these? Did he, even better, try to develop his own conceptual tools from scratch? (Zeeman [1977] gives an excellent example of the merits of working from ignorance in a similar case.)

He did not. He got stuck into the equations in their indexed glory, and ground through. At the end he thought he had a positive result, particular rather than general of course, but that was what he had been asked for. Then, he checked. Two weeks in, he had made a slip in the calculations, invalidating the manipulations of the rest of the semester. The same time spent on conceptual work (with calculations where needed) would have greatly enlarged his understanding of pseudo-Riemannian manifolds, even if nothing publishable resulted. As it was, he had gained only another slab of practice at manipulating indexed-quantity equations.

My claim is not, of course, that nothing without immediate application should be studied. Apart from the non-application virtues of mathematics (compelling, but hard to establish with a listener who *needs* an argument), mathematically natural questions usually do tie up with applications sooner or later, as the algebraists' invention of complex numbers took over electronics and quantum mechanics. Pseudo-Riemannian structures are not just a quirk of the physicists: there is a natural one on, for instance, the group of area-preserving linear transformations of the plane. They would surely have been invented, and almost as surely been applied, even if relativity had not come along, and in an application other than to physical spacetime the dimension might be anything. But in the absence, so far, of such an application, the above work was as "Pure" as anything done in a Pure Mathematics Department, failing only to be pure, and perhaps to be mathematics. (This last depends on definition. Does an IBM 704 do mathematics?)

Not all "Pure Mathematics" is pure either, in this sense. "The future does not lie with the theory of gencralised left pseudo-heaps" (Stewart, 1977), but a look through the journals shows that a substantial part of the present lies with just such forgettable material. Academic Pure Mathematics has vices all its own, but they are not my subject here, which is purity in application.

Purity, it seems to me, is more fundamental a criterion than mathematical rigor. Indeed, rigor is basically a tool for purity, for penetrating to an insight as to just what is really going on. Historically, its meaning has varied, and the notion of a correct proof has usually changed in response to a crisis in understanding. When natural arguments could sum $1 - 1 + 1 - 1 + \ldots$ as 0, 1/2 or 1, it became necessary to sharpen the reasoning tools used. Hilbert foresaw a climax to this process of refinement, but Gödel gave us leave to doubt the finality of all arithmetic arguments, forever. In any case, even Bourbaki "abuses language" at the expense of rigor, to benefit purity. In applications a demand for rigor, as an end in itself and not as a servant of purity, can be even more deadening than the debauch of indices. It can even encourage the growth of bogus "Applied" theories, like the equations of irrotational inviscid flow von Neumann called the study of dry water, by masking the assumptions made in a wreath of technicalities. A crowded map showing every logical leaf of every demonstrational tree may so effectively conceal the wood that nobody will notice that the thing being mapped is not a

forest at all but grassland. Among a list of fifty-three axioms about the cell structure of the plants in the model, who will notice the importance of the presence of lignin?

Rigor has a crucial part to play in clarification. For example the question "In what space do these objects you are calculating with live?" is an appeal for rigor that sheds light from classical electromagnetism to wave mechanics to the buckling of steel plates. Sometimes the questions raised by a wish for purity cannot be quickly answered. Poincaré's creation of topology out of his purity in mechanics raised so many pure mathematical questions that the subject went into purdah for half a century, and has only recently started acquiring its natural prominence in physics. Approximations by Taylor expansions were in use centuries before the techniques associated with catastrophe theory gave lucid, rigorous reasons behind their perfect validity for some purposes, in suitable cases, and proved their inadequacy in others. Purity is a goal and a standard that can never be perfectly met, and must (like rigor) often be compromised for the sake of some numerical answer demanded by a more immediate goal. But the compromise should be conscious, and considered: for if the surrender of purity is complete, the result is first computational ineffectiveness and finally the mad house.

I no longer call myself a Pure Mathematician—indeed, I am currently in a Physics Department. I do not want the name Applied Mathematician, with its British associations and self-exposing illogic (who applies the mathematician?). I do not work in one, single field of science, whose name I could borrow; I have published with coauthors from physics, geography, archaeology. . . . I am still a mathematician. I work, as best I can, in the application of mathematical understanding. To the extent that I succeed, in the meaning here proposed I am a pure mathematician.

References

1. Forman S. Acton. *Numerical Methods that Work*. Harper and Row, New York, 1970.
2. Oliver Heaviside. *Electromagnetic Theory*. D.

Van Nostrand, New York; and "The Electrician," Printing and Publishing Company, London, 1893.

3. C. W. Misner, K. S. Thorne, J. A. Wheeler. *Gravitation*. W. H. Freeman, San Francisco, 1973.

4. T. Poston and A. B. Budgor. "A Geometrical Approach to Calculating the Energy and Frequency Spectra of Crystals." *J. Comp. Phys.* 19 (1975) 1–28.

5. I. N. Stewart. *Concepts of Modern Mathematics.* Penguin, London, 1977.

6. Joseph Weizenbaum. *Computer Power and Human Reason*. W. H. Freeman, San Francisco, 1976.

7. E. C. Zeeman. "Research Ancient and Modern." *Bull. IMA* 10 (1974) 272–281; also in E. C. Zeeman. *Catastrophe Theory: Selected Papers* 1972–77. Addison-Wesley, Reading, Massachusetts, 1977.

Applied Mathematics Is Bad Mathematics

Paul R. Halmos

Paul R. Halmos was born in Budapest, Hungary, and received his Ph.D. in mathematics from the University of Illinois. He has held professional positions at the Universities of Chicago, Michigan, and Hawaii and is currently professor of mathematics at the University of Indiana. He is the author of numerous books and research articles in pure mathematics.

One might suspect from the title that Halmos is about to embalm and then bury applications of mathematics. Well, that is only partially accurate. Halmos intends to establish a perspective on the role that applications of mathematics now play and have played in the history and development of the discipline. His thesis is rather straightforward: first there is mathematics, and only then are there possible applications of mathematics.

In truth, except for the title, there is relatively little in the essay that most applied mathematicians would take issue with. The author recognizes the importance and utility of applications and also the interaction between the world of nature and the evolution of mathematical ideas. What Halmos argues is the impossibility of doing decent applied mathematics without ultimately doing in essence that which any other creative mathematician does, that is, forming abstract systems that involve definitions, theorems, and proofs.

Viewed in this way the author's thesis is less contentious than the title suggests and provides useful counterpoint for those who insist that human activity is important only if it immediately confronts and subdues nature. The secrets of the universe yield, it would seem, not to frontal assault but to an approach more indirect and contemplative.

IT ISN'T REALLY (applied mathematics, that is, isn't really bad mathematics), but it's different.

Does that sound as if I had set out to capture your attention, and, having succeeded, decided forthwith to back down and become conciliatory? Nothing of the sort! The "conciliatory" sentence is controversial, believe it or not; lots of people argue, vehemently, that it (meaning applied mathematics) is not different at all, it's all the same as pure mathematics, and anybody who says otherwise is probably a reactionary establishmentarian and certainly wrong.

If you're not a professional mathematician, you may be astonished to learn that (according to

some people) there are different kinds of mathematics, and that there is anything in the subject for anyone to get excited about. There are; and there is; and what follows is a fragment of what might be called the pertinent sociology of mathematics: what's the difference between pure and applied, how do mathematicians feel about the rift, and what's likely to happen to it in the centuries to come?

What Is It?

There is never any doubt about what mathematics encompasses and what it does not, but it is not

Source: Paul R. Halmos, "Applied Mathematics Is Bad Mathematics," in Lynn Steen, ed., *Mathematics Tomorrow* (New York: Springer-Verlag, 1981), pp. 9–20.

easy to find words that describe precisely what it is. In many discussions, moreover, mathematics is not described as a whole but is divided into two parts, and not just in one way; there are two kinds of mathematics according to each of several different systems of classification.

Some of the dichotomies are well known, and others less so. Mathematics studies sizes and shapes, or, in other words, numbers (arithmetic) and figures (geometry); it can be discrete or continuous; it is sometimes finite and sometimes infinite; and, most acrimoniously, some of it is pure (useless?) and some applied (practical?). Different as these classification schemes might be, they are not unrelated. They are, however, not of equal strengths; the size-shape division, for instance, is much less clear-cut, and much less divisive, than the pure-applied one.

Nobody is forced to decide between vanilla ice cream and chocolate once and for all, and it is even possible to mix the two, but most people usually ask for the same one. A similar (congenital?) division of taste exists for mathematicians. Nobody has to decide once and for all to like only algebra (discrete) or only topology (continuous), and there are even flourishing subjects called algebraic topology and topological algebra, but most mathematicians do in fact lean strongly toward either the discrete or the continuous.

Squares and Spheres

It would be a shame to go on and on about mathematics and its parts without looking at a few good concrete examples, but genuine examples are much too technical to describe in the present context. Here are a couple of artificial ones (with some shortcomings, which I shall explain presently).

Suppose you want to pave the floor of a room whose shape is a perfect square with tiles that are themselves squares so that no two tiles are exactly the same size. Can it be done? In other words, can one cover a square with a finite number of non-overlapping smaller squares all of which have different side-lengths? This is not an easy question to answer.

Here is another puzzle: if you have a perfect sphere, like a basketball, what's the smallest number of points you can mark on it so that every point on the surface is within an inch of one of the marked ones? In other words, what's the most economical way to distribute television relay stations on the surface of the globe?

Is the square example about sizes (numbers) or shapes (figures)? The answer seems to be that it's about both, and so is the sphere example. In this respect the examples give a fair picture; mixed types are more likely to occur (and are always more interesting) than the ones at either extreme. The examples have different flavors, however. The square one is more nearly arithmetic, discrete, finite, pure, and the one about spheres leans toward being geometric, continuous, infinite, applied.

The square problem is of some mild interest, and it has received attention in the professional literature several times, but it doesn't really have the respect of most mathematicians. The reason is not that it is obviously useless in the practical sense of the word, but that it is much too special (petty?, trivial?), in the sense of being isolated from most of the rest of mathematics and requiring *ad hoc* methods for its solution. It is not really a fair example of pure mathematics.

The sphere example, on the other hand, is of a great deal of practical use, but, nevertheless, it is not a fair example of applied mathematics: it is much easier (and much purer) than most applied problems, and, in particular, it does not involve motion, which plays the central role in the classical conception of what applied mathematics is all about.

Still, for what they are worth, here they are, and it might help to keep them in mind as the discussion proceeds.

Fiction or Action

The pure and applied distinction is visible in the arts and in the humanities almost as clearly as in the sciences: witness Mozart versus military marches, Rubens versus medical illustrations, or Virgil's *Aeneid* versus Cicero's *Philippics*. Pure literature deals with abstractions such as love and war, and it tells about imaginary examples of them in emotionally stirring language. Pure mathematics deals with abstractions such as the multiplication of numbers and the congruence of triangles, and it reasons about Platonically idealized examples of them with intellectually convincing logic.

There is, to be sure, one sense of the word in which all literature is "applied." Shakespeare's sonnets have to do with the everyday world, and so does Tolstoy's *War and Peace*, and so do Caesar's commentaries on the wars he fought; they all start from what human beings see and hear, and all speak of how human beings move and feel. In that same somewhat shallow sense all mathematics is applied. It all starts from sizes and shapes (whose study leads ultimately to algebra and geometry), and it reasons about how sizes and shapes change and interact (and such reasoning leads ultimately to the part of the subject that the professionals call analysis).

There can be no doubt that the fountainhead, the inspiration, of all literature is the physical and social universe we live in, and the same is true about mathematics. There is also no doubt that the physical and social universe daily affects each musician, and painter, and writer, and mathematician, and that therefore a part at least of the raw material of the artist is the world of facts and motions, sights and sounds. Continual contact between the world and art is bound to change the latter, and perhaps even to improve it.

The ultimate goal of "applied literature," and of applied mathematics, is action. A campaign speech is made so as to cause you to pull the third lever on a voting machine rather than the fourth. An aerodynamic equation is solved so as to cause a plane wing to lift its load fast enough to avoid complaints from the home owners near the airport. These examples are crude and obvious; there are subtler ones. If the biography of a candidate, a factually correct and honest biography, does not directly mention the forthcoming election, is it then pure literature? If a discussion of how mathematically idealized air flows around moving figures of various shapes, a logically rigorous and correct discussion, does not mention airplanes or airports, is it then pure mathematics? And what about the in-between cases: the biography that, without telling lies, is heavily preju-

diced, and the treatise on aerodynamics that, without being demonstrably incorrect, uses cost-cutting rough approximations—are they pure or applied?

Continuous Spectrum

Where are the dividing lines in the chain from biography to interpretive history to legend to fiction? We might be able to tell which of Toynbee, Thucydides, Homer, and Joyce is pure and which is applied, but if we insert a dozen names between each pair of them, as we pass from interpreted fact to pure fancy, the distinctions become blurred and perhaps impossible to define. The mathematical analogy is close: if we set out to sort a collection of articles that range from naval architecture to fluid dynamics to partial differential equations to topological vector spaces, the pure versus applied decisions that are clear at the two ends of the spectrum become fuzzy in the middle.

To confuse the issue still more, pure mathematics can be practically useful and applied mathematics can be artistically elegant. Pure mathematicians, trying to understand involved logical and geometrical interrelations, discovered the theory of convex sets and the algebraic and topological study of various classes of functions. Almost as if by luck, convexity has become the main tool in linear programming (an indispensable part of modern economic and industrial practice), and functional analysis has become the main tool in quantum theory and particle physics. The physicist regards the applicability of von Neumann algebras (a part of functional analysis) to elementary particles as the only justification of the former; the mathematician regards the connection as the only interesting aspect of the latter. *De gustibus non disputandum est?*

Just as pure mathematics can be useful, applied mathematics can be more beautifully useless than is sometimes recognized. Applied mathematics is not engineering; the applied mathematician does not design airplanes or atomic bombs. Applied mathematics is an intellectual discipline, not a part of industrial technology. The ultimate goal of applied mathematics is action, to be sure, but, before that, applied mathematics is a part of theoretical science concerned with the general principles behind what makes planes fly and bombs explode.

The differences between people are sometimes as hard to discern as the differences between subjects, and it can even happen that one and the same person is both a pure and an applied mathematician. Some applied mathematicians (especially the better ones) have a sound training in pure mathematics, and some pure mathematicians (especially the better ones) have a sound training in applicable techniques. When the occasion for a crossover arises (a pure mathematician successfully solves a special case of the travelling salesman problem that arises in operations research, a relativity theorist brilliantly derives a formula in 4-dimensional differential geometry), each one is secretly more than a little proud: "See! I can do that stuff too!"

Doers and Knowers

What I have said so far is that in some sense all mathematics is applied mathematics and that on some level it is not easy to tell the pure from the applied. Now I'll talk about the other side: pure and applied are different indeed, and if you know what to look for, and have the courage of your convictions, you can always tell which is which. My purpose is to describe something much more than to prove something. My hope is neither to convert the pagan nor to convince the agnostic, but just to inform the traveller from another land: there are two sects here, and these are the things that they say about each other.

The difference of opinion is unlike the one in which one sect says "left" and the other says "right"; here one sect says "we are all one sect" and the other says "oh no, we're not, we are two." That kind of difference makes it hard to present the facts in an impartial manner; the mere recognition that a conflict exists amounts already to taking sides. There is no help for that, so I proceed, with my own conclusions admittedly firm, to do the best I can for the stranger in our midst.

Human beings want to know and to do. People want to know what their forefathers did and said,

they want to know about animals and vegetables and minerals, and they want to know about concepts and numbers and sights and sounds. People want to grow food and to sew clothes, they want to build houses and to design machines, and they want to cure diseases and to speak languages.

The doers and the knowers frequently differ in motivation, attitude, technique, and satisfaction, and these differences are visible in the special case of applied mathematicians (doers) and pure mathematicians (knowers). The motivation of the applied mathematician is to understand the world and perhaps to change it; the requisite attitude (or, in any event, a customary one) is one of sharp focus (keep your eye on the problem); the techniques are chosen for and judged by their effectiveness (the end is what's important); and the satisfaction comes from the way the answer checks against reality and can be used to make predictions. The motivation of the pure mathematician is frequently just curiosity; the attitude is more that of a wide-angle lens than a telescopic one (is there a more interesting and perhaps deeper question nearby?); the choice of technique is dictated at least in part by its harmony with the context (half the fun is getting there); and the satisfaction comes from the way the answer illuminates unsuspected connections between ideas that had once seemed to be far apart.

The last point deserves emphasis, especially if you belong to the large group of people who proudly dislike mathematics and regard it as inglorious drudgery. For the pure mathematician, his subject is an inexhaustible source of artistic pleasure: not only the excitement of the puzzle and the satisfaction of the victory (if it ever comes!), but mostly the joy of contemplation. The challenge doesn't come from our opponent who can win only if we lose, and victory doesn't disappear as soon as it's achieved (as in tennis, say); the challenge is the breathtakingly complicated logical structure of the universe, and victory is permanent (more like recovering precious metal from a sunken ship).

The basic differences in motivation, attitude, technique, and satisfaction are probably connected with more superficial but more noticeable differences in exposition. Pure and applied mathematicians have different traditions about clarity, elegance, and perhaps even logical rigor, and such differences frequently make for unhappy communication.

The hows and the whys listed above are not offered as a checklist to be used in distinguishing applied science from pure thought; that is usually done by a sort of intuitive absolute pitch. The word "spectrum" gives an analogical hint to the truth. In some sense red and orange are the same—just waves whose lengths differ a bit—and it is impossible to put your finger on the spot in the spectrum where red ends and orange begins—but, after that is granted, red and orange are still different, and the task of telling them apart is almost never a difficult one.

Beauty and Boredom

Many pure mathematicians regard their specialty as an art, and one of their terms of highest praise for another's work is "beautiful." Applied mathematicians seem sometimes to regard their subject as a systematization of methods; a suitable word of praise for a piece of work might be "ingenious" or "powerful."

Here is another thing that has frequently struck me: mathematics (pure mathematics), despite its many subdivisions and their enormous rate of growth (started millennia ago and greater today than ever before), is an amazingly unified intellectual structure. The mathematics that is alive and vigorous today has so many parts, and each is so extensive, that no one can possibly know them all. As a result, we, all of us, often attend colloquium lectures on subjects about which we know much less than an average historian, say, knows about linguistics. It doesn't matter, however, whether the talk is about unbounded operators, commutative groups, or parallelizable surfaces; the interplay between widely separated parts of mathematics always shows up. The concepts and methods of each one illuminate all others, and the unity of the structure as a whole is there to be marvelled at.

That unity, that common aesthetic insight, is mostly missing between pure and applied mathematics. When I try to listen to a lecture about fluid mechanics, I soon start wondering and puzzling at the (to me) *ad hoc* seeming approach; then the puzzlement is replaced by bewilderment, boredom, confusion, acute discomfort, and, before the end, complete chaos. Applied mathematicians listening to a lecture on algebraic geometry over fields of non-zero characteristic go through a very similar sequence of emotions, and they describe them by words such as inbred, artificial, baroque folderol, and unnecessary hairsplitting.

It might be argued that from the proper, Olympian, impartial scientific point of view both sides are wrong, but perhaps to a large extent both are right—which would go to prove that we are indeed looking at two subjects, not one. To many pure mathematicians applied mathematics is nothing but a bag of tricks, with no merit except that they work, and to many applied mathematicians much of pure mathematics deserves to be described as meaningless abstraction for its own sake with no merit at all. (I mention in passing that in moments of indulgent self-depreciation the students of one particular branch of pure mathematics, category theory, refer to their branch as "abstract nonsense"; applied mathematicians tend to refer to it the same way, and they seem to mean it.)

New Heresy

Some say that the alleged schism between pure and applied mathematics is a recent heresy at which the founding greats would throw up their hands in horror—the world is going to the dogs! There is a pertinent quotation from Plato's *Philebus*, which doesn't quite refute that statement, but it's enough to make you think about it again.

SOCRATES   Are there not two kinds of arithmetic, that of the people and that of the philosophers? . . . And how about the arts of reckoning and measuring as they are used in building and in trade when compared with philosophical geometry and elaborate computations—shall we speak of each of these as one or two?

PROTARCHUS   . . . I should say that each of them was two.

Is the distinction that Socrates is driving at exactly the pure-applied one? If not that, then what?

The only other curiosity along these lines that I'll mention is that you can usually (but not always) tell an applied mathematician from a pure one just by observing the temperature of his attitude toward the same-different debate. If he feels strongly and maintains that pure and applied are and must be the same, that they are both mathematics and the distinction is meaningless, then he is probably an applied mathematician. About this particular subject most pure mathematicians feel less heat and speak less polemically: they don't really think pure and applied are the same, but they don't care all that much. I think what I have just described is a fact, but I confess I can't help wondering why it's so.

New Life

The deepest assertion about the relation between pure and applied mathematics that needs examination is that it is symbiotic, in the sense that neither can survive without the other. Not only, as is universally admitted, does the applied need the pure, but, in order to keep from becoming inbred, sterile, meaningless, and dead, the pure needs the revitalization and the contact with reality that only the applied can provide.

The first step in the proof of the symbiosis is historical: all of pure mathematics, it is said, comes from the real world, the way geometry, according to legend, comes from measuring the effect of the floods of the Nile. (If that's false, if geometry existed before it was needed, the symbiosis argument begins on a shaky foundation. If it's true, the argument tends to prove only that applied mathematics cannot get along without pure, as an anteater cannot get along without ants, but not necessarily the reverse.)

Insofar as all mathematics comes from the study of sizes (of *things*) and shapes (of *things*), it is true that all mathematics comes from the things of the real world. Whether renewed contact with physics or psychology or biology or economics was needed to give birth to some of the greatest parts of 20th century mathematics (such as Can-

tor's continuum problem, the Riemann hypothesis, and the Poincaré conjecture) is dubious.

The crux of the matter is, however, not historical but substantive. By way of a parable, consider chess. Mathematicians usually but sometimes grudgingly admit that chess is a part of mathematics. They do so grudgingly because they don't consider chess to be "good" mathematics; from the mathematical point of view it is "trivial." No matter: mathematics it is, and pure mathematics at that.

Chess has not been conceptually revitalized in many hundreds of years, but is vigorously alive nevertheless. There are millions of members of chess clubs, and every now and then the whole civilized world spends days watching Bobby Fischer play Boris Spassky. Chess fires the imagination of a large part of humanity; it shows them aesthetic lights and almost mystic insights.

Not only does chess (like many parts of mathematics) not need external, real-world revitalization, but, in fact, every now and then it spontaneously revitalizes itself. The most recent time that occurred was when retrograde chess analysis began to be studied seriously. (Sample problem: a chess position is given; you are to decide which side of the board White started from and whether Black had ever castled.) And here's a switch: not only was the real world not needed to revitalize chess, but, in fact, the life giving went the other way. Retrograde chess analysis challenged computer scientists with a new kind of problem, and it now constitutes a small but respectable and growing part of applied mathematics.

A revitalist might not be convinced by all this; he might point to the deplorable tendency of mathematics to become ultra-abstract, ultra-complicated, and involutedly ugly, and say that contact with the applications remedies that. The disease exists, that is well known, but, fortunately, so does nature's built-in cure. Several parts of mathematics have become cancerously overgrown in the course of the centuries; certain parts of elementary Euclidean geometry form a probably non-controversial example. When that happens, a wonderful remission always follows. Old mathematics never dies—what the Greeks bequeathed us 2500 years ago is still alive and true and interesting—but the outgrowths get simplified, their valuable core becomes integrated into the main body, and the nasty parts get sloughed off.

(Parenthetically: the revitalization argument could, in principle, be applied to painting, but so far as I know no one has applied it. Painting originates in the real world, it has been known to leave that world for realms of abstraction and complication that some find repulsive, but the art as a whole continues alive and well through all that.

A time argument is sometimes mentioned as a good feature of the contact of pure mathematics with applied. Example: if only pure mathematicians had paid closer attention to Maxwell, they would have discovered topological groups much sooner. Perhaps so—but just what did we lose by discovering them later? Would the world be better off if Rembrandt had been born a century earlier? What's the hurry?)

Whether contact with applications can prevent or cure the disease of elaboration and attenuation in mathematics is not really known; what is known is that many of the vigorous and definitely non-cancerous parts have no such contact (and probably, because of their level of abstraction, cannot have any). Current examples: analytic number theory and algebraic geometry.

When I say that mathematics doesn't *have* to be freshened by periodic contact with reality, of course I do not mean that it *must not* be: many of the beautiful concepts of pure mathematics were first noticed in the study of one or another part of nature. Perhaps they would not have been discovered without external stimulation, or perhaps they would—certainly many things were.

As far as the interaction between pure and applied mathematics is concerned, the truth seems to be that it exists, in both directions, but it is much stronger in one direction than in the other. For pure mathematics the applications are a great part of the origin of the subject and continue to be an occasional source of inspiration—they are, however, not indispensable. For applied mathematics, the pure concepts and deductions are a tool, an organizational scheme, and frequently a powerful hint to truths about the world—an indispensable part of the applied organism. It's the ant and the anteater again: arguably, possibly, the

anteater is of some ecological value to the ant, but, certainly, indisputably, the ant is necessary for the anteater's continued existence and success.

What's Next?

The most familiar parts of mathematics are algebra and geometry, but for the profession there is a third one, analysis, that plays an equally important role. Analysis starts from the concept of change. It's not enough just to study sizes and shapes; it is necessary also to study how sizes and shapes vary. The natural way to measure change is to examine the difference between the old and the new, and that word, "difference," leads in an etymologically straight line to the technical term "differential equation." Most of the classical parts of applied mathematics are concerned with change—motion—and their single most usable tool is the theory and technique of differential equations.

Phenomena in the real world are likely to depend on several variables: the success of the stew depends on how long you cook it, how high the temperature is, how much wine you add, etc. To predict the outcome correctly, the variables must be kept apart: how does the outcome change when a part of the data is changed? That's why much of applied mathematics is inextricably intertwined with the theory of *partial* differential equations; for some people, in fact, the latter phrase is almost a synonym of applied mathematics.

Are great breakthroughs still being made and will they continue? Is a Shakespeare of mathematics (such as Archimedes or Gauss) likely to be alive and working now, or to be expected ever again? Algebra, analysis, and geometry—what's the mathematics of the future, and how will the relations between pure and applied develop?

I don't know the answers, nobody does, but the past and the present give some indications; based on them, and on the hope that springs eternal, I'll hazard a couple of quick guesses. The easiest question is about great breakthroughs: yes, they are still being made. Answers to questions raised many decades and sometimes centuries ago are being found almost every year. If Cantor, Riemann, and Poincaré came alive now, they would be excited and avid students, and they would learn much that they wanted to know.

Is there an Archimedes alive now? Probably not. Will there ever be another Gauss? I don't see why not; I hope so, and that's probably why I think so.

I should guess that in the foreseeable future (as in the present) discrete mathematics will be an increasingly useful tool in the attempt to understand the world, and that analysis will therefore play a proportionally smaller role. That is not to say that analysis in general and partial differential equations in particular have had their day and are declining in power; but, I am guessing, not only combinatorics but also relatively sophisticated number theory and geometry will displace some fraction of the many pages that analysis has been occupying in all books on applied mathematics.

Applied mathematics is bound to change, in part because the problems change and in part because the tools for their solution change. As we learn more and more about the world, and learn how to control some of it, we need to ask new questions, and as pure mathematics grows, sloughs off the excess, and becomes both deeper and simpler thereby, it offers applied mathematics new techniques to use. What will all that do to the relation between the ant and the anteater?

My guess is, nothing much. Both kinds of curiosity, the pure and the practical, are bound to continue, and the Socrates of 2400 years from now will probably see the difference between them as clearly as did the one 2400 years ago.

So, after all that has been said, what's the conclusion? Perhaps it is in the single word "taste."

A portrait by Picasso is regarded as beautiful by some, and a police photograph of a wanted criminal can be useful, but the chances are that the Picasso is not a good likeness and the police photograph is not very inspiring to look at. Is it completely unfair to say that the portrait is a bad copy of nature and the photograph is bad art?

Much of applied mathematics has great value. If an intellectual technique teaches us something about how blood is pumped, how waves propagate, and how galaxies expand, then it gives us science, knowledge, in the meaning of the word that deserves the greatest respect. It is no insult to the depth and precision and social contribution of great drafters of legislative prose (with their rigidly traditional diction and style) to say that the laws they write are bad literature. In the same way it is no insult to the insight, technique, and scientific contribution of great applied mathematicians to say of their discoveries about blood, and waves, and galaxies that those discoveries are first-rate applied mathematics; but, usually, applied mathematics is bad mathematics just the same.

Early Years of the Mathematics Program at ONR

Mina Rees

Mina Spiegel Rees earned her Ph.D. at the University of Chicago in 1931 and has received seventeen honorary degrees since. She has been associated with Hunter College since 1926. Rees is currently professor emeritus of mathematics at the City University of New York. She was with the Office of Naval Research from 1946 to 1949, and since then she has held numerous governmental advisory appointments on the National Research Council, National Bureau of Standards, National Science Foundation, National Science Board, and the National Manpower Committee.

The ONR of the title is the Office of Naval Research, the research arm of the United States Navy. Initially this bureau investigated matters that were directly related to practical questions of gunnery, seamanship, and so on. During World War II, however, the problems faced by the Navy drew the department ever more deeply into the support of basic scientific research. For example, the problem of locating enemy submarines underwater came to involve an enormously complex collection of interrelated scientific disciplines. In many of these areas there was little or no basic scientific research upon which an investigation useful to the Navy could be started. Given this fact, the Navy had no choice but to perform its own research and hire or contract for the services of its own scientists. Mina Rees describes here the development of mathematics research at ONR.

AT THE END of World War II, thirty years ago, the birth of the Office of Naval Research signalled the beginning of a series of federal programs that provided significant investments in scientific research and stimulated an expansion of scientific activity that placed the United States in the forefront of scientific achievement. In particular, substantial support of the research of university mathematicians introduced a new dimension into the relationship between the government and mathematicians. It changed the life style of many university people, encouraging young people to seek careers in mathematics and stimulating work in new or previously neglected sub-fields of mathematics. Many of these fields have since blossomed and become familiar aspects of college and university programs. This article will recount some aspects of the genesis of the military support

of mathematics, beginning in 1946, and comment on some of the early achievements of the program.

In 1945, even before the end of World War II, many scientists who had been involved in wartime research were asked for opinions on the creation of an office within the Navy that would give money to universities for basic research in mathematics. My response was one of grave doubts because I thought that mathematicians probably would not be enthusiastic about receiving financial support for their peacetime research from the government, and especially from the military. But the plans went forward and the Office of Naval Research (ONR) was created by an act of Congress in 1946. Later, counterpart offices were created by the other military services, and the three offices together provided wide support for scien-

Source: Mina Rees, "Early Years of the Mathematics Program at ONR," *Naval Research Reviews* 30 (1977): 22–29.

tific research in American universities within their broad mandate to support research of interest to the Defense Department.

In spite of my doubts I was invited to Washington in 1946 to help set up the mathematics program of the new Office of Naval Research. After consulting with some of my wisest friends, I decided to participate in what still seemed to me a somewhat uncertain venture. When I arrived in Washington in August of 1946, it was impossible to find a place to live. No apartments were available and most hotels permitted a guest to stay only five days. When I found one that extended its hospitality for two weeks at a time, I was enchanted. I made a virtue of necessity, and every two weeks vacated my room and went on a trip to a leading mathematics department. On my return I registered for another two weeks.

These were the conditions under which I consulted many of the senior mathematicians of the United States. Together we evolved the first outline of the ONR mathematics program. While it evolved through criticism and change by my Washington colleagues, of course, our basic decision was to support pure and applied mathematics, statistics, and computer development with its related numerical analysis to insure the sophisticated use of electronic digital computers when they became available. Also, we had to establish the philosophy to guide the Navy in providing funds to buy time for able mathematicians to carry on their research and to establish research assistantships for young mathematicians whose support seemed to us the key to the flowering of mathematical research in the country. Because ONR was not authorized to carry on an educational program, the teaching aspects of setting up these new mathematics studies would have to be handled by the universities.

Before World War II, there had been relatively little emphasis in American universities on "applied mathematics" which was strongly represented at a number of German centers, particularly Goettingen, and at other continental universities as well as on British campuses. After the war, with some of the world's most distinguished emigre mathematicians on our campuses, it was possible to contemplate a strong development in these fields in the U.S. The ONR seized the opportunity to support emerging groups like that at New York University under Richard Courant whose work at Goettingen had made his name magic throughout the world. There were also individuals, such as Szego and Polya at Stanford, about whom strong groups could be expected to grow. There was a small number of very able probabilists and statisticians; these included some emigres who were already eminent, such as Feller and Kac at Cornell and Neyman at Berkeley, as well as some native mathematicians who were well established and whose work was just beginning to be acclaimed. All these received encouragement and support from ONR as part of a plan to expand the U.S. activity in applied mathematical research and to increase the numbers of able young people being educated to carry on research in these fields. Only by working toward these goals could ONR be counted on to produce results not only significant for mathematics but useful to the Navy.

Although ONR support of research in the more abstract fields of mathematics was in our original planning, it had not been explicitly authorized without regard to relevance to the Navy's mission when the ONR Mathematics Branch was established. Nevertheless, it seemed clear to us in the Mathematics Branch that the argument for increasing the number of well educated and experienced research mathematicians was a strong one. During the war, the effectiveness of mathematicians in handling troublesome and pressing problems had often depended not so much on their specific fields as on their quality as research investigators. Of course there were some problems, such as the malfunctioning of a rocket, which required specific work in a relevant field but, in general, the pure mathematicians were among the most admired and sought after in seeking answers to many urgent problems. Moreover, there was considerable feeling among us that our program must strive to strengthen mathematical research in the United States, not fragment it, and we did not want to exclude any first class research.

One night early in my tenure, I was working late at my desk when Captain Robert Conrad came in. Captain Conrad was the spiritual father of the Office of Naval Research, a great man and a great leader, whose energy and enthusiasm set the tone of ONR. He sat down and said to me, after a little chit-chat: "Mina, if you want to include pure mathematics in your program, I'll support you in your decision." This was a great day for all of us, for it meant an end to the constant worry as to whether the Navy would see the needs of mathematics as we saw them.

Within this framework, many mathematicians supported by the Navy continued to work in the abstract parts of mathematics that were of greatest interest to them. But there were others who, to quote A. W. Tucker of Princeton, "felt an obligation to reach out beyond customary courses, seminars, and research, to make two-way contact with industrial labs and government undertakings." My own evaluation is that those who were lured into new fields by the Navy's interest were mathematicians who welcomed a reason for exploring new aspects of work in which they had been interested for a long time. When this kind of new research commitment was accompanied by the offering of related courses and seminars at their universities, a lively campus activity was apt to come into being. Thus, Solomon Lefschetz set up at Princeton a broadly based program in differential analysis that provided a home for the work of a number of vigorous young mathematicians. These men became leaders in creating new developments in such areas as stability theory of differential equations, mathematical theory of control processes, and dynamic programming. And the project in the logistics program under Professor Tucker, also at Princeton, produced many of the leading figures now pursuing research in universities or working in business or industry in fields related to the project. Tucker and his former students, particularly David Gale and Harold W. Kuhn made important contributions to the development and systematization of the underlying mathematical theory of linear inequalities. Their work led to significant advances in the related field of game theory and in linear programming.

The Navy's program had a broad effect not only on individual mathematicians across the nation, but also on some departments and institutions as well, who changed their character under the stimulus of federal dollars. The ONR emphasis on analysis, with considerable interest in questions related to continuum mechanics, stimulated increased activity in several university departments. The New York University Graduate Mathematics Department is one of the most striking in its use of the new resources, originally in support of analysis. With the new funding, that Department expanded its activities, assumed a new role in its university, and became one of the most distinguished departments in the country. Some very substantial engineering-oriented mathematical research was supported by ONR's Mechanics Branch. When that Branch joined the Mathematics Division after a few years, the Division's influence was extended into the engineering schools of many universities. Stanford was one of those where the new resources were applied across the span of science and engineering as well as mathematics, including applied mathematics and mathematical statistics.

In the early days, we recognized that ONR had a special obligation to provide for the balanced support and growth of mathematical research in the United States within the framework of the Navy's established policy. In time, it became clear that dedication to these purposes would also provide the Navy with access to first class mathematical talent to aid in the attack on major problems. Thus, when the Defense Department needed help in considering the DEW Line defense of the continent against air attack, a number of our computer mathematicians were asked for advice. When the fleet needed a coordinated system of defense, similar invitations were extended to appropriate mathematicians. And when, in the late 1940's, the staff of our office became aware that some mathematical results obtained by George Dantzig, who was then working for the Air Force, could be used to reduce the burdensome costs of the Navy's logistics operations, the possibilities were pointed out to the Deputy Chief of Naval Operations for Logistics. His enthusiastic reaction led in a short time to the establishment of a Logistics Branch in ONR with a separate research program. This has been a most successful activity of the Mathematics Division, both in its usefulness to the Navy and in its impact on industry and the universities. Our support for the quantitative side of economics, to which two recent Nobel Laureates contributed, was motivated by our concern with decision making processes. The "decision mathematics" fostered by our program strongly affected developments in agricultural economics as well as military command decision systems. Along with the Rand Corporation, we had a major influence on the introduction of operations research and its subdiscipline, management science, into business schools. Operations research also found roots in many universities in new departments and in existing departments of computer science and industrial engineering. The content of operations research as it is taught in these disciplines reflects research areas supported by ONR. ONR's journal, the Naval Research Logistics Quarterly, is highly respected and is extensively used as a reference for source materials in these fields. Game Theory and Gaming as an instructional technique, as well as the mathematical theory of optimization and other aspects of mathematics for social scientists, have also provided teaching content and research interests for members of various university departments.

Another important aspect of the early Mathematics Branch program was the work in computers. It not only made the Logistics program possible but broadly touched the whole span of Naval operations and our society. When I first went to Washington in 1946, ONR was supporting some projects dealing with analog computers. However, little attention was being given to automatic digital computers, although other parts of the Navy had supported significant work in this field. ONR's entry into the field was extensive, much of it in collaboration with the National Bureau of Standards. Initially, we emphasized the development of mathematical results that would be needed if the machines, when they became operative, were to be used properly. With the passage of time, however, a substantial program for component and computer development did emerge. The two computers we supported that had the greatest influence on subsequent developments in the field were the computer at the Institute for Advanced Study, known particularly because of John von Neumann's critical role in its design, and the Whirlwind computer at M.I.T., which provided Jay Forrester with his first claim to fame. As F. J. Weyl summarized it: "The decisive

aspects of stored program computer logic, high speed parallel electrostatic and magnetic core memories, the interaction of high speed small memories with slower, much more capacious ones in the same computer, and many important simplifications in programming and coding were first realized on one or the other of these machines."

The Whirlwind was originally conceived as an element in an advanced flight trainer. After many changes and adaptations to the state of the art, it evolved as a general purpose computer of unusual design. Within months after its completion, it became clear that this computer was particularly well suited to serve as a data processing component in a prototype integrated defense system, then under development at M.I.T. The experience gained on Whirlwind during the second half of the fifties laid the groundwork for the development of the computerized air traffic control systems, the automated reservations facilities, and the computer-managed learning systems of our day. Components of Whirlwind have recently been installed as a permanent display in the Smithsonian Institution.

ONR supported many projects concerned with numerical analysis, which often were led by investigators widely known and respected for their work in pure mathematics. In 1947, the Institute for Numerical Analysis was established at UCLA under the auspices of the Bureau of Standards and with ONR support. Its staff of distinguished mathematicians and mathematical physicists came from the United States and Europe. D. H. Lehmer, a leading U.S. number theorist and a Director of the Institute commented on the nature and quality of the Institute's research in an October, 1969 interview at the Smithsonian Institution. He observed that the Institutes program had naturally focussed on the research interests of its staff. There was work on partial differential equations and systems of linear equations that produced a great variety of significant results. Much of the mathematics was concerned with experiments in methods for the new kinds of numerical analysis problems that would arise with the use of the new, very fast, very sophisticated electronic digital computers. A number of very able young people were trained at the Institute, and large numbers of older mathematicians learned the new approaches that computers required. When the Institute was terminated as a government agency, many of these people went to new positions across the country and spread the word about the computer revolution to many universities that had not yet been involved. Professor Lehmer comments: "It was a little rough on the lot of us, because the laboratories we went to or the campuses we returned to were not supplied with the hardware we needed . . . and it took another ten years for [these] to show up at every university."

Another major application field that owes much to the pioneering support of ONR is mathematical statistics. At first, the principal feature of the ONR work was a basic research program in statistics and probability at those universities which, in the late 1940's, either had such programs or were developing them. The people who headed these university programs were acknowledged leaders in the field or some times junior people who have since assumed positions of leadership. With support from ONR, departments of mathematical statistics flourished on university campuses, and research activity in the field prospered in the United States.

Looking back, we can see that many of the research results produced in the ONR programs have been important both to science and to applications for the Department of Defense, other federal agencies, and industry. Abraham Wald's work in sequential analysis and decision theory, launched during World War II, was carried forward under ONR sponsorship; William Feller produced a notable exposition of probabilistic methods in his two-volume treatise; and a number of theoretical investigations into applied problems such as weather modification, models in medicine, design of experiments and data analysis, were carried on separately by Jerzy Neyman and S. S. Wilks. Junior colleagues and students of these early ONR investigators are now prominent statisticians; and their students, in turn, made possible the staffing of the fifty or more statistics departments that were begun after 1950.

An important part of the statistics program, which continues to this day, evolved from steps taken just prior to and at the beginning of the Korean war. About 1949, the Joint Services Program in Quality Control (now Quality Control

and Reliability) was established. Its purpose was to continue World War II work on quality control and acceptance sampling and to address new reliability problems arising in inspection and quality measurement. A number of Department of Defense Inspection Manuals developed from this research are still in use.

I have not tried to describe the extent of the ONR program in pure mathematics since the Navy's influence was felt primarily in the availability of increased research support rather than in the fields chosen for research. However, a number of very able mathematicians did participate during the fifties in summer studies on a highly classified project and generated new research interests which grew into major mathematical efforts. But on the whole, research in pure mathematics moved forward propelled by its own inner forces; and it was natural that the National Science Foundation should gradually assume the major responsibility for its support.

As I reflect on ONR's thirty years of existence, and particularly the early years when I was part of the organization, I believe there may be some lessons of value to those who are considering the future course of ONR's mathematics program. The most basic of these is the realization that the old perception of what constitutes "applied mathematics" is too limited, and that virtually all mathematics is applicable. In ONR, this was perhaps most striking in some of the work done in the early years for the National Security Agency. This basic precept justifies a policy of constant watchfulness for new developments in mathematics and access to the most productive mathematicians. Such a policy, vigorously encouraged and practiced, can do much to enhance the contributions of mathematics to national needs.

A further implication derives from the recognition that many new applications lie in fields other than the classical fields of physics and engineering. Such applications require collaboration between mathematicians and practitioners who may be less sophisticated mathematically than physicists and engineers. Environmental protection, biomedical research, and medical and public health economics abound with problems in which known methods of data treatment are inadequate. Many of these problems can benefit from skillful model building and research to obtain new mathematical results. But experience has indicated that the best hope of success in such applications lies in immersing an interested and suitably trained mathematician in the field and encouraging close collaborative work toward solutions. Results are seldom obtained quickly, and support for two or three years away from usual academic commitments is needed generally.

Such a program would give able young mathematicians an opportunity to broaden their mathematical perspectives in applications important to the national welfare and could thereby greatly enrich the country's mathematical resources. Concurrently, it could bring new program vitality to many of the nation's mathematics departments and provide ONR with a cadre of able and enthu-

siastic young mathematicians capable of addressing urgent Navy problems.

The management of a program of this type, involving applications of mathematics in new and unfamiliar fields, is a major challenge to the federal scientific officers who must monitor it. The intrinsic difficulty of collaboration across disciplinary boundaries is compounded by the problems of fitting such a program into the appropriate budget categories and pigeonholes, obtaining support money from various sources, and being responsive to the divergent interests of more than one sponsor. We know from experience that such programs sometimes do succeed, and with proper care and courage the results can be extremely worthwhile for the sponsors and the scientists alike.

part four

Sociology and Education

AS INDIVIDUALS, MATHEMATICIANS tend to be a rather drab lot. There is usu-ally little of the spectacular or bizzare in lives devoted to silent and often isolated contempla-tion of abstraction. If it were not for the relative importance of their achievements, certainly no others would pay mathematicians the slightest attention. But the creation of mathematics in an age dominated by technology is a vital activity. For this reason the world of mathe-matics has been the focus of some attention by social scientists. In truth the number of such studies is, in the ocean of sociopsychological investigations in which we all seem to float, a miniscule drop. But they are worthy of our attention nevertheless.

Another aspect of mathematics on which there has been essentially no comment to this point is the subject of mathematics education. It is no accident that the material on mathematics education has been reserved for this catchall section. While there are a few useful insights to be shared and some well-considered advice to be given, in the main mathematics education stands about where it stood during the fifth dynasty of the old Egyptian kingdom. The shrieks and bellows of our friends in the colleges of education notwithstanding, this assertion is rooted in observable fact. Go to any elementary school anywhere in the world, observe the teaching of arithmetic, and then read the surviving relevant texts from the old kingdom. The drills seem the same and the story problems sound similar. Of course, we do have rather more efficient algorithms than did the ancient Egyptians, but the general character of the processes varies not a jot. However, and this should surprise no one, the Egyptians of 5,000 years ago were in their fundamental nature essentially the same as modern Westerners. They pro-cessed, stored, and retrieved information just as we do, they found the same kinds of tasks as easy or as difficult as we do, and quite naturally, they learned mathematics in about the same way we do.

The very nature of the human nervous system suggests that the acquisition of a complex skill such as the ability to do arithmetic should be rooted in the physiology of the brain. It would be astonishing if the average acquisition time for that skill could have dramatically improved in so brief a period as five millennia. This seemingly elementary observation has not been enough, though, to deter an army of divers individuals who over the past thirty years have proposed, suggested, imposed, and, most importantly, sold a staggering variety of nostrums to improve the teaching of mathematics. There have been films and computers, charts and slides, games and plays, puppets and shows, colored rods and jelly beans with brooms, and on and on. While each of these devices has been justified by experiments con-ducted at a college of education before introduction into the market, the fact is, nevertheless, that virtually none has been universally adopted. More importantly, the ultimate test—the level of public mathematical literacy, which is currently dismal—hardly confirms that any of these palliatives is effective. It seems clear that learning mathematics is a process, like the gestation period of the great blue whale, that simply cannot be significantly altered by the rather crude technology of our age.

In mathematics education today too much emphasis is placed on using current technology; educators are trying to divert the students from the unalterable fact that learning mathematics involves work, concentration, thought, discipline, insight, and more work. Education courses overemphasize the understanding of educational methods to the exclusion of understanding the mathematics that is to be taught. While the foregoing assessment sounds rather pessimistic, we do not mean to suggest that all current research in teaching mathematics be abandoned. Since no one can be certain what future studies may find, it would be imprudent to cease all such research. However, researchers need to realize that they face a formidable task. They must be very careful in designing experiments, they need to know much more about the fundamentals of the process of learning, and most importantly, they must stop making absurdly inflated claims for very modest insights.

Finally, very little has been said of the attempts of the mathematical community to influence society. Again, this is no oversight; it is simply an issue about which there has been relatively little concern. In a nation as aggressively democratic as the United States the fate of an abstract and esoteric discipline such as mathematics would seem rather bleak. And over the major portion of our national history this was indeed the case. There was very little of mathematical importance that occurred in America until World War II linked mathematics with science. Since World War II the public support for mathematics has simply followed the ups and downs of public support for science. Only quite recently have some members of the mathematical community come to realize that the community as a whole might benefit from a modest increase in public awareness of mathematics and its contributions to society. The efforts toward gaining such recognition have been rather modest, with an impact substantially less than that of the latest light-beer campaign. But a seminal idea has been implanted in the public consciousness, and mathematicians can be quite clever. Who knows, there may be a C^{∞} manifold in America's future after all!

Sex-Related Differences in Mathematics Achievement: Where and Why

Elizabeth Fennema

Elizabeth Fennema is an associate professor of education at the University of Wisconsin at Madison. She has carried out grants for the National Science Foundation on topics of women and mathematics.

Those readers who still maintain an innocent belief in the scientist as impartial investigator, devotedly following the trail of observable facts wherever it may lead, should avoid this article; it may be hazardous to their faith. The investigator here is female and the topic of investigation is the existence (or nonexistence) of a difference in the abilities of females and males to learn mathematics. It seems clear from almost the first page that the author hopes that no difference can be demonstrated, in spite of a number of earlier studies that do seem to indicate a difference. In a circumstance such as this, the investigator has the dual task of both establishing the credibility of her results and refuting the earlier contradicting studies. This is not the easiest of circumstances in which to conduct a scientific investigation, and the reader should note how Elizabeth Fennema carries it off.

An interesting aspect of this essay emerges from Fennema's refutation of the earlier studies that seemed to contradict the new results. But the refutation may be too successful. The list of uncontrollable variables involved in any such study is formidable. The investigator deals with real children in real schools, taught by real teachers, with real constraints on time, money, children's attention, and so on. Forming uniform samples of reasonable size under such circumstances seems an almost insurmountable difficulty. This article provides more evidence, if any were needed, of how hard it is to do research in mathematics education.

MATHEMATICS EDUCATORS HAVE used sex as a variable in research concerned with mathematics achievement for a number of years, and many summaries of mathematics achievement have been published that include information about comparative learning of mathematics by women and men. Basically, all reviews published before 1974 concluded that while there might not be a sex-related difference in mathematics achievement in young children, male superiority was always evident by the time learners reached upper elementary school or junior high school. In addition, males were definitely superior on higher-level cognitive tasks: "The evidence would suggest to the teacher that boys will achieve higher than girls on tests dealing with mathematical reasoning" (Glennon and Callahan, 1968, p. 50); "from junior high school and beyond . . . boys now surpass girls in studies involving science and mathematics" (Suydam and Riedesel, 1969,

Source: Elizabeth Fennema, "Sex-Related Differences in Mathematics Achievement: Where and Why," in L. H. Fox et al., eds., *Women and the Mathematical Mystique* (Baltimore: The Johns Hopkins University Press, 1980), pp. 76–90. Reprinted by permission of The Johns Hopkins University Press.

p. 129); "sex differences in mathematical abilities are, of course, present at the kindergarten level and undoubtedly earlier" (Aiken, 1971, p. 203).

Reviews published since 1974 do not show the same consensus about male superiority. In a 1974 review synthesizing information from thirty-six studies, the conclusion was that there were no sex-related differences in elementary-school children's mathematics achievement and little evidence that such differences exist in high-school learners. However, there was some indication that boys excelled in higher-level cognitive tasks and girls excelled in lower-level cognitive tasks (Fennema, 1974). Callahan and Glennon (1975) agreed with this conclusion, while Maccoby and Jacklin, in a highly quoted review (1974), disagreed. They stated that one "sex difference that [is] fairly well established . . . is that boys excel in mathematical ability" (pp. 351–52). From these reviews it is evident that currently there is not a consensus on whether sex-related differences in mathematics achievement exist.

The question of whether there are sex-related differences in mathematics achievement is more complicated than it at first appears. While there is no doubt that many more men than women are involved in post-high-school mathematics study and in adult occupations that involve mathematics, whether this unequal representation is due to less adequate knowledge of mathematics on the part of women or to their deliberate choice not to study mathematics has been unclear. Both of these issues will be addressed here.

Sex-Related Differences in Mathematics Achievement

In order to clarify the reality of sex-related differences in mathematics achievement, four major studies of sex-related differences in mathematics achievement will be specifically noted: Project Talent, the National Longitudinal Study of Mathematical Abilities (NLSMA), the First National Assessment of Educational Progress (NAEP-I), and the Fennema-Sherman studies. In addition, some studies from other cultures will be briefly reviewed, as well as the Stanley study of mathe-

matically precocious youth and scores on college boards.

Data for Project Talent were gathered about 1960 (Flanagan et al., 1964). This study assessed (among many other things) the mathematics achievement of a random sampling of high-school students in the United States (N ≈ 440,000). The data indicated that in ninth grade, sex-related differences in mathematics achievement were negligible but that by twelfth grade boys tended to do better. The mean difference at the twelfth-grade level, although statistically significant, may have little educational significance, since one item may account for the difference. Also, no attempt was made to control the number of mathematics courses the subjects had taken previously. Higher percentages of boys than of girls were enrolled in college-preparatory courses, so males undoubtedly had taken more mathematics courses and were more apt to say they were preparing for a career in which mathematics was needed. Undoubtedly a population of boys with more mathematical background was being compared with a population of girls with less mathematical background.

In 1975, a follow-up to the 1960 Project Talent study was done. Data were collected from approximately 1,800 students in grades nine through eleven in seventeen of the original schools (Flanagan, 1976). Careful statistical checks on reliability of the comparisons, as well as adjustments for any change in the schools' socio-economic status, were made, and the following conclusions were reached (see Table 1): (1) While the mathematics test scores were fairly stable from 1960 to 1975, the differences between females and males had been reduced; (2) male scores on computation tasks had declined 17 percent, while female scores had declined 11 percent, and the female mean score was 8.2 points higher than the male mean score; (3) and quantitative-reasoning scores declined 8 percent for each sex, and female scores were 0.6 points lower in 1975. A close inspection of these data makes it difficult to conclude that the mathematics achievement of males was much higher than that of females in 1960 or 1975.

Support for the belief that females do not achieve as well as males in mathematics could

Table 1   Project Talent 1960 and 1975 Mathematics Results

	Males			Females		
	Raw Score		Tenth-grade Percentile Difference	Raw Score		Tenth-grade Percentile Difference
Skill	1960	1975		1960	1975	
Computation	25.7	18.7	− 17%	30.8	26.9	− 11%
Mathematics	10.5	10.7	+ 2	9.9	10.3	+ 3
Quantitative reasoning	8.5	7.8	− 8	8.0	7.2	− 8

Source: Abstracted from Flanagan, 1976.

come from the NLSMA data that were gathered from 1962 through 1967. In these multitudinous studies, sex was used as a control variable. Analyses were done independently by sex whenever significant interactions between sex and any other variable were found. Unfortunately, the results from these studies have been inadequately reported and interpreted, making the knowledge they could contribute to the study of sex-related differences largely unavailable. However, a summary statement says: "Differences favoring girls were for variables at the comprehension level (the lowest cognitive level tested) and the differences favoring the boys were for variables at the application and analysis level" (Wilson, 1972, p. 94). The number of mathematics courses that had been taken previously by the subjects in the NLSMA studies was controlled, so the conclusion reached undoubtedly was statistically valid in 1967. The size of the differences between the mean female performance scores and the mean male performance scores and the educational significance of that difference are unknown.

The 1972–73 mathematics data collected by the NAEP-I have received much publicity, and one statement has been widely quoted: "In the mathematics assessment, the advantage displayed by males, particularly at older ages can only be described as overwhelming" (Mullis, 1975, p. 7); inspection of these data, shown in Figure 1, confirms that males did outperform females at ages seventeen and between the ages of twenty-six and thirty-five. However, at ages nine and thirteen, differences were minimal and sometimes in favor of females. The problem of comparable populations is a concern here, as it was with the Project Talent data. The population was selected by sophisticated random-sampling techniques but without control for educational or mathematical background. Since males have traditionally studied mathematics more years than have females, once again a population of males with more background in mathematics was being compared with a population of females with less background. At ages nine and thirteen, when the educational and mathematical backgrounds of boys and girls were similar, their levels of achievement were also similar.

The Fennema-Sherman study, data for which were collected in 1975 and 1976, investigated mathematics achievement in grades six through twelve (Fennema and Sherman, 1977, 1978; Sherman and Fennema, 1977). This National Science Foundation-sponsored study investigated a variety of levels of mathematics learning, as well as cognitive and affective variables hypothesized to be related to differential mathematics achievement by females and males. The results of this study can be widely generalized because of the diverse, carefully selected sample. In grades nine through twelve (N = 1,233)—carefully controlling subjects' mathematics backgrounds—significant differences in achievement in favor of males (approximately two items) were found in two of four schools. In grades six through eight (N = 1,330), significant differences in achievement were found in favor of females in a low-cognitive-level mathematical task in one of four school areas tested. In another of the four school areas significant differences were found in favor of males in a high-cognitive-level mathematical task.

Sex differences in mathematics have also been found on the Scholastic Aptitude Test (SAT), a college-entrance examination with a verbal component and a mathematics component, usually administered to high-school seniors. According to

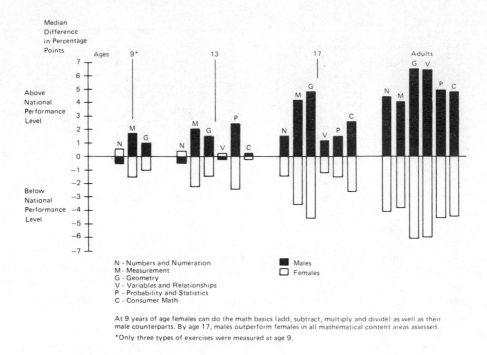

N - Numbers and Numeration
M - Measurement
G - Geometry
V - Variables and Relationships
P - Probability and Statistics
C - Consumer Math

■ Males
□ Females

At 9 years of age females can do the math basics (add, subtract, multiply and divide) as well as their male counterparts. By age 17, males outperform females in all mathematical content areas assessed.

*Only three types of exercises were measured at age 9.

Figure 1   Median-difference in performance between males and nation and females and nation on mathematics content areas.

the publishers of the test, the mathematics required is that which is taught in grades one through nine. Over a period of years women have scored lower than men on this test. However, the following trend is interesting: "In 1960, the mathematical component means were 465 for women, 520 for men. Twelve years later, the average for women was virtually unchanged, but the average for men had dropped by 14 points (to 506)" (Wirtz, 1977, p. 16). Although the advisory panel appointed to review the decline in SAT scores concluded that one reason the scores declined between 1962 and 1970 was that more women were taking the test (Wirtz, 1977), the data do not confirm that women's scores dropped.

Once again, however, conclusions about male superiority are being drawn from populations in which males and females have studied different amounts of mathematics. Even though the mathematics required for the SAT may be taught before disparity in enrollment between the sexes is evident, continued use of such mathematics in ad-

vanced high-school classes undoubtedly aids one in solving items of the type included on the SAT.

In summary, the following can be concluded about sex-related differences in mathematics learning in the United States in 1978: (1) No sex-related differences are evident—at any cognitive level, from computation to problem solving—at the elementary-school level (this conclusion has been accepted for a number of years); (2) after elementary school, differences do not always appear; (3) starting at about the seventh grade, if differences appear, they tend to be in the males' favor, particularly on tasks involving mathematical reasoning; (4) there is some evidence that sex-related differences in mathematics learning in high school may not be as great in 1978 as they were in previous years; and (5) conclusions reached about male superiority have often been gathered from old studies or from studies in which the number of mathematics courses taken was not controlled. Therefore, males with more mathematics background were being compared with females with less mathematics background. In reality, then, the comparison was not between females and males, but between students who had studied mathematics from one to three years in high school and students who had studied mathematics for two to four years in high school.

An examination of cross-cultural differences in mathematics performance is interesting. In Australia, Clements and Watanawaha report female superiority on problem-solving and computation tasks in grades five through eight, while males performed at high levels in space tasks (in Clements and Foster, 1977). However, Keeves (1973) reports male superiority in mathematics achievement within all the ten countries that participated in the First International Study of Educational Achievement.

A different perspective on sex-related differences in mathematics achievement is noted if one examines performances of highly precocious males and females. In the Stanley Study of Mathematically Precocious Youth, many males outperformed any female; for example, in the 1973 talent search, junior-high-school youths who had scored above the ninety-eighth percentile on subtests of standardized achievement tests were asked to volunteer to be tested on a college-entrance examination. Seven percent of the boys scored higher than any girl, and the boys' mean score was significantly higher than the girls' mean score (Fox, 1976). . . .

Sex-Related Differences in the Studying of Mathematics

There *are* sex-related differences in the studying of mathematics. This is indicated by females choosing not to enroll in mathematics courses in high school and by the paucity of females in university mathematics courses. . . . Undoubtedly, the most serious problem facing those concerned with equity for the sexes in mathematics education is how to ensure that females will continue their study of mathematics. In support of this statement, consider some data from Wisconsin. During the 1975–76 academic year, while approximately the same number of females and males

were enrolled in algebra, many more males were enrolled in the advanced courses (see Table 2).

Table 2   Males and Females Enrolled in Mathematics Courses in Wisconsin

Course	Males	Females
Algebra*	41,404	41,579
Geometry	20,937	20,280
Algebra II	11,581	9,947
Pre-calculus	3,234	1,917
Trigonometry	4,004	2,737
Analytic geometry	1,752	970
Probability/statistics	1,113	581
Computer mathematics	3,396	1,481
Calculus	611	262

Source: Konsin, 1977.
Note: Data obtained from Wisconsin Department of Public Information Enrollment Statistics, 1975–76.
*Students enrolled in one-year and two-year courses.

Although only symptomatic of the effect of many variables, electing not to study mathematics in high school beyond minimal or college requirements is the cause of many females' nonparticipation in mathematics-related occupations. The one variable that can be positively identified as causing sex-related differences in mathematics learning is the differential number of years females and males spend formally studying and using mathematics. Such a simplistic explanation of such an important problem seems too good to be true. However, this author believes strongly that if the amount of time spent learning mathematics were somehow equated for females and males, educationally significant sex-related differences in mathematics performance would disappear.

Contributing Factors

In order to gain an understanding of why so many males leave educational institutions knowing a great deal more mathematics than do females, selected cognitive, affective, and educational variables will be discussed.

Cognitive Variables. "Mathematics is essentially cognitive in nature; and the principle, distinguishing goals or objectives of mathematics instruction are (and should be) cognitive ones" (Weaver, 1971, p. 263). Since mathematics is a cognitive endeavor, the logical place to begin to look for explanatory variables of sex-related differences in mathematics performance is in the cognitive area. It is within this area that the most important variable can be found, that is, the amount of time spent studying mathematics. This variable, as well as its impact, has already been discussed.

Another cognitive variable that may help explain sex-related differences in mathematics performance is spatial visualization, a particular subset of spatial skills. Spatial visualization involves visual imagery of objects, movement by the objects themselves or change in their properties. In other words, objects or their properties must be manipulated in one's mind's eye—or mentally. Even though the existence of many sex-related differences is currently being challenged, the evidence is still persuasive that in the American culture male superiority on tasks that require spatial visualization is evident beginning during adolescence (Fennema, 1975; Maccoby and Jacklin, 1974). However, even this difference appears to be moderating.

The relationship between mathematics and spatial visualization can be logically demonstrated. In mathematical terms, spatial visualization requires that objects be (mentally) rotated, reflected, and/or translated. These are important ideas in geometry. In fact, James and James (1968), in defining geometry as "the science that treats of the shape and size of things . . . the study of invariant properties of given elements under specified groups of transformation" (p. 162), are describing accurately most of the conditions that are met by items on spatial-visualization tests.

Many mathematicians believe that all of mathematical thought involves geometrical ideas. According to Bronowski (1947), the total discipline of mathematics can be defined as the language for describing those aspects of the world that can be stated in terms of "configurations." Meserve (1973) believes that each person who makes extensive use of all areas of mathematics uses the modes of thought of geometry at every turn and that "even the most abstract geometrical

thinking must retain some link, however attenuated, with spatial intuition" (p. 249). In the Russian literature, mathematics and spatial abilities are regarded as inseparable (Kabanova-Meller, 1970). Therefore, if spatial-visualization items are geometrical in character and mathematical thought involves geometrical ideas, spatial visualization and mathematics are inseparably intertwined.

Not only are spatial-visualization activities similar to ideas within the structure of mathematics, but spatial representations are increasingly being included in the teaching of mathematics; for example, the Piagetian conservation tasks, which are becoming a part of many preschool programs, involve focusing on correct spatial attributes before quantity, length, and volume are conserved. Most concrete and pictorial representations of arithmetical, geometrical, and algebraic ideas appear to rely heavily on spatial attributes. The number line, which is used extensively to represent whole numbers and operations on them, is a spatial representation. Commutativity of multiplication, illustrated by turning an array ninety degrees, involves a direct spatial-visualization skill. Many other examples could be cited.

Although the relation between the content of mathematics and spatial-visualization skills appears logical, results from empirical studies that have explored the relationship are not consistent. Many factor-analytic studies have explored this relationship, and several authors have reviewed the literature. Some investigators have concluded that spatial skills and learning of mathematics definitely are not related. In 1967, Very concluded: "Research on spatial ability has failed to produce any significant correlation of [the spatial factor] with any facet of mathematics performance" (p. 172). Fruchter (1954) stated that "spatial ability is unrelated to academic performance with the possible exception of a few very specialized courses such as engineering drawing" (p. 2). Smith (1964) concluded that although "there are several studies which indicate consistently that spatial ability is important in tests which are genuinely mathematical as distinct from those which involve purely mechanical or computational processes . . . the question whether the mathematical ability is dependent on the visual factor (or factors) has not been definitely answered" (pp. 127 and 68, respectively).

Even in geometry, where one would expect to find the strongest relationship, empirical findings do not indicate clearly that the two are related. Lim concluded in 1963, after a thorough review of relevant literature, that the evidence for a relationship between geometric ability and spatial visualization was inconsistent and unreliable. Werdelin (1971) was not willing to conclude definitely that spatial-visualization ability and geometric ability were related; however, he felt that "there is strong pedagogical reason to believe in a connection between the ability to visualize and geometric ability" (p. 39).

Other authors have felt that research indicated a positive relationship. In 1951, Guilford, Green, and Christensen concluded that spatial-visualization ability helped in solving mathematics problems. French (1951, 1955) showed that successful achievement in mathematics depended to some extent on spatial-visualization skills. In a more recent review, Aiken (1973) concluded that spatial-perceptual ability was one of the "most salient" mathematical factors extracted in various investigations. Obviously, the relationship between learning in mathematics and spatial ability is not clear, and the need for more data is great.

Even less is known about the effect that differential spatial visualization has on the mathematics learning of females and males. One indication that the relationship between the learning of mathematics and spatial visualization is an important consideration is the concurrent development of sex-related differences in favor of males in mathematics achievement and spatial-visualization skills. No significant sex-related differences in either mathematics achievement or spatial-visualization skills have been consistently reported in subjects four through eight years old. Sex-related differences in performance on spatial-visualization tasks become more pronounced between upper elementary years and the last year of high school (Maccoby and Jacklin, 1974). Sex-related differences in mathematical achievement also appear during this time (Fennema, 1974). Perhaps less adequate spatial-visualization skills may partially explain sex-related differences in mathematics achievement.

The Fennema-Sherman study specifically investigated the relationship between mathematics achievement and spatial-visualization skills. The data from this study do not support the idea that differences in spatial-visualization ability are helpful in explaining sex-related differences in mathematics achievement. In this study of females and males (grades six through twelve) enrolled in mathematics courses, few sex-related differences in either mathematics achievement or spatial-visualization skills were found. The two were related ($r \simeq .5$) similarly for both sexes, and spatial-visualization ability appeared to influence both females and males equally to continue studying mathematics.

Affective Variables.   The *confidence-anxiety dimension in mathematics.* One tends to do those things that one feels confident to do and to avoid activities that arouse anxiety. This confidence-anxiety dimension, as it relates to mathematics learning, is one of the more important affective variables that helps explain sex-related differences in mathematics learning. The relationship of anxiety and mathematics learning has been explored by a variety of methodologies and with instruments purported to measure debilitative or facilitative anxiety in general and/or specific to mathematics. Callahan and Glennon (1975) concluded that "anxiety and mathematics are related," that "in general high anxiety is associated with lower achievement in mathematics" (p. 82). Reports from NLSMA indicate that between grades four and ten, facilitating anxiety decreased; females' scores decreased more than males'. Debilitating anxiety increased for females between these grade levels (Crosswhite, 1975).

Confidence per se as it relates to mathematics has not been given specific attention except in the Fennema-Sherman study. However, self-concept, which appears to be defined in many scales as self-confidence, has received much study. Leviton (1975) and Primavera et al. (1974) reviewed the literature dealing with self-concept, and both concluded that a positive relationship exists between academic achievement and self-esteem. Brookover and Thomas (1964) offer evidence that self-concept is not generalizable but is related to specific academic areas. Callahan and Glennon (1975) concluded that there is a positive relationship between self-esteem and achievement in mathematics. Others have also recognized the importance of academic self-concept in learning mathematics (Bachman, 1970; Fink, 1969).

Although confidence and anxiety have been defined as separate traits, it appears that in relation to mathematics, they are very similar. In the Fennema-Sherman study an attempt was made to measure both confidence and anxiety. A high rating on the confidence scale correlated highly ($r = .89$) with a low rating on the anxiety scale. While it may be possible to talk about the two independently, it doesn't appear to be useful.

The literature strongly supports the belief that there are sex-related differences in the confidence-anxiety dimension. It appears reasonable to believe that lesser confidence, or greater anxiety, on the part of females is an important variable that helps explain sex-related differences in mathematics course-taking. Crandall et al. (1962) concluded that girls underestimate their own ability to solve mathematical problems. Others have concluded that females feel inadequate when faced with a variety of intellectual, problem-solving activities (Kagan, 1964). Maccoby and Jacklin (1973) reported that "girls tend to underestimate their own intellectual abilities more than boys do" (p. 41).

In the Fennema-Sherman study, at each grade level from grade six through grade 12, boys were significantly more confident in their ability to deal with mathematics than were girls. In most instances this was true when there were no significant sex-related differences in mathematics achievement. In addition, confidence in learning mathematics was more highly correlated with mathematics achievement than was any other affective variable ($r \simeq .40$). Confidence was almost as highly related to achievement as were verbal ability and spatial visualization.

Stereotyping mathematics as a male domain. It is commonly accepted that mathematics is stereotyped as an activity more appropriate for males than for females. It has been believed that the sex typing of mathematics as male began in elementary school, became stronger during adolescent years, and was solidly entrenched by adult years.

However, Stein (1971) and Stein and Smithells (1969) provide evidence that mathematics is not considered masculine by females and males until adolescent years, and even during these years it is not ranked as highly masculine as are spatial, mechanical, and athletic tasks. Bobbe (1971) found that among fourth- and sixth-grade subjects, arithmetic was judged to be feminine by girls, while boys judged it to be appropriate for both sexes. Among adults, it is a fact that the use and creation of mathematics is predominantly a male domain. Stein and Smithells (1969) offered evidence that in the twelfth grade, females perceived this fact and were responding to the reality.

The Fennema-Sherman study indicated that females in grades six through twelve deny that mathematics is a male domain. While the males in the study did not strongly stereotype mathematics as a male domain, at each grade they stereotyped it at significantly higher levels than did females. This is an interesting and highly significant finding. The cross-sex influence on all aspects of behavior is strong during adolescent years. Since males stereotype mathematics as a male domain, they undoubtedly communicate this belief in many subtle and not so subtle ways to females, which influences females' willingness to study mathematics. This has strong implications for the development of intervention programs designed to increase female participation in mathematics.

Usefulness of mathematics. A different kind of affective variable is belief in the personal usefulness of mathematics. Hilton and Berglund (1974) and the Fennema-Sherman study provided data indicating that females believe that mathematics is personally useful to a lesser degree than do males. The difference was not as great, however, in the Fennema-Sherman study as it was in the Hilton-Berglund study. This may indicate that the beliefs of females are becoming more similar to those of males in this respect.

Effectance motivation in mathematics. One variable that has been hypothesized to show a sex-related difference is effectance motivation. This motive can be "inferred specifically from behavior that shows a lasting formalization and that has characteristics of exploration and experimentation" (White, 1959, p. 323). It is closely related to problem-solving activity and is often called intrinsic motivation. This motivation would encourage learners to participate in mathematics activities at high cognitive levels. Some believe that females are not so involved in problem-solving activities as are males (Carey, 1958; Kagan, 1964); however, the Fennema-Sherman study found no sex-related difference in this variable at any grade level from grade six through twelve. It appears that the belief that females are not as intrinsically motivated in mathematics as males is merely a myth.

Educational Variables.   There are sex-related differences in the final outcome of mathematical education due in large part to females' reluctance—if not refusal—to elect to study mathematics. Some intervention is essential at the present time to ensure equity in mathematics education for both sexes; however, before effective intervention can be planned, more information is needed about critical school variables that are amenable to change and important in the educational process.

Teachers. Teachers are the most important educational influence on students' learning of mathematics. From kindergarten to high school, learners spend thousands of hours in direct contact with teachers. While other educational agents may have influence on educational decisions, it is the daily contact with teachers that is the main influence of the formal educational institution. Part of the teachers' influence is in the learners' development of sex-role standards. These sex-role standards include definitions of acceptable achievement in the various subject areas. It is believed that this influence by teachers is exerted through their differential treatment of the sexes as well as through their expectation of sex-related differences in achievement.

Many studies have indicated that teachers treat female and male students differently (Schonborn, 1975). In general, males appear to be more salient in the teachers' frame of reference. Teachers' interaction with males is greater than their interaction with females in both blame and praise contacts. Teachers also reinforce in both females and males sexually stereotypic behavior (Sears and Feldman, 1966). Brophy, Good, and their colleagues—whose main interest has been teachers' treatment of males—have been the major investigators of teachers' treatment of females and males. In several studies they have concluded that girls and boys receive equal treatment. The data from one of their major studies, however, show that while the sex of the teacher was unimportant, high-achieving high-school boys received significantly more attention in mathematics class than any other group (Good, Sikes, and Brophy, 1973). Another study involving first-grade reading replicated this trend at nonsignificant levels (Good and Brophy, 1971). They concluded from these studies that teacher bias was not evident. One must question why no conclusion was reached about inequitable treatment of high-achieving females.

The investigation of the relationship between teacher behavior and sex-related differences in mathematics appears to be crucial to understanding why females do not participate in higher-level mathematics. In particular, information in the following areas would be helpful: (1) What are the effects of differential teacher treatment and expectations on achievement in and election of mathematics courses? (2) Do teachers differentially reinforce males and females for specific kinds of mathematical and/or sexually stereotypic activities? Are males being reinforced more for problem-solving activities, while females are reinforced for computational activities? (3) What is the effect of sex of teacher on mathematical achievement of boys and girls? While O'Brien (1975) reports no sex-of-teacher effect, Good, Sikes, and Brophy (1973) and Shinedling and Pederson (1970) report that male students do best in quantitative scores when taught by male teachers.

School organization. There is some evidence, and much belief, that schools do influence sexual stereotypes. Minuchin (1971) concluded that children who attended schools categorized as traditional differed in their sex-typed reactions from those who attended schools categorized as modern. The interaction of the sexes was different in those schools, also. In the most traditional school, boys became leaders in problem solving, while girls became followers. This was not so in the less traditional schools. The sex-role behavior of children attending traditional schools was more rigid than that of children attending liberal schools.

Some schools are remarkably more effective in persuading females to attempt high achievement in mathematics. Casserly identified thirteen high schools that had an unusually high percentage of females in advanced-placement mathematics and science classes. The schools had identified these girls as early as fourth grade, and the girls' teachers and peers were supportive of high achievement by females. . . . Rowell (1971) pursued the same type of investigation in attempting to identify schools and school characteristics that produced females with high achievement in science. Studies identifying and describing schools that are particularly successful in encouraging females to enroll in mathematics beyond minimal requirements are needed.

Many people are advocating that female-only classes will result in equity in mathematics education. The argument for this type of school organization goes something like this: Because peer pressure against female competitiveness is too strong a force, females will not compete against males in mixed-sex classrooms; female leadership (in problem solving, in this case) is only able to emerge when competition with males is eliminated; teachers will not have different sex-related expectations and behaviors if only one sex is present. Single-sex classrooms appear to provide a simple solution to a complex problem. However, the weight of evidence found does not support this type of grouping. Conway (1973) convincingly argues that throughout history separate education for the sexes has resulted in inferior education for females. Keeves (1973), after a careful and thorough review of mathematics and science education in ten countries, concluded that the "extent to which a community provides for education in single-sex schools would appear to indicate the extent to which it sees its boys and girls requiring different preparation for different societal roles" (p. 62). He argues that "in so far as a community has different expectations for different groups of its members and proceeds to mold its future members through different organizations, then it fails to provide equal opportunities for individual development" (p. 52).

Before single-sex classrooms are embraced as a panacea for educational equity for females, there must be careful examination concerning long-term effectiveness of such programs. In reality, this may be a partially nonresearchable problem. No one can foresee the implications for females fifty years from now of being isolated in their mathematical training. Because of what has happened to females as well as blacks over the last century, single-sex classrooms must be approached with caution.

Conclusions

What, then, is known about sex-related differences in mathematics and factors related to such differences? Certainly, when both females and males study the same amount of mathematics, differences in learning mathematics are minimal and perhaps decreasing. Far fewer females elect to study mathematics, and therein lies the problem. Factors that appear to contribute to this nonelection are females' lesser confidence in learning mathematics and a belief that mathematics is not useful to them and males' belief that mathematics is a male domain.

There is nothing inherent in females that keeps them from learning mathematics at the same level as do males (Sherman, 1976). Intervention programs that will increase females' participation in mathematics can and must be designed and implemented within schools. Such programs must include male students, female students, and their teachers. Only when such intervention programs become effective can true equity in mathematics education be accomplished.

References

1. Aiken, L. R. 1971. Intellective variables and mathematics achievement: Directions for research. *Journal of School Psychology* 9: 201–9.

2. ———. 1973. Ability and creativity in math. *Review of Educational Research* 43: 405–32.

3. Bachman, A. M. 1970. The relationship between seventh-grade pupils' academic self-concept and achievement in mathematics. *Journal for Research in Mathematics Education* 1: 173–79.

4. Bobbe, C. N. 1971. Sex-role preference and academic achievement, Ph.D. diss., Yeshiva University.

5. Brookover, W. B., and Thomas, S. 1964. Self-concept of ability and school achievement. *Sociology of Education* 37 (3): 271–79.

6. Bronowski, J. 1947. Mathematics. In *The quality of education,* ed. D. Thompson and J. Reeves, pp. 179–95. London: Muller.

7. Callahan, L. G., and Glennon, V. J. 1975. *Elementary school mathematics: A guide to current research.* Washington, D.C.: Association for Supervision and Curriculum Development.

8. Carey, G. L. 1958. Sex differences in problem-solving performance as a function of attitude differences. *Journal of Abnormal and Social Psychology* 56: 256–60.

9. Clements, M. A., and Foster, J., eds. 1977. *Research in mathematics education in Australia.* Vol. 2.

10. Conway, J. K. 1973. Perspectives on the history of women's education in the United States. Paper presented at the annual meeting of the American Educational Research Association, New Orleans, 1973.

11. Crandall, V. J.; Katkovsky, W.; and Preston, A. 1962. Motivational and ability determinants of young children's intellectual achievement behaviors. *Child Development* 33: 643–61.

12. Crosswhite, F. J. 1975. Correlates of attitudes toward mathematics. National Longitudinal Study of Mathematics Achievement, report no. 20. Abstracted by L. R. Aiken. *Investigations in Mathematics Education* 8 (3): 38–40.

13. Fennema, E. 1974. Mathematics learning and the sexes: A review. *Journal for Research in Mathematics Education* 5: 126–39.

14. ———. 1975. Spatial ability, mathematics, and the sexes. In *Mathematics learning: What research says about sex differences,* ed. E. Fennema, pp. 33–44. Columbus, Ohio: Educational Research Information Center, Center for Science, Mathematics, and Environmental education, College of Education, Ohio State University.

15. Fennema, E., and Sherman, J. A. 1977. Sex-related differences in mathematics achievement, spatial visualization and affective factors. *American Educational Research Journal* 14 (1): 51–71.

16. ———. 1978. Sex-related differences in mathematics achievement and related factors: A further study. *Journal for Research in Mathematics Education* 9 (3): 189–203.

17. Fink, M. B. 1969. Self-concept as it relates to academic underachievement. *California Journal of Educational Research* 13: 57–61.

18. Flanagan, J. C. 1976. Changes in school levels of achievement: Project TALENT ten- and fifteen-year retests. *Educational Researcher* 5 (8): 9–12.

19. ———, et al. 1964. *The American high-school student.* Pittsburgh: University of Pittsburgh Press.

20. Fox, L. H. 1976. Sex differences in mathematical precocity: Bridging the gap. In *Intellectual talent: Research and development,* ed. D. P. Keating, pp. 183–214. Baltimore: The Johns Hopkins University Press.

21. French, J. W. 1951. The West Point tryout of the guidance battery. Research bulletin 51-12. Princeton: Educational Testing Service.

22. ———. 1955. The West Point tryout of the guidance battery, part 2. Research bulletin 55-6. Princeton: Educational Testing Service.

23. Fruchter, B. 1954. Measurement of spatial abilities: History and background. *Educational and Psychological Measurement* 14: 387–95.

24. Glennon, V. J., and Callahan, L. G. 1968. *A guide to current research: Elementary school mathematics.* Washington, D. C.: Association for Supervision and Curriculum Development.

25. Good, T. L., and Brophy, J. E. 1971. Questioned equality for grade one boys and girls. *Reading Teacher* 25: 247–52.

26. Good, T. L.; Sikes; J. N.; and Brophy, J. E. 1973. Effects of teacher sex and student sex

on classroom interaction. *Journal of Educational Psychology* 65: 74–87.

27. Guilford, J. P.; Green, R. F.; and Christensen, P. R. 1951. A factor analytic study of reasoning abilities. II. Administration of tests and analysis of results. Report no. 3. University of Southern California Psychology Laboratory.

28. Hilton, T. L., and Berglund, G. W. 1974. Sex differences in mathematics achievement: A longitudinal study. *Journal of Education Research* 67: 231–37.

29. James, G., and James, R. C. 1968. *Mathematics Dictionary*. 3d ed. Princeton: Van Nostrand.

30. Kabanova-Meller, E. N. 1970. The role of the diagram in the application of geometric theorems. In *Soviet studies in the psychology of learning and teaching mathematics*, ed J. Kilpatrick and I. Wirszup, trans. M. Ackerman, pp. 7–50, vol. 4. Stanford: School Mathematics Study Group, Stanford University.

31. Kagan, J. 1964. Acquisition and significance of sex typing and sex role identity. In *Review of child development research*, ed. M. L. Hoffman and L. Hoffman. pp. 137–67. New York: Russell Sage Foundation.

32. Keeves, J. P. 1973. Differences between the sexes in mathematics and science courses. *International Review of Education* 19: 47–63.

33. Konsin, M. A. 1977. Enrollment in Wisconsin high school mathematics classes, by sex, during 1975–76. Mimeographed. Madison: University of Wisconsin-Madison.

34. Leviton, H. 1975. The implications of the relationship between self-concept and academic achievement. *Child Study Journal* 5: 25–36.

35. Lim, H. 1963. Geometry and the space factors. Stanford: School Mathematics Study Group, Stanford University.

36. Maccoby, E. E., and Jacklin, C. N. 1973. Sex differences in intellectual functioning. In *Assessment in a pluralistic society: Proceedings of the 1972 Invitational Conference on Testing Problems*, pp. 37–51. Princeton: Educational Testing Service.

37. ———. 1974. *The psychology of sex differences*. Stanford: Stanford University Press.

38. Meserve, B. E. 1973. Geometry as a gateway to mathematics. In *Developments in mathematical education*, ed. A. G. Howson, pp. 241–53. Cambridge: Cambridge University Press.

39. Minuchin, P. P. 1971. Sex-role concepts and sex typing in childhood as a function of school and home environments. In *Social development and personality*, ed. G. C. Thompson, pp. 371–87. New York: John Wiley & Sons.

40. Mullis, I.V.S. 1975. *Educational achievement and sex discrimination*. Denver: National Assessment of Educational Progress.

41. O'Brien, C. W. 1975. Pupil achievement, attendance, and attitudes, and the relationship between teacher perception, teacher sex, and pupil sex. Ph.D. diss., University of Michigan.

42. Primavera, L. H.; Simon, W. E.; and Primavera, A. M. 1974. The relationship between self-esteem and academic achievement: an investigation of sex differences. *Psychology in the Schools* 11: 213–16.

43. Rowell, J. A. 1971. Sex differences in achievement in science and the expectations of teachers. *Australian Journal of Education* 15: 16–29.

44. Schonborn, B. G. 1975. *An investigation of the attitudes of elementary school teachers toward sex-role behaviors of elementary school children*. Ph.D. diss., University of Illinois.

45. Sears, P. S., and Feldman, D. H. 1966. Teacher interactions with boys and girls. *National Elementary Principal* 46 (2): 45–48.

46. Sherman, J. A. 1967. Problem of sex differences in space perception and aspect of intellectual functioning. *Psychological Review* 74: 290–99.

47. Sherman, J. A., and Fennema, E. 1977. The study of mathematics among high school girls and boys: Related factors. *American Educational Research Journal* 14 (2): 159–68.

48. Shinedling, M., and Pederson, D. M. 1970. Effects of sex of teacher and student on children's gain in quantitative and verbal performance. *Journal of Psychology* 76: 79–84.

49. Smith, I. M. 1964. *Spatial ability*. San Diego: Knapp.

50. Stein, A. H. 1971. The effects of sex role standards for achievement and sex role preference on three determinants of achievement motivation. *Developmental Psychology* 4: 219–31.

51. Stein, A. H. and Smithells, J. 1969. Age and sex differences in children's sex role standards about achievement. *Developmental Psychology* 1: 252–59.

52. Suydam, M. N., and Riedesel, C. A. 1969. *Interpretive study of research and development in elementary school mathematics, vol. I. Introduction and summary: What research says.* U.S. Department of Health, Education and Welfare final report, project no. 8-0586.

53. Very, P. S. 1967. Differential factor structures in mathematical ability. *Genetic Psychology Monographs* 75: 169–207.

54. Weaver, J. F. 1971. Seductive shibboleths. *Arithmetic Teacher* 18: 263–64.

55. Werdelin, I. 1971. *The geometrical ability and space factor in boys and girls.* Lund, Sweden: University of Lund.

56. White, R. W. 1959. Motivation reconsidered: The concept of motivation. *Psychological Review* 66: 297–333.

57. Wilson, J. W. 1972. *Patterns of mathematics achievement in grade 11: Z population.* National Longitudinal Study of Mathematical Abilities, no. 17. Stanford: Stanford University Press.

58. Wirtz, W. 1977. *On further examination: Report of the advisory panel on the Scholastic Aptitude Test score decline.* New York: College Entrance Examination Board.

Rigor Versus Intuition in Mathematics

John G. Kemeny

John George Kemeny, born in Budapest, Hungary, received his doctorate from Princeton in 1949. He was chairman of the department of mathematics at Dartmouth from 1955 until 1967. He has been president of Dartmouth since 1970. Kemeny has received numerous honorary doctorates from all over the world for his efforts in mathematics education.

John Kemeny is currently president of Dartmouth College. At the time that this article was written he was head of the mathematics department of that institution. He has achieved a national reputation in mathematics for his achievements in making the mathematics curriculum of Dartmouth relevant without loss of substance. In this essay he suggests that developing the proper kind of mathematical intuition in students is essential to their enjoyment of the subject. The context of this discussion is the explosion of the "new" mathematics curriculum in the 1960s.

The initial idea behind the new mathematics was to present students with a modern and developmental approach to the subject. The result was a generation of mathematical illiterates unable to do the rote arithmetic of their parents and bored and confused by the "new" orthodoxy. The reasons for this disaster were many but prominent was the fact that the teachers did not understand the "new" approach any better than the students. Indeed, since most teachers were and are now trained in colleges of education, they learned their "new" mathematics not from mathematicians but from educators. The professors of education were convinced that the new methodology would be better just as soon as they learned the new mathematics themselves. The professors never did. Kemeny's address was directed to teachers of mathematics and teachers of teachers of mathematics. He gently chides the education establishment for what were the increasingly apparent failures of the new system and suggests how a proper development of mathematics can make a difference.

I THOUGHT THAT I might make some informal remarks this evening about the role of rigor and the role of intuition in both mathematical research and in the teaching of mathematics. The best way to contrast these two very important trends is by a story told about one of our leading graduate schools. There was an advanced seminar in topology in which the lecturer devoted the entire hour to writing out a proof with complete rigor. After having filled all the blackboards, he had everyone in the room completely lost, including one of his own colleagues, who jumped up and said, "Look, I just don't understand this proof at all. I tried to follow you, but I got lost somewhere. I just didn't get it at all." The lecturer stopped for a moment, looked at him, and said, "Oh, didn't you see it? You see, it's just that the two spaces connect like this," intertwining his

Source: John G. Kemeny, "Rigor Versus Intuition in Mathematics," *The Mathematics Teacher* (Feb. 1961): 66–74. Banquet address, National Council of Teachers of Mathematics, Salt Lake City, August 23, 1960.

two arms in a picturesque fashion. And then his colleague exclaimed, "Oh, now I get the whole proof."

There is something in this story that is typical of a great deal of mathematical research. You can write down long formulas to make a proof complete and rigorous. Indeed, you *have* to write down long formulas and justify every step. Yet very often there is one key idea which, once understood, makes the rest of it purely routine. And if this one idea is not understood, the whole proof is meaningless to the student or to the research worker.

My basic theme this evening is that I am somewhat worried that amongst all the very fine reforms that are being suggested, tried out, and patiently worked out on the high school level, there may have come an overemphasis on rigor and a playing down of intuition in mathematics. This evening I am going to try to plug for continued emphasis on the role of intuition in the teaching of mathematics.

If you look at the problem historically, you will find that rigor always enters mathematics quite late. Euclidean geometry is identified as one of the high points in mathematical rigor. Yet Euclid is full of holes from any modern standpoint. A great deal of publicity has been given to this, and I won't dwell on it. Let us take only one small point. It is impossible to prove from Euclid's axioms that a circle has an inside and an outside. Of course, it is quite important to know that a circle has an inside and an outside; however, since this proof requires a considerable effort in an advanced graduate course in mathematics, it was perhaps fortunate that Euclid didn't realize that he couldn't prove this. In the last analysis he knew very well that a circle does have an inside and does have an outside. This does not mean that the Jordan Curve Theorem is not of importance to modern mathematics. It is tremendously important, but the fact that this major hole exists in Euclidean geometry does not destroy the value of Euclid's work.

Let me jump over several centuries to Newton's work on the calculus. If any of our freshman students in calculus should perform in the sloppy, unjustifiable way in which Newton did the calculus, we would surely refuse to pass him. Never-

theless, I would like to maintain that Newton's work was, in the long run, quite valuable.

I come to one of the greatest names in the history of mathematics, that of Euler. Euler was quite capable of doing rigorous mathematics, but occasionally he did hair-raising things. His manipulation of some infinite series, for example, was completely unjustifiable. As a matter of fact, it took the next two hundred years of mathematical progress to find out that practically everything that Euler did could be justified, though there was no real reason why Euler should have suspected this. Euler was just "plain lucky"— with dozens of major ideas, almost every one of which turned out to be right. His remarkable mathematical intuition has never been equaled.

The following story is told about a very famous modern mathematician, one of the co-founders of a great branch of mathematics. He had published a certain paper in which he mentioned a theorem without proof, and a Russian mathematician wrote to him, asking whether it would be possible to receive a proof. Our distinguished mathematician answered the Russian request. After about a month or so he had a reply. The Russian mathematician thanked him profusely; however, he had to point out that the proof sent was for a completely different theorem and that the proof was incorrect. As a matter of fact, this particular mathematician is credited with many incorrect proofs, and yet there isn't a single creative mathematician who would not list him as one of the greatest mathematicians of the century.

After this very elaborate historical introduction, I want to ask you a simple question. If it is possible for Euclid, for Newton, for Euler, and for many contemporary mathematicians to go down in history as among the great, even though they were far from completely rigorous, don't you think that the same sin might be forgivable on the part of high school students?

Let me be more specific. Let us talk a little about definitions. Everybody knows that one has to be very rigorous in definitions. There has been a strong trend in recent years to make modern concepts—like that of a function—exceedingly rigorous. I was particularly pleased that in this trend, set theory has played a major role. It so happens that I wrote my Ph.D. thesis on set theory, and therefore I am exceedingly fond of it. Perhaps I may perform a public service by seeing to it that, as long as we define functions in terms of sets, we make sure that the definition is really rigorous.

You all know that a function, when correctly defined, is a set of ordered pairs. Of course, people don't quite take the trouble to distinguish between an ordered pair and an unordered pair. There happens to be a very nice way of doing this. It is the standard method in set theory: to get an ordered pair in set theory (which deals with unordered sets), you just define an ordered pair as a set having two sets as elements. For example, if you want the ordered pair $\langle A, B \rangle$, one of the elements is the pair $\{A, B\}$ and the other element is a set whose only element is A. Now you can identify which is which, because A belongs to both of these and B only to one of them. Then you've got something that will serve as an ordered pair.

The mathematical logician would then define a function as follows: "A function is a set of sets of sets, such that each element is a two-element set consisting of a one-element set and a two-element set, and the one-element set is a subset of the two-element set. Furthermore, for each object whose unit set is an element of an element of the function, there is at most one other object which is an element of one of the elements of the elements of the function to which the given object belongs." I am delighted that this kind of highly enlightening and intuitive material has finally reached the high school level. We couldn't dream of teaching it to undergraduates in college, but I am delighted to see that you are teaching this material in high school.

My point obviously is that there *must* be a more intuitive way of defining a function. This is a particularly amusing example to a logician who happens to know the history of this particular subject. Around the turn of the century, for the first time, mathematicians interested in the foundations of mathematics developed two fundamentally different approaches to the foundations of mathematics. In one of them, pioneered by Zermelo, the basic idea was that of *set*. In the other, pioneered by Russell and Whitehead, the basic idea was that of *function*. Of course, both of these

concepts are fundamental to mathematics and, therefore, in the theory of types, in which function is the basic idea, they had to introduce sets by some sort of trick. The other basic approach—of set theory—had to introduce functions by a trick. It happened to be a rather complicated trick, but was useful, nevertheless. And therefore, if you insist on making sets fundamental, you have to do something very complicated to define functions. It never occurred to mathematical logicians that anyone would ever use this as the basic definition of a function in an elementary course. Somehow, half of this history has been made public; which shows that certain branches of mathematics ought, perhaps, to be classified.

The impression has been created that the *only* way to define a function is in terms of sets. I'll put it to you that research mathematicians never think of a function in this particular manner. They may differ in ways of looking at it—there are three or four different ways—but they have certain similarities, and they are highly intuitive. A function is a mapping, an assignment where you have certain objects in one set, and to each object you assign some specific object, usually from a different set. Now this is a very simple idea, and of a type met in everyday life. Examples familiar to all students can be given.

For example, every human being has a father and a mother. Well, *father* and *mother* are perfectly good functions, defined over the set of human beings, where to each human being "father of" assigns a specific male human being and "mother of" determines a specific female human being. One can illustrate a great many basic ideas connected with functions in terms of simple examples of this sort.

Let me take one of the ideas that has caused most trouble in the study of functions, namely that of the idea of a composite function, where one function is applied to another function. A student may have trouble at first recognizing as a composite function something like $(3x + 2)^4$, but in everyday life it is not terribly hard to explain to him what a maternal grandfather is—father of your mother—and this is a typical composite function.

Actually these simple everyday examples have great pedagogical advantages, because the usual examples of numerical functions are too special for the use of the research mathematician. In advanced mathematics courses you rarely deal with something as simple as a numerical function, and family relations illustrate the general nature of a function much better than do the ordinary numerical functions.

Let us next discuss the simultaneous solution of linear equations (like $3x + 4y = 5$). There is a very elaborate theory in advanced mathematics, known as linear algebra, which has relevance to some of the material being suggested for high school curricula. But if we attempted a complete, rigorous treatment of everything one ought to know about such equations, it would ruin high school algebra, and I don't believe that anyone has ever suggested this.

But what is commonly taught about these equations? It is usually taught as a bag of tricks and techniques which have two serious limitations. One limitation is that these tricks only work in special situations. For example, one of the favorite methods of solving equations—by means of determinants—works only if you happen to have the same number of equations as unknowns and where the key determinant is not zero. So for the advanced mathematician, the solution of an equation by determinants is very rarely of value. (Also, the method as usually taught happens to work only for 3×3 determinants.) The second serious objection is that the methods usually taught for solving simultaneous equations are highly dated and have long lost their practical importance. In the age of computing machines, we must rethink what is a practical way of solving equations and what is an impractical way.

On the related topic of finding roots of an algebraic equation, we had a debate once at Dartmouth about how useful Horner's Method is. I offered to put this to a test. A colleague of mine and I each had a desk computer and a fifth-degree equation for which we had to find a root to five decimal places. He was going to use Horner's Method and I was using successive approximations, i.e., organized common sense. I am sorry to say that this particular test of the practicability of Horner's Method turned out to be quite inconclusive because, unfortunately, I had the root to five decimal places before my colleague remem-

bered Horner's Method. Which was a great pity, because it was the first (and presumably last) time in his career as a professional mathematician that he ever had the least excuse for using Horner's Method.

Let me come back to linear equations. What are some of the key ideas? I think there are two key ideas that one should understand about linear equations, and they do not require tremendous rigor, only a feeling for the subject matter and a degree of understanding. First, one must know what it means to solve simultaneous linear equations, and more generally, what it means to solve equations. A great deal of worthwhile work has been done and various different approaches to this have been suggested. Students should understand that solving an equation will mean finding a certain set of numbers about which a particular assertion is true—about which the equation holds. And solving simultaneous equations means finding a set of numbers about which several assertions hold, in other words, numbers which have all these special properties; in short, finding the intersection of several sets.

Secondly, it is important to connect this idea of a set of solutions with geometry, for one's geometric intuition is usually stronger than one's numerical intuition. For example, if you plot the solution of an equation in two unknowns in the plane, it comes out to be a straight line. If we plot a second equation, it is also represented by a straight line; and to ask for numbers (or rather number pairs) which satisfy both of these equations will obviously be asking for the point or points that the two lines have in common; it is the intersection of the two lines. It is very interesting that when you formulate the same thing set-theoretically, there too the word "intersection" occurs.

Let us illustrate in three dimensions the major theorem that all students should know about simultaneous equations. *One of three things must happen: you may have no solutions; you may have a unique solution; or you may have infinitely many solutions.* This is by far the most important fact known about simultaneous linear equations. There are no solutions, one solution, or infinitely many.

If you think of it geometrically, this fact is obvious. In three dimensions each equation represents a plane. Let us begin with two of them, and let us suppose that they intersect in a line L. Now we ask what happens if we add an additional plane. If we have bad luck, the new plane may be parallel to the line L, and we will have no solution. Normally the new plane will cut L in one and only one point, and we have a unique solution. Or it may happen that the third plane passes through L. In that case we will have infinitely many solutions. This is the most general possible situation for simultaneous linear equations.

It is also easy to see that what happens is not determined by the number of different equations or the number of different unknowns. You could have just two equations in three unknowns and have no solution, because the two planes may be parallel. You may have a hundred different equations in three unknowns and they may still have a unique solution if, by chance, they all go through the same point. And you may have a hundred different equations in three unknowns and you may have infinitely many solutions. Just think of a number of planes, at different angles, all going through a given line.

This simple fact, that I explained here in about five minutes, can be explained to students in one class period. And yet, it is the fundamental fact about solving simultaneous linear equations. It is obvious, *if you teach it intuitively*.

I feel very strongly that, although a degree of rigor is important in teaching because a student should be able to understand what a proof is, it is vastly more important to emphasize basic ideas and to build up the intuition possessed by the student.

Of course, we do not know what constitutes intuition. Even what is intuitively obvious can be a matter of great controversy. You know that the mathematician's favorite word is "trivial," which is a shorthand way of saying "intuitively obvious." There are endless stories about the word "trivial." My favorite is the one about the mathematician who, in a lecture, asserted that a result is trivial. One of his colleagues challenged him, and they got into a long argument which was still going on at the end of the class. The class tiptoed out, and the two mathematicians were seen arguing vehemently for over two hours. When they

finally showed up outside, students eagerly queried the challenger about the outcome. He replied: "Oh, he was right. It *is* trivial."

While I maintain that *rigor* is not a necessity in much high school mathematics teaching, I feel quite differently about *abstraction*, which has been tied to it (somewhat accidentally) in many developments. Mathematics by its very nature is abstract. It is the power of abstraction that enables mankind to rise above lower animals. The power to abstract should be developed in students as early as possible.

There has been a feeling that the only way to teach abstraction is to take an abstract axiom system and develop it in detail. This is a worthwhile undertaking; I am not criticizing it. But this is not the only way to develop a feeling for abstraction.

Abstraction should start from simple, concrete examples. An idea can be abstract and still be highly intuitive. For example, a measure space is a very important abstract concept. It is an advanced idea, but it can be explained in the simplest possible terms. (I personally like to do it in terms of probabilities, though it can be done in other ways.)

Just take a collection of objects, say a set of five objects, and assign a weight to each one. Think of each subset as being weighed, literally, by putting all the weights in the subset on scales. This can be used to introduce the basic idea of a measure space. If the weights are all positive and happen to add up to one, you have begun to do probability theory. If the weights don't necessarily add up to one, you may be measuring areas; and if we allow negative weights, then you are doing generalized measure theory—which you are not supposed to be doing until graduate school. It is a natural generalization then to go over to an abstract approach to the idea of area, and a student can see that some of the basic rules governing area govern much wider ranges of mathematical and applied disciplines. Indeed, eventually these same rules are going to apply to all kinds of integrals found in geometry, in physics, in applications, and in several advanced branches of mathematics.

A second important role of abstraction is to connect unrelated ideas. If you have a large number of unrelated ideas, you have to get quite a distance away from them to be able to get a view of all of them, and this is the role of abstraction. If you look at each one too closely, you see too many details. You have to go far away to see what they have in common. And it is by no means true that if you get far away things are going to become less clear. They may appear simpler, because you can only see the large, broad outlines; you do not get lost in petty details. This has been the secret of a great deal of modern mathematics.

Let me take up two unorthodox examples, one from algebra and one from geometry. In algebra, let us select the idea of an *isomorphism*, which is central in modern algebra. Two structures which are alike are said to be isomorphic. More precisely, you've got two sets and you do something with each of them. If you can match up the objects in the two sets in such a way that whenever you do something in one, exactly the same thing happens to corresponding elements in the other set, then one speaks of an isomorphism. This concept is useful because it is so general.

Let us apply it to something that is well known to you; let us apply it to real numbers and to the operations of multiplication and addition. Take two sets: one consists of the positive real numbers, and the other collection has all the real numbers in it. I'm going to concentrate on one type of operation for each of them. In the first set it will be multiplication; in the second set it will be addition. Let us ask whether we can establish an isomorphism. Is it possible to match up the positive real numbers with all the real numbers in such a way that every time you multiply two positive numbers, and you add the corresponding real numbers, the results will correspond? The answer is "yes," even if we require a "continuous" matching.

As a matter of fact, if you try doing this, you quickly convince yourself that you have a certain amount of freedom. If I use the letter f to stand for the correspondence, and I take the positive real number one, we first find that what will correspond to it will be zero (because if you think of your basic laws of multiplication, one plays exactly the same role for multiplication as zero plays for addition), i.e., $f(1) = 0$. If you try raising positive numbers to powers, you will quickly find that this operation corresponds to multiplication,

i.e., $f(x^y) = y \cdot f(x)$. After all, raising to powers is essentially repeated multiplication, and hence should correspond to repeated addition, which is multiplication. This formula almost gives us our complete matching, namely, all we have to do is to find a number b, such that $f(b) = 1$. The moment you have found that number, b^y will correspond to $y \cdot f(b)$, which is y, and then you have found the whole secret of how to match the two sets. What you have, of course, are logarithms to the base b.

The amount of choice you have is the freedom of choosing a base for logarithms. You quickly find that your base can be anything except one, and therefore you will have as many different isomorphisms here as you can choose bases for logarithms—any positive real number other than one.

If you look at the same mapping in the opposite direction, you have exponential functions. This is one of many useful ways of looking at logarithms and exponentials; what they really do is establish an isomorphism, a complete structural matching-up, of the positive real numbers under multiplication with real numbers under addition.

I am going to select my other example from topology, the celebrated abstract version of geometry. Let me quote a famous result and show you something that can be done with it. Take any simple polyhedron, and count the number of vertices, the number of faces, and the number of edges. For example, in a box you find eight corners, so the number of vertices is equal to eight. The number of faces on a box is equal to six. And the number of edges—there are four on top, there are four on the bottom, and there are four on the sides—so there are 12 edges. The number of vertices, plus the number of faces, is 14; if you subtract the number of edges, you get two. A remarkable fact, discovered by Euler, is that you can take absolutely any simple polyhedron—any three-dimensional figure with straight edges and plane faces, without holes—and you will always get two as an answer. For example, for a tetrahedron, you get four vertices plus four faces, which equals eight; subtract six edges, and you get two. You can reshape the figure as you like, except that you must not cut a hole in it, because this is a topological property. Actually, there is a more general formula where the number of holes enters into the formula. There are also formulas for other numbers of dimensions.

This fascinating topic should, even without proofs, interest a great many high school students.

But how can we tie this abstract idea to high school topics? Well, for example, one rather isolated, interesting topic in solid geometry (or what is left of solid geometry) is the study of the five regular polyhedra. But why are there just five of them? We will use Euler's formula to answer the question.

Let there be f faces, each being a regular polygon of s sides, and let k faces meet at each vertex. Then the number of edges is $sf/2$ and the number of vertices is sf/k. Hence Euler's formula asserts that $f + sf/k - sf/2 = 2$ or

$$(2k + 2s - ks)f = 4k.$$

Obviously, k and s must be at least three. Thus there are only five possible combinations of integer value for k and s, since larger values would make the left side zero or negative:

$k = 3,\quad s = 3,\quad f = 4\quad$ (tetrahedron)
$k = 3,\quad s = 4,\quad f = 6\quad$ (cube)
$k = 3,\quad s = 5,\quad f = 12\quad$ (dodecahedron)
$k = 4,\quad s = 3,\quad f = 8\quad$ (octahedron)
$k = 5,\quad s = 3,\quad f = 20\quad$ (icosahedron)

This simple mixture of intuition and rigorous proof shows us why there are just five regular solids.

Whatever you may think about my views on rigor, intuition, and abstraction, I hope that we have one common goal: to develop in students early their ability to create new ideas. I feel that able students need only a slight lead, especially if you are fortunate enough to have sections in which you separate off the good students. Once they are amongst their peers they can be encouraged to develop ideas freely; though a certain amount of guidance is very important even here.

I recently finished teaching at a summer institute that Dartmouth co-sponsored. In addition to a number of high school teachers we had two dozen very able secondary school juniors. It was an interesting and enlightening experience. The students were wonderful; I would be happy to

have had any one of them at Dartmouth. It was an outstandingly able group, but they were badly in need of some channeling of their unguided mathematical abilities. They seemed to be under the impression that the highest-possible use of high school mathematics is solving puzzles. This is not too surprising since high school libraries usually have mathematics sections loaded with puzzle books. The rest of their time was spent on problems of the same sort as they had for homework, only harder—something that took more time or ingenuity. Of course, this has some value, but a really good student should be given a task that is somewhat higher and more challenging to him than doing hard versions of homework problems or solving uninstructive puzzles.

The first thing that we can all do is to give the students a good book to read. An able high school student is old enough to read books. There are many books on the market that can be given to a student. SMSG (School Mathematics Study Group, Stanford University) is undertaking a major effort to turn out special pamphlets and monographs for just this type of use in high school, and other groups are doing the same. A list compiled by Mu Alpha Theta tried to prove to you that for $180 you can build up a superb high school mathematics collection. And, indeed, that list with $180 worth of books in it is more than enough for any high school collection. Half of it would do very well. I was pleasantly surprised by the number and quality of really good books that are available and readable by high school students.

Even better than giving them books is to give them *good* problems. There are lots of good problems suitable for students. Take a book like that marvelous one by Professor G. Pólya, *Induction and Analogy in Mathematics* (Princeton, N.J.: Princeton University Press, 1954). I will cite just one of his classic examples. He asks the question, "Suppose you have a number of planes, say 10 planes, and you partition a room with these; into how many pieces will a room be cut with ten partitions? How about n partitions?" I assure you that it is not an easy problem, unless you go at it just right. The right way to solve the three-dimensional problem is to consider it first in one and two dimensions. In one dimension we have a line with n points on it, and the number of pieces is clearly $n + 1$. Then do it in two dimensions, using the solution of the one-dimensional case, and then go to three dimensions. Your best student will not only have no trouble in doing this, but will come back with the solution for four, five, and—hopefully—for n dimensions.

Or give these students a little bit of number theory—the theory of whole numbers. There are dozens of opportunities for the student to develop his own formulas. Nothing is more thrilling than to find a mathematical formula that holds without exception. If you want them to do geometry, why stick to three-dimensional geometry? It is rather dull. Why not let them do four- or five-dimensional geometry? Let them try to argue by anology (or rigorously, if they can) theorems in four- and five-dimensional geometry, using their experience in two and three dimensions. If you want to do abstract algebra, the beginnings of the theory of groups are easily accessible to a high school group. I have often used that as a talk for high school students. The vast majority of them grasped the idea the first time. I certainly don't say that you should do this in a single lecture, but spend a week on it, then challenge them to go out and develop their own examples of groups. Finally—if they are really ambitious—let them form their own axiom system for something more abstract, let them work it out, and see for themselves what actually happens.

I think in all fields we owe it to our best students to encourage creative endeavor. The great advantage that we have in mathematics is that, again and again, examples have shown it possible to get students at a remarkably early age to do creative mathematics. There have been major contributions to mathematics by men in their late teens. Even if your students aren't going to do creative work, at least give them a first taste of developing something that may not be new to the mathematical world, but is new to them; something that has not been spoon-fed, but that they have honestly discovered for themselves—preferably something that you, yourself, have never heard of. I know that at first it is frightening to have your students know something you don't know, but it is the greatest achievement of a teacher to enable his students to surpass him.

I would like to close by citing the example of Galois, the great young French mathematician. He died at the age of 21, yet he will remain for all time one of the great creative mathematicians because in his late teens he created entirely new ideas, the first really deep insight into group theory. This will remain fundamental mathematics for centuries to come. Galois's biography is more fascinating than any currently featured on television, but it is also very disturbing. He had to fight against traditional school curricula that strait-jacketed thinking, and against teachers who neither understood nor had tolerance for the unorthodox mind. His good fortune was to be exposed to writings of Legendre, Lagrange, and Abel, and to find one high school teacher with the vision to encourage the young genius. What would be the fate of Galois today? Would he find anyone to encourage him in exploring entirely new paths, and would anyone help him find the mathematical literature that would inspire him, or would he be doomed to eternal boredom by being kept within the limitations of the traditional curriculum?

Some Social Characteristics of Mathematicians and Their Work

Charles S. Fisher

Charles Samuel Fisher received his Ph.D. in mathematics in 1964 at Berkeley and then switched to postgraduate work in sociology as a social science research fellow at the Courant Institute. He has been a professor of sociology at Brandeis University since 1972.

The devoted reader, one who has faithfully followed the path of these volumes to this point, must surely have formed an opinion about how mathematicians act and how they approach their subject. In this essay a mathematician turned social scientist gives his views on the same topic. While much of the author's presentation is anecdotal, he is clearly most knowledgeable and well qualified to discuss this subject. The insights that Fisher provides are somewhat subjective and frequently not the stuff of which surveys or group samples can be made. In this sense the essay is frequently more philosophical than scientific, but its conclusions are worth pondering. The reader is urged to tackle the article and then compare it with the views of mathematicians contained in other readings in these volumes. Does it ring true?

Introduction

The effectiveness of science has often been seen to lie in its ability to solve the problems posed by its subject matter. Scientific progress is displayed by inverted pyramids of ever more concise and comprehensive solutions: Newton, Lagrange, Einstein. For some scholars, problems are the essence of science.[1] But problems do not exist by themselves. Like all intellectual products, they are social artifacts within the complex communities whose members create them.

In this essay, I will examine the relationships between some characteristics of the contemporary world of mathematics and the actions of mathematicians attempting to solve a long-standing problem. To do this, I will indicate some social structures of the contemporary community of mathematicians, and then look at them as they interact with the historically given problem. Finally, I will point to some consequences this situation has for the men and their discipline. Together they will illustrate the kinds of variability that exist in what to outsiders appears to be a unified scientific activity. Before proceeding, some comments are necessary concerning the nature of problem solving, the scope of this study, and the methods of research used.

The expression "problem solving" can have a wide variety of meanings. In the everyday world, it refers to anything from a problem in an arithmetic book to the problem of achieving happiness. What constitutes the problem and its solution in each of these situations differs. Arithmetic creates a simple task which is accomplished when a number placed upon a sheet of paper is accepted

Source: Charles S. Fisher, "Some Social Characteristics of Mathematicians and Their Work," *American Journal of Sociology,* 78 (1972/3): 1094–1118.

by the teacher. But the definition of happiness and the criteria of achievement are unclear.

When problem solving is mentioned with respect to science, the arithmetic book usually comes to mind; that is, problems are simply given and the possession of their solution is immediately recognized. Most routine scientific problems are of this nature: the mathematician finds maxima and minima, and the chemist tests acidity. In their daily work, scientists pinpoint problems the form of whose solutions they are sure of. This is the model activity of the scientist which Thomas Kuhn has called normal science.[2] In contrast, more important problems often occur in a less well-defined form, that is, in a form in which the statement and the meaning of the problem are open to interpretation and in which the significance or, in fact, the existence of a solution may be disputed. Three famous examples are the nature of electrical forces, the foundation of the calculus, and the age of the earth (Williams, 1965; Boyer, 1959; Toulmin and Goodfield, 1966). Problems leading to scientific revolutions are generally of this character. This is sometimes also true for less significant problems. If a number of scientists are dedicated to a problem, each possesses a slightly different view of what the problem is. The more difficult the problem and the longer it remains unsolved, the more likely it is that the opinions will vary and the more likely it is that it will have revolutionary significance.

In this essay we will examine the efforts of mathematicians to solve a problem which has been recognized as difficult for more than half a century, the so-called Poincaré conjecture. Our focus is on the nature of the problem as it is differentially socially constituted in the opinions and actions of different individuals and groups of mathematicians. The problem chosen for consideration is rather special in that it is long standing and in that enough interest has centered upon it in the last 20 years to make it a hotly contested issue. No fewer than six men have proposed solutions to this problem in recent years. The fact that none of these solutions has proven adequate makes the problem unusual. Further, the problem remains unsolved; hence, we are considering only the first half of the process of formulation, struggle for solution, actual solution, and assimilation of the solved problem.

The reason for presenting this singular instance is not that it is typical of what the average mathematician usually does. Here, the Poincaré conjecture is treated as an ideal-typical case of the process of problem solving. Because of intractability and fame of the conjecture, this process is more easily observed. It is hoped that a case study will illuminate the structure of problem solving both in other parts of mathematics and in other disciplines. Some of the structures which emerge in this essay are characteristic of all intellectual pursuits while others are particular to mathematics and the special problem. An understanding of the peculiar character of science and mathematics rests on the sorting of these differences.[3]

The materials on which this study is based were gathered between 1965 and 1967. They are composed of a review of relevant mathematical papers and general articles, interviews, and field notes. As a mathematician and sociologist, in the course of interviewing some 100 scientists, I formally interviewed 15 famous mathematicians who were associated with the conjecture. These men worked at Princeton, NYU, Harvard, Wisconsin, Brandeis, and Berkeley. They were selected because they represented a cross section of the different approaches to the problem. I spoke to them as both peer and social inquirer. The interviews were open ended, among other things, focusing on the subjects' biographical relationship to the problem. Additional materials were gathered from informal contacts I had with mathematicians while working and wandering about a number of departments of mathematics. The gossip of mathematics professors and their students was an invaluable source of information. Finally, my own experience as a mathematician sensitized me to significant issues and events.[4]

Some Elements of the World of Mathematicians

In order to understand the setting for this particular problem, a number of social features of the community concerned must be described. These features, or social structures, distinguish the mathematical community from others. It should be noted that these features do not exhaustively describe the world of mathematicians, because that world is made up of quite different groupings whose interests and activities frequently diverge. The social structures outlined here all bear upon the particular problem chosen for examination.[5] If other problems were considered, such things as the application or the relationship between mathematicians and logicians might be emphasized. For the purposes of this study, mathematics is seen as self-contained, done in universities, and dealing with intuitive objects whose relationships are established by proof. The community is diffuse, its members relatively isolated, and two styles of work are evident. We will examine these briefly.

To the mathematicians described, only their academic positions and the opinions of their colleagues who like themselves are exclusively occupied with the creations of mathematical ideas are relevant. Although some mathematicians attend to the activities of men outside their discipline, this is not the case with those who work on the given problem.

Mathematicians are trained in universities and work their way up the ladder of job security there, so that the contingencies of academic careers are the only worldly subject matter with which the mathematician need be concerned. The occasional man who makes contributions from outside the university will require special attention.

Mathematics differs from much science, in that, as mathematicians often say, their subject matter is independent of events in the "real world." Despite this, the existence of mathematical objects radically delimits the domain of appropriate mathematical speculation. While arbitrary axiomatic systems can be pondered, in most concrete situations, mathematicians speak of themselves as exploring objects which have some sort of real intuitive existence. This intuition is developed in the course of a mathematical apprenticeship and centers upon historically given problems. Unlike the empirical scientist, the mathematician does not have to go into the laboratory to test his ideas, but he does have to make

them come to terms with his own and others' conceptions of a set of intuitive objects.[6]

The relationships among mathematical objects are presented in the form of theorems. These, in turn, are composed of a statement or proposition and its proof. Whereas a physicist seeks control over nature by means of theories and experiments, the mathematician requires that statements be proven before they are accepted as true or as certified mathematical knowledge. This fact effects the kind of activities the mathematician undertakes. Most of the time, mathematicians sit around trying to prove things. One man's success in this endeavor is verified by another, like, sitting man who checks the first's efforts. The explicit role of proof in mathematics is a complex and much disputed subject which, though important, does not bear on this investigation.[7] For the purposes of this essay, proof will stand as the criterion of successful mathematical problem solving.

Since physics is the paradigm case of science, I note one of its features in order to bring out the contrasting properties of the world of mathematics. In contemporary physics, the investigation of elementary particles is generally acknowledged to be the most fundamental area of research. Many physicists feel that theory is forged in attempts to understand the interactions of particles and that theory is then passed down to other areas of physics. Hence, there is a generally accepted notion of what is fundamental and a vaguely defined hierarchy of prestige based on theory production.[8] Mathematics, on the other hand, is a more diffuse, less focused discipline, the members of which often work in relative isolation. The roots of this lie in three interrelated features of the mathematical community: two concern the training which mathematicians receive, and the other, the theoretical structure of mathematics. These are considered in order.

The first relevant aspect of the training of mathematicians is a learned feeling of independence. This contributes to the isolation of mathematicians. Mathematicians like to claim that they could carry on their activities independently of the rest of the people in the world. They feel that, having reached a certain stage of maturity, their discipline is so internalized they could, given the fundamentals of a theory, develop all of its conclusions while living on a desert island. This assertion is usually accompanied by examples of the few famous mathematicians who, isolated in their youths and unaided, were able to make great progress in mathematics.[9] These exotic claims do correspond to some everyday mathematical realities. For instance, mathematicians often work alone for years with the feeling of assurance that their ouput is mathematically correct.

The second aspect of training is the common course of study which mathematicians of the same generation and locale experience. This promotes the feeling that the discipline is unified and vitiates against the forces toward diffuseness to be mentioned next. Students of mathematics follow a common course of study until the last years of their graduate education. As a student proceeds into a specialty he may learn a number of very particular theorems, but the years of common study allows him to follow, if only rather vaguely, the specialized study of his fellow students. Because of the extent of shared knowledge specialists do not have much difficulty in moving into neighboring areas. The ease of mobility declines in proportion to the removal in time and space of the mathematicians from their neighboring specialty.

The third factor lies in the theoretical structure of mathematics. It contributes to the diffuseness of the discipline. Unlike unidirectional physics, mathematics is made up of three broad substantive areas of equal theoretical status. These are algebra, geometry, and analysis.[10] It is from them that the basic training of students is drawn. Within these three are many theories of greatly differing ranges. They can be encompassing, like the theory of numbers, or they can be restricted to a more or less technical domain, like the theory of topological semigroups. A mathematician could cultivate either of these specialties for long periods of his scientific life and remain completely unaware of the activities of men in the other. A man in either of the specialties need not have a feeling that others are working on more fundamental problems than he. When the number of wide-ranging theories is multiplied by 10 and the

number of narrow ones by 100—all potentially independent, equally mathematical subject areas—then the diversity of the discipline is even more evident. This extreme statement of the situation can be modified and it is this modification which provides for the claim of mathematicians that their activities are unified. This modification will also play a key role in the later discussion of problem solving, so it will be considered very briefly.

Many problems of mathematics are so stated that a person with only a high school education could understand and entertain the notion that he might solve them. A number of mathematical theories use techniques which require little more background than is contained in the common mathematical training. For example, much work in number theory can be stated and explained in language which is the property of all mathematics graduate students. The universality of access to these theories and problems lends substance to the feeling that mathematics is, indeed, all of one sort. In contrast to this are the many other theories or specialties which are highly technical and require long periods of training in a particular technique or perspective. Both of these kinds of specialties coexist.

Putting together the three features of mathematics, while noting their counterinstances, we can understand both the discipline's diffuseness and the isolation of its practitioners. The unfocused nature of mathematics arises from the multiplicity of activities of equal status which lie side by side and yet are only partially visible to the men who cultivate one or another of them, while the relative isolation of the men comes from a combination of their feeling of independence and their ability to cut out one of the many specialties for themselves irrespective of other mathematical goings-on.

A final feature of the community of mathematicians lies in the men's relationship to their techniques. Two stereotypical styles of work are evident. One is based upon adherence to technique. Men in this category search for problems which can be solved by their methods, while those in the other try out many techniques in their attempts to solve a given set of problems. The former are much more frequent, if for no other reason than the latter requires a greater mathematical ability. Many mathematicians combine these styles; they attempt to solve a narrow range of problems using the few techniques which they can easily master.

Having noted these structural elements, I will examine the ways in which the mathematicians' attempt to solve a particular problem are fashioned by the structures of their world and in turn how problem solving itself organizes these structures. I begin with some comments concerning the development of the problem and the men who work on it.

The Background and the Men

At the turn of the century, Henri Poincaré put forth a proposition concerning the equivalence of certain kinds of topological objects[11] This conjecture has neither been definitely proven nor disproven. Many men thought they had established its truth only to discover some error. As the 20th century progressed, topology became one of the central concerns of mathematics and the conjecture came to be considered an outstanding problem of topology. In the early 1930s, a basic text in topology mentioned the conjecture as one among several fundamental topological puzzles (Seifert and Threlfall, 1934).

The conjecture as presented in the text appears to be simple and straightforward. Its statement is short and the relationships claimed seemed intuitively obvious. One man related that, on reading the conjecture, he thought that he could prove it in a couple of hours. He soon discovered that the problem was very difficult and that, although he believed that he had solved it a number of times, he was invariably disappointed. Soon after the statement of the conjecture was published, a well-known mathematician published a proof of it. He immediately uncovered an error in his demonstration and in the next issue of the journal pointed out his mistakes. The experience of these two mathematicians was to be repeated over and over again. In the past 10 years a number of erroneous proofs have been made public. This places the problem in a rather special light which makes it easier to examine the men who are attempting to solve it.

In the years following the publication of the text, mathematicians actively cultivated the areas of mathematics which included the conjecture. The problem did not directly stimulate this development. It stood as a well-known difficulty on which men were likely to try out their new techniques. As topology developed and the conjecture remained intractable, it gained the reputation of being unsolvable. Older mathematicians who at one time or another had, without result, spent time thinking about it tended to discourage younger men from wasting any effort on the problem. This is how things stood in the late 1940s when the oldest of the men who were interviewed entered the scene.

Among the men I studied who are currently working on the conjecture are three generations.[12] Each generation is old enough to have been the successive generation's teachers, though this was only occasionally the case. The oldest generation consists of men who finished their graduate work in the middle or late 1940s. They are all about 50 years old. The second generation is made up of men who were trained in the early to middle 1950s. Their ages range from 33 to 40. The youngest group is composed of men who obtained their degrees in the late 1950s and early 1960s. They are all under 35 years old. While these generational differences are significant, they do not determine the attitudes of these men.

Cutting across the generations is one very important theoretical development which had an effect on the work in which they are engaged. During the 1950s a mathematical specialty called "differential topology," was elaborated. Its techniques were used to solve a variation of the conjecture.[13] This proof was taken to be one of the crowning achievements of the new specialty. Although a number of people tried to extend the proof to the case of the original problem (which I will sometimes call the classical conjecture), none was successful. The latter two generations of men are closely associated with these new techniques. The second generation was involved in their elaboration, while the third learned them during their apprenticeships.

With the development of the new set of techniques and the presentation of some of the incorrect proofs of the problem, interest in it has increased. Growing from a few men in the late forties there are now 20–50 mathematicians who take a direct interest in the conjecture, the first figure being the maximum of those who seriously work on the problem, while the second includes those who are aware of the work connected with the conjecture.

The Problem

As a social entity, the conjecture has different relevance and meaning to mathematicians depending upon their placement in the community, the structures of the community, and their relationship to the problem. In examining how it is differentially constituted by the various men, the conjecture will emerge more as a vaguely defined social feature of the working world of mathematicians than as a clear-cut intellectual item. This is not to imply that its statement as found in textbooks is vague or that when asked the men would not all recite equivalent mathematical versions of the problem; it is to assert that, in their ongoing world, mathematicians see and do things very differently and that these differences, as they make up the activity, have consequences for the men involved in it.

In order, we will look at (1) recruitment to the problem, (2) its perceived significance, (3) commitment to the problem, (4) the mathematicians' adherence to particular techniques as means of solving it, and (5) their opinions as to the conjecture's truth. Mathematicians differ in each of these categories according to their generation, their specialty, and their particular set of personal idiosyncrasies. The following analysis could have been made at any stage of the development of the conjecture. The difficulty (if not impossibility) of treating the whole history of the problem in a similar manner restricts me to the period covered by the memories of the interviewed men.

Recruitment.   For men in each of the generations, the atmosphere in which they came to work on the conjecture was quite different. For men of the first generation and for mathematicians from countries in which topology was not taught, the source of the conjecture was the previously mentioned textbook. Until well into the 1950s this book was the primer on topology and consequently the problem was universally available. In opting to work on the conjecture, the men of the first generation had to go against popular opinion. Those of their teachers who had pondered it felt that the problem was unsolvable and any time spent on it would be wasted. To choose the problem in such circumstances the men of the first generation had to be strong individuals. As one man relates:

Q: What did other people think of your getting involved with this?

A: Some of them thought I was a damned fool. Others thought that if a problem like this was going to be solved, you might as well stick to it.

He did. Another man came across the conjecture in his self-appointed mission to solve all of the problems in the basic text. He was successful until he came to the conjecture. He has been working on it ever since. Yet another chose the problem because he was only interested in long-standing problems. He discounted its presumed unsolvability, having just solved another impossible problem.

The members of the second generation took up the problem because it seemed amenable to their newly developed techniques. They solved the generalization of the conjecture, but when the classical case proved intractable, they left it for their students to finish up. So for the members of the third generation the problem was in the air, but the decision to work on it did not place one in the forefront of research.

Significance.   Various opinions as to the importance of the conjecture are distributed throughout the mathematical community. I begin by locating a general climate of opinion and move progressively towards the feelings of those men who take a more specialized interest in the problem. Almost all mathematicians have heard of the conjecture, and some would class it among one of the outstanding problems of mathematics. It is sufficiently well known to be compared to the few great problems of mathematics: Fermat's last theorem, the four-color problem, the three-body problem. These are part of the store of common knowledge of most mathematicians. Although many mathematicians may not be able to locate the specific importance or implications of one or another of these problems they would grant laurels to anyone who solved them.

This accent on solving historically given problems is a major feature of the rhetoric of mathematicians. As I noted in the section on structure, one of the unifying elements of mathematics is a relatively uniform basic training allowing for a widespread understanding of the content of a common set of problems. The most famous can be understood by laymen—they are simply stated and stand by themselves. Yet these problems have resisted solution for centuries. The conjecture, similarly unsolved, requires more specialized knowledge to be understood, and as the mathematicians concerned become more knowledgeable about it, their opinions become more refined.

Topologists are farther along the spectrum of specialization. For them the problem appears in more detail. While the development of their specialty does not depend upon the solution of the conjecture, the problem does occupy a very visible position. One topologist who himself has worked on the conjecture characterized it as follows:

It hasn't been a successful problem in the sense that none of the work that has been done on it has lead anywhere. There are great differences in unsolved problems in this respect. The most successful example of an unsolved problem is Fermat's last theorem. This is a problem hundreds of years old which has never been solved and yet some of the most important parts of modern mathematics were developed in attempts to solve it. It lies in the center of the whole subject of algebraic number theory. This is an example of a useful unsolved problem. One of the standard examples of a non-useful problem is the four-color problem in topology. A great deal of effort has been spent on this and absolutely nothing interesting has come out of it. Now I think the con-

jecture is much better than this. Certainly some interesting work has come out of it. And also the solution would be meaningful. It would take us a long way in our understanding (of certain topological objects). I think the four-color problem is an example where the solution wouldn't prove much. You would know the answer and nothing else. The conjecture is important especially since the generalized case has been solved. The classical one stands as a stumbling block on the way to further progress, so that if someone could solve it, it would be extremely useful. And also I think that there is at least hope that the solution is just around the corner.

The more aggressive specialists in the new technique used to solve the generalized conjecture cite the generalization as evidence for the unimportance of work on the classical case. Discounting the few results which have been generated by attempts to solve the classical conjecture, these men see it as interesting but only a special case and hence not worth much effort. A central element of this group's view of mathematics is that the discipline progresses by the creation of algebraic classificatory systems. Having obtained such a system through the solution of the generalized conjecture, they feel that there is not much more to be done on the subject. Therefore they have taken their techniques into new areas, carrying with them—in their opinion—the mainstream of mathematics. Those who tarry with the classical problem are viewed as behind the times. They exempt from this a few members of the third generation, students of the specialists, who are encouraged because success by means of the special techniques will further help to certify the usefulness of those techniques.

Finally, there are the experts on the conjecture. They hold a variety of opinions as to its significance within mathematics. One man, having spent many years pondering the conjecture, thinks it is the most important mathematical problem: "The conjecture is much more important than Fermat's last theorem. If the latter were solved then one would have nothing more than its solution. With the conjecture you would have much more." The added knowledge concerns the objects of our experience. For this man, the conjecture lies at the heart of intuition about topological objects, and he is compelled to investigate it because of what it can tell about the world: if the conjecture could be proven then the objects of topology could be ordered and hence they would become understandable. This view is stated as the passionate belief of a man whose world is composed of the ideas about which he thinks. To him the ideas are alive and naturally important. The conjecture will help order this world, therefore giving the conjecture its importance.

Such a radical opinion was not offered by any of the other experts. While several cited the fact that the solution would aid in ordering topological objects, this is only part of the reason for its importance. "Of course it is interesting, because lots of things depend upon it, but this is to a certain extent irrelevant. I don't know, but I consider mathematics like a growing organism: it sort of develops along natural lines of itself. The conjecture has a very, very central position in a very central part of mathematics. It is important for the development of the organism that this problem should be solved one way or another." He explained this by saying that the objects with which the conjecture dealt appeared everywhere and that mathematicians would like to characterize them; in attempting to do so the first problem confronted is the conjecture. This man goes beyond the previous one by indirectly giving mathematically organic reasons for the problem's importance.[14] Another expert claims the problem's importance on more personal grounds: "No, it isn't the consequences that interest me. The importance I attach to the problem is not predicated on corollaries I could deduce from it. *I would just like to know* the answer to that problem. To me problems like this are what mathematics is all about." A member of the first generation, this man is influenced by the public image of a mathematician. Disregarding the interest and opinions of his colleagues, he has spent many years working on the conjecture. In an extreme fashion, he embodies the characteristics of an independent problem solver. He is potentially one of the heroes of mathematics.[15]

Looking over these various opinions, we note the spiral toward expertise, giving rise to judgments as to the conjecture's importance—the more expertise, the less problematic its importance. At the center of the spiral, where to impute irrelevance to the conjecture is to attack the expert, we find opinions based both on personal feelings and visions concerning the nature of mathematics. Given this spectrum of opinions we might expect quite different degrees of commitment to the conjecture.

Commitment.   The amount of time mathematicians spend on a problem depends upon their conception of its importance, their emotional involvement with it, and their feelings as to the likelihood of their being able to solve it. In the 1940s, few men spent much time thinking about the conjecture since it had the reputation of unsolvability. Later, as more attention was focused on the conjecture, mathematicians were more likely to consider attempting to solve it.

There are two major factors which influence the amount of time nonspecialists spend on the problem. One has to do with the simplicity of the problem's statement and the other with the manner in which mathematicians follow their ability to handle a particular set of techniques. Since the conjecture is easily grasped by anyone who has studied topology, it has often been toyed with. When there were not a number of men visibly working on the problem, topologists, in general, were not aware of the amount of specialized knowledge necessary for solving the problem. Hence they often considered the problem for a while and then put it aside. As the body of specialized knowledge grew, men were less likely to become involved with the conjecture. The second factor was mentioned in the section on structure. Mathematicians who follow their techniques into problem areas only become involved with the conjecture if they feel that the technique can handle it. An example of both of these points is contained in the following:

Q: What about the classical conjecture? Are you at all interested in that?

A: Yes, but I don't know what to do, I am not an expert on these things. The techniques are different from the ones I am accustomed to using. It is a very difficult field in itself and there are a lot of special techniques I am not as familiar with as the ones that I use. It seems to me to be much harder to use my techniques in the classical case. So I haven't done anything.

It is interesting to note that this man became interested in the problems on which he works because he discovered that some of the techniques he learned elsewhere were applicable to them. He was so pleased that he could solve problems in his new area that he just continued doing so. An additional factor which influences involvement with the conjecture is the pull of other interests. Several men who themselves were making slow progress on the conjecture gradually moved away from it as they became interested in other areas. These men were young and had spent the first years out of the university working on the conjecture. Their movement can be associated with their growing ability to see what other kinds of things could be done.

Other members of the third or youngest generation who continue to work on the conjecture are those closely associated with the new techniques. These men have, in some sense, been left behind to complete the unfinished work. They realize this, and although they are primarily occupied with the conjecture, they carefully watch the development of the new techniques in other areas. When talking to these men, one has the feeling that, in agreeing with the rhetoric of their teachers (that is, with the aggressive promoters of the new techniques), they might at any time give up their work on the conjecture. One man replied to the question of how long he felt it would take to settle the conjecture:

A: In a small number of years from now it will be decided.

Q: How much longer would you work on it?

A: It is hard to say.

Q: Could you conceive of working on it for 20 more years?

A: No, definitely not.

In contrast, dedicated men of the first generation have spent that length of time and more trying to solve the problem. Some have given over their entire professional existence to a search for the solution. More common are the men who, though spending long periods of time working on the conjecture, combined that effort with interest in other mathematical problems. One man worked on the conjecture constantly for eight years with little result. "Yes, I worked on that for many, many years and got out of it one research paper which I haven't published. I thought that when I finished the result of this paper that surely I should be able to prove the conjecture. But I devoted the equivalent of three to four years of full time to work on it after that with absolutely no luck." Taken together, the mathematicians interested in the problem illustrate a complete range of involvement.[16] Both the long- and short-term unsuccessful involvement have consequences for the men and mathematics which will be considered later.

Technique.   The reasons mathematicians choose one rather than another approach in attempting to solve a problem are embedded in his particular milieu. A mathematician does not sit down with all the various theories and techniques spread before him and ask himself which he should choose. The methods of attack are not rationally chosen.[17] They are derived from a combination of training, taste, and personal predilection. As noted before, there are two stereotypical manners of proceeding employed by mathematicians. One is to follow the problem through various techniques, and the other is to adhere to a technique, seeking problems amenable to it. The limits on the former are observable in the actions of many mathematicians working on the conjecture. Each of the men working on the problem uses only a few of the possible routes of attack. Not one of them has systematically tried all of the different techniques. Although aware of other techniques, a man is usually skilled only in the ones he uses constantly. Choice of technique is not capricious. The mathematicians can give good technical reasons for their choice of tools, but on being pressed or confronted with another man's reasons, each will admit that the basis of their selection is taste and a hunch that their techniques might work.

The most apparent division among the men with respect to their methods of attack lies along the lines of generations. The older men do not use the techniques of the specialty developed in the 1950s. Several members of this generation follow the developments of the specialty, but do not make use of them. One characterized the newer techniques as a fashion and, as he said, "I don't use fashionable techniques." This same man views these techniques with sadness, for though he has seriously followed their development, he has discovered nothing in them which he feels might be useful in settling the conjecture. For him they are ephemeral. Other members of the first generation shy away from the newer techniques because they feel the approach is less pure; that is, it requires more theoretical apparatus and therefore removes the conjecture from its intuitively appropriate, native setting. One member of this first generation pays little attention to the newer methods:

Q: What about the new techniques?

A: I don't know them and I would have to work like a dog to understand them because I don't know the basic theory for one thing.

Q: What about their application to the conjecture; do you follow it?

A: No, I don't know it. Since I came here I have devoted practically no attention to the research literature.

When asked whether these techniques will work in solving the conjecture, he replied: "I find this awfully hard to believe. My hunch is that if it is true, and I am no longer convinced that it is, then the chances are that it will be proved by a new primitive proof. That is, nobody is going to use prefabricated pieces of anything at all to get a proof of the conjecture." Like the other members

of his generation this man felt that the solution would come from either one of their own numbers using unorthodox methods or from some yet unheard of young man who went directly to the core of the problem without any complicated apparatus, that is, the solution required a person who shared their socio-technical characteristics.

In spite of their common feeling about the new techniques, these men do not agree on the best approach to the problem. Each man has a style of his own, and it would be difficult to say that any two of the men used the same techniques. The men themselves point to the variations which constitute grounds for saying that the other men really see the problem in a different light. One reduces the problem to algebra and tries to solve it algebraically; another looks at the pathologies which develop when objects are twisted in space; and a third looks at the problem only as it can be expressed in very special settings.[18]

The members of the younger generations tend to be more tolerant in their choice of tools. They mix older ideas with the newer techniques. Some of the youngest work exclusively with the newer techniques. These men partake of the rhetoric of the specialty built on the techniques and, as indicated, they wish to add the conjecture to the list of conquests so that they can proceed with the main battle.

The younger men are no more uniform than their elders when it comes to selecting methods of attack. One looks at the problem topologically, another algebraically, while yet a third wishes to make it a special case of an even more encompassing theorem. Thus, even though there is a trend toward the use of newer techniques, the members of the younger generations select their tools according to their own personal predisposition.[19]

Truth or Falsity. A final element dividing the men is their conviction about the truth or falsity of the conjecture. Most think it is true, some are uncertain, and a few believe it is false. Their opinions do not follow generational lines. Because of their personalities, the men in the first generation tend to be more outspoken, but there are representatives of all three views in each of the generations.

As was indicated in the description of the conjecture, interest stems from the fact that the relationship which is claimed to hold true is easy to grasp and seems intuitively obvious. On being introduced to the conjecture, many topologists feel that it is a simple matter to establish its truth. Further investigation reveals the existence of hidden difficulties. In attempting to reduce the supposedly equivalent objects to one another, complications arise: objects naively not thought to exist have to be taken account of. Yet most mathematicians think that the conjecture is true. Some of the experts hold this view with great passion. One man has such a strong belief in its truth that, thinking about the conjecture, he cannot fall asleep. For him the conjecture's truth is intimately connected with his ideas of order among the objects concerned. He never has encountered anything which would lead him to feel that the conjecture is false. Moreover, he never works on the conjecture with an eye to proving its falseness; that is, he never looks for a counterexample. The truth of the conjecture is a matter of belief.

This man, with several others who hold that the conjecture is true, makes a mathematical as well as social investment in his opinions. He has proved a number of theorems which will be true if the conjecture can be proven to hold true. If the conjecture turns out to be false, then his efforts are mathematically in vain.[20] A less emotional view is revealed by a second generation expert: "Any serious attack on a problem like this looks at both sides at once. One tries to construct counterexamples and one tries to prove the theorem at the same time. If one fails in one, one tries to use that as a step in doing the other. I certainly don't have any conviction that it must be true." But the consequences of the conjecture's falsity are much worse. Things would be simpler if it were true. If it turns out that it is false, then simplicity is also to be desired. "If the conjecture is false, then this implies that things are much more complicated. If the conjecture is false then it would be a good thing to have a simple example in which one could see why it is false rather than a horridly complicated pathology which would be unenlightening."[21]

With the passage of time and the problem's continued resistance to solution, a member of the first generation has lost his once-held conviction of the conjecture's truth.

Q: You thought at one time that it was true and now you don't?

A: There was a time when it seemed to be self-evidently true. Now I have my doubts.

Q: You think someone could construct a counterexample?

A: No. I really don't have any strong conviction that anybody will. I will not be especially surprised if the answer turns out to be an example.

Yet even this man would rather have the conjecture be true. In contrast there are one or two radicals who stand out against the majority: "As a matter of fact I have a feeling that the problem is false, that the conjecture is a false one. In recent years I have spent time doing two things: putting enough extra conditions on the conjecture to make it true and trying to get an example showing that the thing is not true without the extra conditions." This man has made his opinion known in public on several occasions and takes pride in the fact that he differs from so many others.

Again we are presented with a range of opinion, but on the issue of truth the lines are drawn sharply. In no sense is there a consensus. For many mathematicians intuition would push the scale in one direction. But as the last cited man indicates, the other direction has its adherents. As will be noted in the next section, choice of sides involves possible social denigration by those who differ.

Consequences

The social order implied in the structural features and the social characteristics of the problem have a number of consequences.[22] These fall into several categories: consequences for the careers of the men who attempt to solve the problem, interactional consequences for the men as expressed in their interpersonal behavior, and consequences for mathematics as a problem-solving venture. I will consider each of these.

Consequences for Careers.   I noted earlier that almost all of our mathematicians are employed in universities and must contend with the career contingencies which arise in these institutions. None of the members of the first generation felt that their involvement with the problem, even for long periods of time, affected their advancement. Given the common notion that promotion is based upon productivity, this should be accounted for. The explanation lies in a series of observations. First, each of the members of the first generation established himself as a good mathematician previous to his involvement with the conjecture. Even while working on the problem, they produced some publications, most of which are derivative of their main occupation. Therefore, in no case did their years of commitment to the problem appear entirely barren.

Further, as mentioned above, members of the first generation had to go against a climate of opinion in choosing to work on the problem although their decision to do so was in accord with the rhetoric of mathematics. Some considered them "damn fools," but they were tackling recognizably difficult problems which, as one man put it, is "what mathematics is all about." Finally, these men were tenured members of academic departments long before Sputnik lifted mathematics from relative obscurity to a strategically important science. Thus, although teaching in prestigious institutions, their promotions were not contingent upon the number of listings in their bibliographies. They could have obtained security solely on the basis of their teaching abilities. These men were permitted to pursue their monomania because they were already established, were marginally producing, were engaged in an appropriate activity, and were working when academic production was not vital.

One member of the first generation avoided the possibilities of career problems. He never held an academic position. Living off a meager personal income and an occasional stipend, he dedicated his entire time to a search for a solution to the problem. In avoiding the responsibilities of a professor, he also did not have the latter's security. In gaining time and freedom for his mathematical occupations, he risked economic failure. Other eras have seen such men go under (Fisher, 1967, pp. 216–44).

The younger generations of mathematicians involved with the conjecture find that their concerns do have some effect on their advancement. The consequences are only in terms of each mathematician's entire activities and the conditions prevailing in universities over the last 15 years.

Members of the second generation, having certified themselves as great mathematicians, suffered few adverse consequences. Since they are not closely identified with the conjecture (being promoters of the new techniques) and are, in any case, extremely productive men, they have not had to consider the effects on their career of an interest in the problem. Men in the third generation are more conscious of their commitment to the problem. They realize they must produce in order to obtain reputations and the attendant security within prestigious schools. For some, there are no difficulties. Since they are students of the aggressive new specialty, they have contributed toward its advancement, linking their names and futures to its progress.

Other members of the third generation can be greatly affected by their involvement with the problem. These are young Ph.D.'s and students (who may be seen as a potential fourth generation). These people are very much aware of the need to produce a good piece of mathematics in order to establish themselves. For students, the characteristics of mathematical careers are unclear. Although they see an emphasis on the production of great ideas, they do not associate this with the attainment of academic security. It is their observations of those who work on the conjecture which helps form their feeling about it. At institutions where more eccentric (independent) experts teach, students view the problem in terms of the gossip which abounds about these people. A reputation for independence and years of relatively unproductive research tend to put off the students. In contrast, a member of the first generation who avoids such a reputation has no trouble in recruiting students. He sets them to work on parts of the conjecture, not with the expectation that they will solve it, but with the hope that in trying something very difficult they will come up with interesting ideas. He related that he has never been disappointed with this strategy. Neither apparently have the students. Unaware of the professional risks they might be taking and guided by their established mentor, their advancement is not inhibited.

Young Ph.D.'s, as distinct from students, are clearly aware of the need to produce in order to maintain academic positions. Therefore, if they do concern themselves with the problem, they are likely to do so on a short-term basis. The rule of thumb goes something like, "If you don't produce any results within two or three months work, move on." This applies to any problem. The alternative is to be resigned to teaching at a less prestigious university. Several young men interested in the problem have taken this path. Most Ph.D.'s in topology rule out the conjecture as a possible problem. They know the tales of years of unproductive research and they have heard stories about the six incorrect proofs, so they look elsewhere for tractable problems.

The careers of those involved with the conjecture is affected in still another way. It might be termed a psychological consequence arising out of the experts' years of unproductive concern with the problem. After a number of years, some of the men found they were going mathematically stale. They felt a waning of creativity combined with an ever-growing frustration. As a result of this, they slowly began to move in other directions. They either put more effort in their teaching or began to ease off on their research. In no case have they stopped thinking about the problem. It just no longer occupies them so completely. They still retain the hope that they might solve it.

Interactional Consequences.   Competition and years of unrewarded dedication to the conjecture have given rise to intense competitive feelings among the men, especially members of the first generation. These are sometimes openly displayed as subtle remarks in research papers, but more

often are evident in the men's pattern of association, in the gossip of the community, and from the men's own reports. When asked how he would feel if another person settled the conjecture, one of the older men made a very sad face and returned the question. Another replied:

A: I would feel horribly disappointed. To be honest, I take a dog-in-the-manger attitude to this problem.

Q: You mean you would just as soon not see it solved if someone else were to solve it?

A: That's right, that's right. I am sure that this is morally irresponsible, but that is the way I feel about it. I don't burn black candles or anything.

Besides being competitive, the older men tend to be secretive. They do not work cooperatively and only present their ideas to others when they are quite sure that the ideas are correct and cannot be used by someone else to prove the conjecture. That is, if they have a good idea, they do not make it known until they have taken the idea as far as it will go. If they think the idea can be used to prove the conjecture and it is just that they are not able to construct the proof, but someone else might, they do not reveal their thoughts. The fear of coming in second makes the men very cautious in their conversations with others.

Intense competition has other effects. One man could not work for a while because he suspected that the man in the office next to him had already solved the problem. Also, the men tend to belittle the work of others. While having great respect for their competitors as mathematicians, they often say that what the others are doing is somewhat off the point or misguided. For the most part, they cannot imagine that the techniques or approach of anyone else will solve the problem. One expression of this denigration is found in the style of mutual kidding. In asides—again very subtle—a speaker will make it clear that he thinks some of the other workers are rather silly fellows. A major avenue of such characterizations lies in opinions regarding the truth of the conjecture. One gets the impression that those who believe the conjecture is still true, feel that those of the opposite opinion are somewhat evil; while those who hold that it is false feel their counterparts are naïve and a bit stodgy.

The younger men do not possess such strong feelings if for no other reason than they have not invested as much time and emotion in the problem. These men tend to be more relaxed and to have wider interests. In addition they have mathematical friends with whom they talk. The fact that they cooperate in attempting to solve parts of the problem and feel themselves part of a larger movement mediates the tone of their involvement. Yet, since the prize is worth having and the competition so intense, the younger men also maintain some degree of secrecy.

There is one additional factor which influences the mathematicians both young and old not to publicize their activities connected with the conjecture. It is fear of being ridiculed or shamed. To let others know that one is working on the problem is to run the risk of being compared to the eccentric men who are already associated with it. To announce a proof of the conjecture is to open oneself to the possibility of error and the shame which accompanies public exposure. The likelihood of making a mistake and the intensity of shame are perceived to be very great. This is because of the number of good mathematicians who have already publicly stubbed their toes on the problem.

Given the competition and secrecy which exists among the experts, a vicious circle arises. Because so many men have been shamed by displaying erroneous proofs and because there is fear of intellectual theft, the men usually do not show anyone their results prior to public presentation. This unmonitored presentation of proofs has led to many errors being exposed at the time of presentation. Hence, a fear of loss of originality and the possibility of being shamed leads to circumstances which are more likely to produce error and shame, and the reverse.[23]

Consequences for Mathematics.   There are two consequences for mathematics in terms of providing men to solve problems by means of techniques which are eventually successful. The first

of these is a two-edged sword. On one side is independence and relative isolation which allows men to work on acceptable problems even though there are differing opinions as to the problem's significance. On the other side, once the problem and its proponents gain reputations for difficulty and social oddity, respectively, then, given the current pressures for publication, young men are not likely to make a long-term commitment to the problem. Yet some young men choose to work on it and in doing so they run the risk of gaining an adverse social reputation and having to work at a less prestigious university. As indicated earlier, talent or association with the new specialty vitiates the chance of these effects. And what is important here is that research on the problem is recognized as legitimate. The first consequence for mathematics then is that there are men who work on a large number of problems, even though their work may be viewed by their colleagues as legitimate but insignificant or oddball.

The second consequence for mathematics is that adherence by the experts to different techniques provides a wide range of intensive investigations of the problem. In selecting only a few approaches, they give their tools a thorough testing. From the fact that no one utilizes all the techniques of which he is aware, it seems likely that he literally cannot be so encyclopedic and still create the emotional and intellectual investment in one approach that is necessary to carry him to a successful solution. Since the problem has resisted the efforts of many intelligent men, it is unlikely (as in athletics) that some one will solve it without almost complete dedication. Such dedication is not usually accompanied by an aloof rational choice of weapons. Therefore, on the one hand, emotional and intellectual commitment provides for intensive cultivation of the problem from many viewpoints. On the other, it introduces the irrationalities of such commitment and with these, as elsewhere in life, the possibility of strain and conflict.

Conclusion

The exploration of mathematical problem solving offered here isolates structures and relationships thereby providing insight into what mathematics is like as a social activity. Such characteristics of mathematicians as specialization and commitment are evident in many other intellectual activities found in modern universities. Hence the descriptions given here may be applicable to other disciplines. On the other hand, there do exist differences among disciplines and these differences are evident in the contexts which make mathematical and scientific problem solving what they are. The analytic schema put forth in this essay offers a device for comparing and contrasting disciplines by focusing on such elements as structure, the particular history of the men and the problem, recruitment, significance, commitment, and consequences. In presenting this schema it is hoped to further an understanding of intellectual and scientific life in a way that looks beyond the rhetorical claims of these undertakings and achieves greater insight into the social nature of problem solving.

References

1. Agassi, Joseph. 1863. "Towards an Historiography of Science." *History and Theory.* Beiheft 2.
2. Boyer, Carl B. 1959. *The History of the Calculus.* New York: Dover.
3. Cicourel, Aaron. 1964. *Method and Measurement in Sociology.* New York: Free Press.
4. Dieudonne, J. 1964. "Recent Developments in Mathematics." *American Mathematical Monthly* 71 (February): 239–48.
5. Euclid. 1908. *The Thirteen Books of the Elements,* translated with commentary by H. L. Heath. Cambridge: Cambridge University Press.
6. Fisher, C. S. 1966. "The Death of a Mathematical Theory." *Archive for History of Exact Sciences* 3 (2): 37–59.
7. ———. 1967. "The Last Invariant Theorists." *European Journal of Sociology* 8 (2): 216–44.
8. Fleck, Ludwig. 1935. *Enstehung und Entwicklung einer Wissenshaftlicter Tatsache.* Basel: Schwabe.
9. Garfinkel, H. 1960. "The Rational Properties of Scientific and Common Sense Activities." *Behavioral Science* 5 (1): 5.
10. Glaser, B., and A. L. Strauss. 1969. *Discovery of Grounded Theory.* Chicago: Aldine.
11. Hagstrom, Warren O. 1965. *The Scientific Community.* New York: Basic.
12. Hanson, Norwood. 1958. *Patterns of Discovery.* Cambridge: Cambridge University Press.
13. Kuhn, T. S. 1961. "The Function of Measurement in Modern Physical Science." *Isis* 52 (June): 161–93.
14. ———. 1962. *The Structure of Scientific Revolutions.* Chicago: University of Chicago Press.
15. Mannheim, Karl. 1952. "The Problem of Generations." *Essays on the Sociology of Knowledge.* London: Routledge & Kegan Paul.
16. Massey, W. S. 1967. *Algebraic Topology.* New York: Harcourt, Brace & World.
17. Merton, R. K. 1957. "Priorities in Scientific Discovery." *American Sociological Review* 22 (6): 635–59.
18. Popper, K. 1963. *Conjectures and Refutations.* New York: Basic.
19. Seifert, H., and W. Threlfall. 1934. *Lehrbuch der Topologie.* Leipzig: Teubner.
20. Smale, S. 1960. "Generalized Poincaré Conjecture in Higher Dimensions." *Bulletin of the American Mathematics Society* 66 (5): 373–75.
21. ———. 1963. "Developments in Differential Topology." *Bulletin of the American Mathematical Society* 69 (2): 131–45.
22. Toulmin, Steven. 1961. *Foresight and Understanding.* Bloomington: Indiana University Press.
23. Toulmin, Steven, and G. J. Goodfield. 1966. *The Discovery of Time.* New York: Harper & Row.
24. Waterman, Alan T. 1966. "Social Influences and Scientists." *Science* 151 (January): 61–64.
25. Williams, L. Pierce. 1965. *Michael Faraday.* London: Chapman Hall.

Notes

1. Popper (1963) and Kuhn (1962). The former focuses upon the intellectual function of prob-

lems in generating new problems, while the latter places problems within a broader psycho-social model of science. Sociologists only peripherally address the function of problems. See Hagstrom (1965) and Merton (1957).

2. Kuhn (1961, pp. 161–93). The evils of seeing all science as made up of arithmeticlike problems have been dealt with by a number of authors. They banish the "inductivist" view which paints sciences as a list of necessary achievements. In so doing they help lay the groundwork for a more sociological description of the activities of scientists (Agassi, 1963; Hanson, 1958; Toulmin, 1961).

3. This essay can be viewed as an exercise in gathering instances for the purpose of theory building in the spirit of B. Glaser and A. L. Strauss (1969).

4. The nature and limitations of my general mode of procedure have been much discussed. For the general problems of sociological data, see Cicourel (1964).

5. There is no intention here of reifying those entities which are referred to as "social structures." Their existence as social objects is not claimed. The term "social structure" is purely organizational. It is a convenient title for a series of observations.

6. This discussion glosses over a very complicated subject. The "existence" of mathematical objects has changed in nature over the centuries. From the standpoint of Euclid, mathematics dealt with worldly objects. Euclid's axioms were "common notions." With the advent of non-Euclidian geometry and set theory in the 19th century and the shift toward abstraction in the 20th century, the "existence" of mathematical objects became more a matter of their logical existence within deductive systems. Although on the formal level this has been a general trend, some working mathematicians still speak of themselves as investigators of the world in which we live. See Euclid (1908) and Boyer (1959).

7. A discussion of proof from a sociological viewpoint can be found in Fisher (1967).

8. Again one must refine this generalization against the very complicated situation in modern physics. The hierarchy is by no means universally accepted and though many men pay lip service to it, it has no meaning in their scientific lives. The case of the experimentalists working on superconductivity is an apt one. Some of these men tend to downgrade the high-powered mathematical physicists as men with mere formalism. The former see real physics as lying in their manipulations and the theory of the latter as something which comes after the fact. In Hagstrom (1965), prestige is incorrectly described as being based on the logical form of theory. See Fisher (1966, pp. 137–59) which points to the interesting case of continuum mechanics.

9. For instance, Gauss and Ramanujan.

10. The reader should remember here that the structural features of mathematics are being selected so as to bear upon the particular problem being studied. Algebra, geometry, and analysis are the classical subject area of mathematics. They only partially delineate the great number of theories which go to make up mathematics. As far back as the 17th century the analytic geometry of Descartes bridges these categories. Over time, the content of the categories changes and their boundaries disappear. Such obvious subjects as mathematical logic and probability theory belong to none of them. Some contemporary mathematicians claim they are useless. Others feel the entire discipline is being algebraized. In any case they help to indicate the diversity of mathematical ideas (Dieudonne, 1964, pp. 239–48).

11. Let me try to clarify the mathematical meanings surrounding the description of the conjecture. First of all, topology, like New Math, is concerned with sets. It deals with the properties of sets defined to be continuous. Two topological spaces (i.e., sets with continuous structures) are said to be topologically equivalent when there is a function which maps one set onto the other so that points are identified in a one-to-one manner and both the function and its inverse are continuous. In modern dress, the Poincaré conjecture claims that any simply connected closed three dimensional topological manifold is topologically equivalent to a three dimensional sphere (Smale, 1960;

Massey, 1967). The technical content of the problem need not concern us here. A more detailed study of the elements which go into the solution of the problem would require a completely different format than is presented in this paper.

There are several logical points about the nature of the problem which may be confusing. When a mathematician offers a conjecture, it is as though he were saying to his colleagues, "I think such and such ought to be the case." He cannot *prove* his statements, but in his belief they should be provable. If a proof of the statements is produced and the proof contains neither logical nor substantive mathematical errors then the conjecture is said to be established or true. The mathematician puts forth a claim to the truth of his statement; it requires proof to establish that truth.

In the case of the Poincaré conjecture, many men have offered proofs of its validity. In each case the proofs have been shown to be faulty. This does not mean that the conjecture is wrong or false, but only that the proofs offered were not sufficient to establish what they claimed. To show that the conjecture is false it is necessary either to exhibit a counterexample or to prove that it logically contradicts another already established theorem. In the case we are considering, a number of men have looked for counterexamples.

12. This term is to be interpreted broadly. It divides the men into vaguely defined age groups. Many similarities between two or more of the men cut across generations. See Mannheim (1952).

13. This is called the generalized Poincaré conjecture. It covers the case of higher dimensions but does not include the original problem for three dimensions. Therefore it is not strictly a logical generalization (Smale, 1963).

14. References to "natural lines of development" to justify interest is typical for scientists. The ways in which they, after the fact, characterize the success of a theory or technique leaves out the potentially efficacious elements of alternate approaches. They constantly describe their worlds in terms of good, correct, effica-

cious, natural theories versus bad, incorrect, useless, unnatural ones (Fisher, 1966; Kuhn, 1962).

15. The fact that he was never able to solve the problem, unlike actual heroes, had a number of consequences for him which we will consider later.

16. The constellation of how a man came across a problem, his rationale for its importance, and his commitment to it seem to undercut Hagstrom's (1965) functional "Information-Recognition Exchange" model of the social mechanism of science. Aside from the fact that the model creates dupes who deny they are in the game for its rewards, it tends to attribute motive on a much too uniform basis. If we begin to survey the complexity of any realm of human activity we often find that motives for given acts are grounded in the on-going events of the realm. Dedicated mathematicians are sometimes oriented almost completely toward the subject matter of their discipline. The justification for a man's involvement may lie within the subject matter. With regard to the conjecture: *Q:* "Why should a man spend so many years working on it?" *A:* "To find out whether it is true. This problem is logically so simple and natural, that it seems to me intolerable for the answer not to be known." This man worked on the problem despite the fact that his colleagues felt he was wasting his time. Either he is a "deviant" (if he is, then so are most great mathematicians) or he is to be seen as taking a long-shot gamble on fame. The analysis in this essay urges neither of these alternatives; the man is inextricably involved in the subject matter of his discipline and that subject matter often seems to dictate courses of action. Compare Hagstrom (1965) with Waterman (1966, pp. 61–64).

17. Rational in the sense of Garfinkel's scientific rationalities (1960).

18. The fine distinctions men draw are important. When characterizing other mathematicians, they might classify each as belonging to one or another schools of thought, but on considering the work of an individual, they are aware of details which distinguish the man

from everyone else. Even a student of a great man (if the former is at all creative) is carefully separated from his teacher. Scientists, like other men, live in densely filled worlds. The historian or sociologist in attempting to describe that world requires simple categories in which to place people. Without simplicity the story would be untellable. The scientist uses highly refined distinctions because he only has to *live* in his world. See Fleck (1935, chap. 2).

19. This is true even for men who collaborate. They use the same methods in one piece of work then go their separate ways afterward.

20. The logical form of these theorems is: given the conjecture, then X holds. If now the conjecture is shown to be false or remains unproven, then one can say nothing about the truth of X.

21. In order to disprove the conjecture one might have to construct what amounts to an inconceivable object, i.e., something which is both counterintuitive and not "seeable." Such pathologies abound in mathematics. Some are objects whose existence can be proven, but for which no intuitive model can be made. Although many mathematicians look upon pathologies with distaste, they have played an important role in the development of the discipline, for example, the pathologies of set theory and measure theory.

22. The observations in this section differ from those in the earlier ones only in their order of presentation. There is no claim that they stand to each other as cause and effect. From both a commonsensical and a descriptive standpoint these facts appear as posterior to the others. No clear dividing line exists between them; the causes of any structural or problem-solving feature could be multiplied ad infinitum. After all, everything described is just phenomenon. If we want to establish one as prior to another in the causal sense of physics, then we would have to perform experiments which we are by no means able to do. Therefore, the use of the word "consequence" is admittedly in a sense contrary to one of its usual meanings.

23. The social stigma attached to the presentation of erroneous proofs will be examined elsewhere.

Mathematics as Propaganda

Neal Koblitz

Neal Koblitz received his Ph.D. in mathematics at Princeton in 1974. He spent the years 1974, 1975, and 1978 at Moscow University doing postdoctorate studies. From 1975 to 1979 he was a Benjamin Peirce Instructor at Harvard University. Koblitz is currently an associate professor at the University of Washington in Seattle.

Koblitz is a self-confessed (and apparently repentant) mathematical propagandist. Having been guilty of the offense, he writes with the purpose of arming the unwary against the onslaughts of those who would deceive with pseudomathematics. While the tone of the essay is not ponderous the topic treated is important. The general level of public understanding of mathematics is quite low. It is no trick for charlatans or even for the well-meaning but ignorant to express a bit of nonsense in pseudomathematical jargon in order to increase its acceptability. This practice is so common that in one guise or another one meets it almost daily. To eliminate such pseudomathematics we must first be aware that it is done. If we routinely scrutinize advertisements, governmental studies, reports of quasi-scientific research, and so on, for attempts to validate lies with equations, graphs, functions, and all the rest, then we would see much less nonsense in the world. And that would benefit all of us.

ONE NIGHT SEVERAL years ago while watching TV, I was surprised to see a mathematical equation make an appearance on the "Tonight Show." The occasion was an interview with Paul Ehrlich, author of *The Population Bomb* and popularizer of population control as a solution to the world's problems. At that time the ecology movement had just started to capture the attention of the public, and Mr. Ehrlich was arguing that the solution, as always, was in population control.

Johnny Carson was in top form, but the show could have bogged down if his guest had delved into subtleties or overly serious discussion. However, Ehrlich had the perfect solution. He took a piece of posterboard and wrote in large letters for the TV audience:

$$D = N \times I.$$

"In this equation," he explained, "D stands for damage to the environment, N stands for the number of people, and I stands for the impact of each person on the environment. This equation shows that the more people, the more pollution. We cannot control pollution without controlling the number of people."

Johnny Carson looked at the equation, scratched his head, made a remark about never having been good at math, and commented that it all looked quite impressive.

Who can argue with an equation? An equation is always exact, indisputable. Challenging someone who can support his claims with an equation is as pointless as arguing with your high school math teacher. How many of Johnny Carson's viewers had the sophistication necessary to question Ehrlich's equation? Is Ehrlich saying that the "I" for the president of Hooker Chemicals (of Love Canal notoriety) is the same as the "I" for you and me? Preposterous, isn't it? But what if the viewer is too intimidated by a mathematical

Source: Neal Koblitz, "Mathematics as Propaganda," in Lynn Steen, ed., *Mathematics Tomorrow* (New York: Springer-Verlag, 1981), pp. 111–120.

equation to apply some common sense? Ehrlich knew how to use his time on the show well.

Political Theory

Of course, it will surprise no one to find low standards of intellectual honesty on the "Tonight Show."

But we find a less trivial example if we enter the hallowed halls of Harvard University, where Professor Samuel Huntington lectures on the problems of developing countries. His definitive book on the subject is *Political Order in Changing Societies* (1968), in which he suggests various relationships between certain political and sociological concepts: (a) "social mobilization," (b) "economic development," (c) "social frustration," (d) "mobility opportunities," (e) "political participation," (f) "political institutionalization," (g) "political instability." He expresses these relationships in a series of equations (p. 55):

$$\frac{\text{social mobilization}}{\text{economic development}} = \text{social frustration}$$

$$\left(\frac{a}{b} = c\right);$$

$$\frac{\text{social frustration}}{\text{mobility opportunities}} = \text{political participation}$$

$$\left(\frac{c}{d} = e\right);$$

$$\frac{\text{political participation}}{\text{political institutionalization}} = \text{political instability}$$

$$\left(\frac{e}{f} = g\right).$$

When he is called upon to summarize his book (e.g., in *Theories of Social Change*, Daniel Bell, ed.), he emphasizes these equations.

Huntington never bothers to inform the reader in what sense these are equations. It is doubtful that any of the terms (a)–(g) can be measured and assigned a single numerical value. What are the units of measurement? Will Huntington allow us to operate with these equations using the well-known techniques of ninth grade algebra? If so, we could infer, for instance, that

$$a = b \cdot c = b \cdot d \cdot e = b \cdot d \cdot f \cdot g$$

i.e., that "social mobilization is equal to economic development times mobility opportunities times political institutionalization times political instability!"

A woman I know was assigned an article by Huntington for her graduate seminar on historical methodology. The article summarized his work on modernization and cited these equations. When she criticized the use of the equations, pointing out the absurdities that follow if one takes them seriously, both the professors and the other graduate students demurred. For one, they had some difficulty following her application of ninth grade algebra. Moreover, they were not used to questioning an eminent authority figure who could argue using equations.

Huntington's use of equations produced effects—mystification, intimidation, an impression of precision and profundity—which were similar to those produced by Paul Ehrlich's use of an equation on the "Tonight Show." But Huntington operates on a more serious level. He is no mere talk-show social scientist. When he is not teaching at Harvard, he is likely to be advising the National Security Council or writing reports for the Trilateral Commission or the Council on Foreign Relations.

Slavery

Before leaving Harvard, let us look in on another professor, this time in the Department of Economics. Robert W. Fogel's specialty is applying quantitative methods to economic history. He and a collaborator, Stanley Engerman, produced a sensation in 1974 with a book called *Time on the Cross*. Using statistical arguments with voluminous computer-processed data, they purported to show that the slave system in the South was both more humane and economically more efficient than the free labor system that existed at that time in the North.

Although this thesis contradicted the conclusions of all major conventional historians, the book was received enthusiastically. Harvard historian Stephan Thernstrom called it "quite simply the most exciting and provocative book I've read in years," and Columbia economist Peter Passel wrote in his *New York Times* book review that it has "with one stroke turned around a whole field of interpretation and exposed the frailty of history done without science."

The initial acclaim lasted long enough to produce an effect outside academia. Fogel appeared on the "Today Show"; the book was reviewed in the *Wall Street Journal, Time* magazine, *Newsweek*, and over three dozen other major publications. The public was told that a sentimental and subjective view of slavery had given way to a "scientific" view based on computer analysis of hard quantitative facts.

But then historians of the slave period and specialists in the use of quantitative methods in history ("cliometricians") undertook careful studies of the book, and the honeymoon ended. They found such an accumulation of outright errors, fallacious inferences, dubious assumptions, and disingenuous use of statistics that the entire project lost any validity. Here is a typical example, as explained by Thomas L. Haskell in the *New York Review of Books:*

> . . . readers of *Time on the Cross* are inclined toward a benign view of slavery when they read that the average slave on the Barrow plantation received only 0.7 whippings per year. In the first place the figure is too low because it is based on an erroneous count both of the number of slaves Barrow owned and the number of times he whipped them. But more important, the figure is not the most relevant measure of the importance of whippings. A whipping, like a lynching, is an instrument of social discipline intended to impress not only the immediate victim but all who see or hear about the event. The relevant question is "How often did Barrow's slaves see one of their number whipped?"—to which the answer is every four and a half days. Again, the form in which the figures are expressed controls their meaning. If one expressed the rate of lynchings in the same form Fogel and Engerman chose for whippings, it would turn out that in 1893 there were only about 0.00002 lynchings per black per year. But obviously this way of expressing the data would cause the reader utterly to misunderstand the histo-

rical significance of the 155 Negro lynchings that occurred in 1893.

Other examples would take too long to go into here; the interested reader is referred to Haskell's excellent article (*NYRB,* Oct. 2, 1975) and to the three volumes critiquing *Time on the Cross* which Haskell reviews.

Haskell regards *Time on the Cross* as an aberration, and refrains from indicting the entire "cliometric" approach because of one unfortunate case. However, he makes some insightful comments on the dangers inherent in any application of mathematics to the social sciences:

> On the surface, cliometrics is an austere and rigorous discipline that minimizes the significance of any statement that cannot be reduced to a clear empirical test ("operationalized"). But beneath the surface one often finds startling flights of conjecture, so daring that even the most woolly-minded humanist might gasp with envy.
>
> The soft, licentious side of cliometrics derives, paradoxically, from its reliance on mathematical equations. Before the cliometrician can use his equation to explain the past, he must assign an empirical value to each of its terms, even if the relevant empirical data have not been preserved or were never recorded. When an incomplete historical record fails—as it often does—to supply the figures that the cliometrician's equations require him to have, it is considered fair play to resort to *estimation,* just so long as he specifies the assumptions underlying his estimates. And although cliometrics requires that these and all other assumptions be made explicit, it sets no limit at all on the *number* of assumptions one may make, or how high contingent assumptions may be piled on top of each other—just so they are explicit.

Fogel, like Huntington, understands the propaganda value of mathematics. In some quarters, invoking an equation or statistic can be even more persuasive than citing a well-known authority. An argument which would be quickly disputed if stated in plain English will often acquire some momentum if accompanied by numbers and formulas, regardless of whether or not they are relevant or accurate. The threshold of expertise and self-confidence needed to challenge an argument becomes much higher if it is enshrouded in science. It is no wonder that quantitative methods have become a bit of a fad in the social sciences.

The impact of *Time on the Cross* reached outside the academic world. Slavery is perhaps the most profound and emotional issue in American history. How one regards slavery has clear implications for attitudes toward present-day grievances of black people and methods proposed to address those grievances, such as busing, affirmative action, compensatory education, etc. It was because of these implications that the book received so much attention outside scholarly circles.

Another example of pseudo-quantitative argument injected into an emotional issue with wide repercussions is the IQ controversy.

IQ

Cyril Burt is often regarded as the father of educational psychology. During a prolific research career that spanned several decades he influenced much thinking among both psychologists and educators in Great Britain and the United States. He was knighted, and his recognition in America included the Edward Lee Thorndike Award of the American Psychological Association.

One of his major achievements was his studies of identical twins separated at birth, which purported to show that intelligence is determined predominantly by heredity rather than by environment. The idea of these studies was that such twins have the same genes but are raised in different environments, so that the correlation between their performance on IQ tests gives a measure of the relative influence of heredity. Burt concluded from his studies that IQ is about 80% heredity and 20% environment.

These studies became especially well known in the late 1960's and early 1970's, because they provided the most important scientific argument for the position popularized by Berkeley Professor Jensen, Stanford Professor Shockley and Harvard Professor Herrnstein that inequalities in society are explained largely by the genetic inferiority of those on the bottom. Jensen and Shockley maintained that 4/5 of the roughly 15 point difference in the measured average IQ of blacks and whites is due to racial differences in intelligence; Herrnstein claimed that "as technology advances, the tendency to be unemployed may run in the genes of a family about as certainly as bad teeth do now." Of course, this viewpoint met vigorous opposition: scholars in various fields pointed out the inaccuracies and cultural biases of IQ tests, the effect of the testing situation, the logical fallacy of extrapolating from interpersonal to intergroup differences, and so on. But for a long time no one went back to examine in detail Burt's original studies.

The first person to do so was Princeton psychologist Leon Kamin. His curiosity aroused by the stormy controversy, Professor Kamin started reading Burt's papers and trying to locate his raw data. Almost immediately he came upon startling irregularities. For example, Burt published three reports in 1955, 1958 and 1966, during which time the total number of identical twins reared apart and the total number of identical twins reared together increased, presumably as more data came in. The reported correlation of IQ's in each group remained identical to three decimal places!

The chance of this happening by honest coincidence is infinitesimal. It began to look like Burt faked his data. The more Kamin examined Burt's work, the more evidence he found of fabrication. (The interested reader may consult Kamin's fascinating book *The Science and Politics of IQ* [John Wiley & Sons, 1974], from which the chart below is taken.)

Burt's Reported Correlations for IQ's of Identical Twins

	Reared Apart		Reared Together	
1955	0.771	($N_1 = 21$)	0.944	($N_2 = 83$)
1958	0.771	($N_1 = $ "over 30")	0.944	(N_2 unspecified)
1966	0.771	($N_1 = 53$)	0.944	($N_2 = 95$)

Backed up by his quantitative "studies," such as the series on identical twins, Cyril Burt had an enormous impact on educational practice as well as theory.

His view that intelligence was predetermined at birth and largely unchangeable helped to shape a rigid, three-tier school system in England based on an I.Q. test given to children at the age of 11. ("Briton's Classic I.Q. Data Now Viewed as Fraudulent," *New York Times*, Nov. 28, 1976.)

More recently, Jensen has used Burt's research in a long article in the *Harvard Educational Review* (1969) to argue the futility of compensatory education programs such as Head Start.

Finally, it is amusing to note how those who are ideologically wedded to the hereditarian position reacted to the exposure of Burt. First of all, they fell back on other studies that seemed to support Burt. These studies were also analyzed by Kamin and shown to be full of holes (though not because of deliberate falsification). But it would take more than Kamin's scientific analysis to shake the self-confidence of Burt's disciples. Interviewed by the *Harvard Crimson* (Oct. 30, 1976), Herrnstein said that even "if he did fake his data, then he faked it truly."

A Game Anyone Can Play

The manipulative use of quantitative arguments is most glaring and annoying when the result is distasteful. But such methodology is merely a tool, and like most tools can be used for good or evil. The word "propaganda" in my title is not necessarily meant to be pejorative. All I mean by that word is a device that makes it possible to disseminate and popularize a point of view without a thorough and careful argument. If frightening statistics on smoking and cancer or drinking and auto accidents are presented in the high schools in a slightly over-simplified and misleading manner, then that is propaganda; but most people would feel that in such cases "the ends justify the means."

I remember using this tool once for a polemical purpose. The year was 1969, and I, together with other anti-War activists, was supporting striking workers at a General Electric plant near Trenton, New Jersey. We were attempting to build ties between workers and students, at the same time encouraging workers' increasing disillusionment with the Vietnam War. In addition to moral and material support for the strike, we brought leaflets. My contribution to one of the leaflets was the graph in Figure 1. Its message is clear: as a defense contractor, GE's profits went up after the escalation of the War, at the same time as workers were paying for the War through battle deaths and declining real wages.

My use of the graph was admittedly an example of "mathematics as propaganda." Someone unsympathetic to my purpose could complain that the graph unfairly implies that GE profits *cause* GI deaths. I was exploiting the basic fact that the graphs of any two increasing functions can be made to resemble one another if the scales and intervals for the two variables are suitably chosen. On the other hand, someone who agreed with what we were doing would probably consider the graph to be a permissible short-cut to get the point across.

Implications for Teaching

Whether mathematical devices in arguments are used for fair ends or foul, a well-educated person should be able to approach such devices critically. Indeed, for many people it may be as important to be able to identify misuses of mathematics as it is to know about the correct uses. More generally, discussions of the fallacies of the pseudo-sciences (astrology, laetrile, biorhythms, etc.) should be included as part of the basic science program in the schools.

Concretely, how can we impart the analytical abilities and the qualities of skepticism and sophistication needed to be able to deal intelligently with quantitative arguments about social and psychological phenomena? This is a difficult challenge. All I can hope to do here is illustrate with a couple of examples.

When students study the use of graphs, they could be shown (or asked to find) examples from

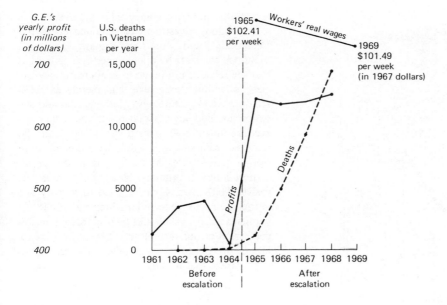

G.E.'s yearly profit (in millions of dollars): 700, 600, 500, 400

U.S. deaths in Vietnam per year: 15,000, 10,000, 5000, 0

1965 • $102.41 per week

Workers' real wages

1969 • $101.49 per week (in 1967 dollars)

Profits

Deaths

1961 1962 1963 1964 | 1965 1966 1967 1968 1969

Before escalation

After escalation

Figure 1

the newspapers and newsmagazines which illustrate how graphs can be set up so as to exaggerate a trend or over-simplify a situation. A homework problem might be: Find at least three ways in which the graph in Figure 2 manages to convey an exaggerated impression of the data. (Answer: the vertical scale starts at 400 rather than zero, the vertical scale is larger to the right than to the left, and actual dollars, rather than inflation-adjusted dollars, are used.)

The table in Figure 3 illustrates an example I have used with first year calculus students who are just learning about differential equations. I describe three possible models for world population growth, all plausible, all based on the same empirical data (present population 4 billion, present growth rate 2% per year), and all leading to differential equations which can readily be solved by the technique of separation of variables. I then ask the students what one can conclude from the widely disparate predictions of the three models. Usually, none of them knows what to say, since mathematics is always supposed to provide a definitive precise answer. Of course, the moral of the story is that world population is far too complex to follow any simplistic model.

Mathematicians in a More Public Role

In addition to our influence as teachers, mathematicians can affect public attitudes through various institutions and media. Just as the medical profession tries to combat medical quackery, members of the mathematical profession can take a stand against mathematical quackery.

I know of one recent example of a remarkably effective effort in this direction by a mathematician: Serge Lang's campaign against Seymour Martin Lipset's ill-conceived "Survey of the Professoriate." Lang's comprehensive critique of the biases, improprieties and methodological fallacies in the survey has led many people to a re-examination of surveying in general and of the use of pseudo-quantitative techniques in sociology. I cannot go into Lang's critique here; the reader is referred to his article in the *New York Review of Books* (May 18, 1978) and to the volume of correspondence on this issue . . . published by Springer-Verlag [The File: Case study in correction (1977–1979), New York, 1981].

To stem the tide of pseudo-science and educate the public to an accurate appreciation of science and mathematics is a Sisyphean task. Major prog-

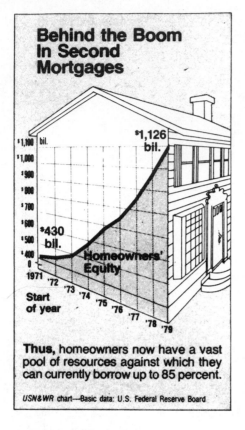

Behind the Boom In Second Mortgages

$1,126 bil.

$430 bil.

Homeowners' Equity

Start of year

1971 '72 '73 '74 '75 '76 '77 '78 '79

Thus, homeowners now have a vast pool of resources against which they can currently borrow up to 85 percent.

USN&WR chart—Basic data: U.S. Federal Reserve Board

Figure 2   (With permission from *U.S. News and World Report*, Nov. 12, 1979.)

ress in this endeavor comes only at the expense of a tremendous investment of time and energy, as Leon Kamin and Serge Lang can attest.

But we can start by opening our eyes to the fact that the relationship between mathematics and society is far more extensive than merely its direct relationship to technology. Mathematical and statistical methodology is playing an increasing and even dominant role in many fields which are far removed from what one would have thought to be readily quantifiable. As we have seen, this proliferation is not an unmixed blessing. Abuse is pervasive. Mathematics can be used to mystify and intimidate rather than to enlighten the public. As mathematicians, we should take an interest in this perversion of our discipline. There is no easy solution. But the first step in solving the problem is to recognize that it exists.

Figure 3

Assumption for Model of World Population Growth	Differential Equation	Solution (in Billions of People)	Predicted Population in 100 Years (in Billions of People)
(1) Growth rate remains constant at 2% per year	$y' = 0.02y$	$4e^{0.02t}$	29.6
(2) An inhibiting effect proportional to the population decreases the growth rate	$y' = 0.02y\left(2 - \dfrac{y}{4}\right)$	$\dfrac{8}{1 + e^{-0.04t}}$	7.9
(3) The growth rate itself decreases by 2% per year	$y' = 0.02y\, e^{-0.02t}$	$4e^{1 - e^{-0.02t}}$	9.5

Can We Make Mathematics Intelligible?

R. P. Boas

Ralph Philip Boas, Jr., was born in Walla Walla, Washington. He did his undergraduate and graduate work at Harvard. He has been professor of mathematics at Northwestern University since 1950. He was executive editor of *Mathematical Reviews* from 1945 to 1950. He has been a Guggenheim fellow, president of the Mathematical Association of America and vice-president of the American Mathematical Society.

This essay is a bit of advice written by a mathematician to mathematicians. Boas asserts that making mathematics intelligible to students or the public is important and suggests how it might, in part, be done. Why, one may ask, is there need for an article on a topic so elementary that it is surely the first concern of anyone communicating mathematics? The reason, faithful reader, is that, historically, making mathematics intelligible has often been the last concern of those communicating it. Throughout history mathematics has generally been supported by an educated elite. Whether the elite understood what it supported was often unimportant. What was important was that the product reaffirmed the special position of the elite. What rational nobleman would waste his substance in support of investigations that even peasants could appreciate?!

History suggests that pure mathematics and democracy are not allies. If voted upon, pure mathematics would follow cockroach breeding on the list of vital public concerns, that is, those for which taxes should be levied. Applied sciences, however, tend to be popular in democracies since the benefits of such a science are more uniformly distributed and quite immediate. The problem faced by mathematics and the basic sciences in a democracy is obvious: They need to sell themselves. Mathematicians and scientists need to convince the public that without basic science and mathematics there can be no applied science and therefore no profits to distribute.

The advantages of such a publicity campaign are manifold. But by nature and training mathematicians are not the best agents to conduct such a campaign. Perhaps the discipline will be advanced regardless of public attitude toward mathematics. But mathematicians could help a bit, and some modest effort to communicate effectively is not a bad place to start.

WHY IS IT that we mathematicians have such a hard time making ourselves understood? Many people have negative feelings about mathematics, which they blame, rightly or wrongly, on their teachers.[1] Students complain that they cannot understand their textbooks; they have been doing this ever since I was a student, and presumably for much longer than that. Professionals in other disciplines feel compelled to write their own accounts of the mathematics they had trouble with. However, it was not until after I became editor of the *Monthly* that I quite realized how hard it is for mathematicians to write so as to be understood even by other mathematicians (outside of fellow

Source: R. P. Boas, "Can We Make Mathematics Intelligible?" *American Mathematical Monthly* 88 (1981): 727–731.

specialists). The number of manuscripts rejected, not for mathematical deficiencies but for general lack of intelligibility, has been shocking. One of my predecessors had much the same experience 35 years earlier.[2]

To put it another way, why do we speak and write about mathematics in ways that interfere so dramatically with what we ostensibly want to accomplish? I wish I knew. However, I can at least point out some principles that are frequently violated by teachers and authors. Perhaps they are violated because they contradict what many of my contemporaries seem to consider to be self-evident truths. (They also have little in common with the MAA report on how to teach mathematics.[3])

Abstract Definitions

Suppose you want to teach the "cat" concept to a very young child. Do you explain that a cat is a relatively small, primarily carnivorous mammal with retractile claws, a distinctive sonic output, etc.? I'll bet not. You probably show the kid a lot of different cats, saying "kitty" each time, until it gets the idea. To put it more generally, generalizations are best made by abstraction from experience. They should come one at a time; too many at once overload the circuits.

There is a test for identifying some of the future professional mathematicians at an early age. These are students who instantly comprehend a sentence beginning "Let X be an ordered quintuple $(a, T, \pi, \sigma, \mathcal{B})$, where . . ." They are even more promising if they add, "I never really understood it before." Not all professional mathematicians are like this, of course; but you can hardly succeed in becoming a professional unless you can at least understand this kind of writing.

However, unless you are extraordinarily lucky, most of your audience will not be professional mathematicians, will have no intention of becoming professional mathematicians, and will never become professional mathematicians. To begin with, they won't understand anything that starts off with an abstract definition (let alone with a dozen at once), because they don't yet have anything to generalize from. Please don't immediately write me angry letters explaining how important abstraction and generalization are for the development of mathematics: I *know* that. I also am sure that when Banach wrote down the axioms for a Banach space he had a lot of specific spaces in mind as models. Besides, I am discussing only the communication of mathematics, not its creation.

For example, if you are going to explain to an average class how to find the distance from a point to a plane, you should first find the distance from $(2, -3, 1)$ to $x - 2y - 4z + 7 = 0$. After that, the general procedure will be almost obvious. Textbooks used to be written that way. It is a good general principle that, if you have made your presentation twice as concrete as you think you should, you have made it at most half as concrete as you ought to.

Remember that *you* have been associating with mathematicians for years and years. By this time you probably not only think like a mathematician but imagine that everybody thinks like a mathematician. Any nonmathematician can tell you differently.

Analogy

Sometimes your audience will understand a new concept better if you explain that it is similar to a more familiar concept. Sometimes this device is a flop. It depends on how well the audience understands the analogous thing. An integral is a limit of a sum; therefore, since sums are simpler (no limiting processes!), students will understand how integrals behave by analogy with how sums behave. Won't they? In practice, they don't seem to. Integrals are simpler than sums for many people, and there may be some deep reason for this.[4]

Vocabulary

Never introduce terminology unnecessarily.[5] If you are going to have to mention a countable intersection of open sets—just once!—there is no justification for defining G_δ's and F_σ's.

I have been assured that nobody can really understand systems of linear equations without all the special terminology of modern linear algebra. If you believe this you must have forgotten that people understood systems of linear equations quite well for many years before the modern terminology had been invented. The terminology allows concise statements; but concision is not the alpha and omega of clear exposition. Modern terminology also lets one say more than could be said in old-fashioned presentations. Nevertheless, at the beginning of the subject a lot of the students' effort has to go into memorizing *words* when it could more advantageously go into learning mathematics. Paying more attention to vocabulary than to content obscures the content. This is what leads some students to think that the real difference between Riemann and Lebesgue integration is that in one case you divide up the *x*-axis and in the other you divide up the *y*-axis.

If you think you can invent better words than those that are currently in use, you are undoubtedly right. However, you are rather unlikely to get many people except your own students to accept your terminology; and it is unkind to make it hard for your students to understand anyone else's writing. One Bourbaki per century produces about all the neologisms that the mathematical community can absorb.

In any case, if you *must* create new words, you can at least take the trouble to verify that they are not already in use with different meanings. It has not helped communication that "distribution" now means different things in probability and in functional analysis. On the other hand, if you need to use old but unfashionable words it is a good idea to explain what they mean. A friend of mine was rebuked by a naïve referee for "inventing" bizarre words that had actually been invented by Kepler.

It is especially dangerous to assume either that the audience understands your vocabulary already or that the words mean the same to everybody else that they do to you. I know someone who thinks that everybody from high school on up knows all about Fourier transforms, in spite of considerable evidence to the contrary. Other people think that everybody knows what they mean by Abel's theorem, and therefore never say which of Abel's many theorems they are appealing to.

An even more serious problem comes from what (if it didn't violate my principles) I would call geratologisms: that is, words and phrases that, if not actually obsolete in ordinary discourse, are becoming so. Contemporary prose style is simpler and more direct than the style of the nineteenth century—except in textbooks of mathematics. While I was writing this article I was teaching from a calculus book that begins a problem with, "The strength of a beam varies directly as . . ." I do not know whether the jargon of variation is still used in high schools, but in any case it isn't learned: only one student in a class of 45 had any idea what the book meant (and he was a foreigner). Blame the students if you will, blame the high schools; for my own part I blame the authors of the textbook for not realizing that contemporary students speak a different language. Another current calculus book says, "Particulate matter concentrations in parts per million theoretically decrease by an inverse square law." You couldn't get away with that in *Newsweek* or even in *The New Yorker*, but in a textbook. . . .

Authors of textbooks (lecturers, too) need to remember that they are supposed to be addressing the students, not the teachers. What is a function? The textbook wants you to say something like, "a rule which associates to each real number a uniquely specified real number," which certainly defines a function—but hardly in a way that students will comprehend. The point that "a definition is satisfactory only if the students understand it" was already made by Poincaré[6] in 1909, but teachers of mathematics seem not to have paid much attention to it.

The difficulties of a vocabulary are not peculiar to mathematics; similar difficulties are what makes it so frustrating to try to talk to physicians or lawyers. They too insist on a rich technical language because "it is so much more precise that way." So it is, but the refined terminology is clearer only when rigorous distinctions are absolutely necessary. There is no use in emphasizing refined distinctions until the audience knows enough to see that they are needed.

Symbolism is a special kind of terminology. Mathematics can't get along without it. A good deal of progress has depended on the invention of appropriate symbolism. But let's not become so fascinated by the symbols that we forget what they stand for. Our audience (whether it is listening or reading) is going to be less familiar with the symbolism than we are. Hence it is not a good idea (to take a simple example) to say "Let f belong to L^2" instead of "Let f be a measurable function whose square is integrable," unless you are sure that the audience already understands the symbolism. Moreover, if you are not actually going to use L^2 as a Hilbert space, but want only the properties of its elements as functions, the structure of the space is irrelevant and calling attention to it is a form of showing off—mild, but it *is* showing off. If the audience doesn't know the symbolism, it is mystified; if it does know, it will be wondering when you are going to get to the point.

My advice about new terminology applies with even greater force to new symbolism. Do not create new symbolism, or change the old, unnecessarily; and admit (if necessary) that usage varies and explain the existing equivalences. If your $\Phi(x)$ also appears in the literature as $P(x)$ or $P(x) + \frac{1}{2}$ or $F(x)$, *say so.* Irresponsible improvements in notation have already caused enough trouble. I don't know who first thought of using θ in spherical coordinates to mean azimuth, whereas θ had almost always previously stood for colatitude, as it still does in physics and in advanced mathematics. It's superficially a reasonable convention because it makes θ the same as in plane polar coordinates; however, since r is different anyway, that isn't much help. The result is that students who go beyond calculus have to learn all the formulas over again. Such complications don't bother the true-blue pure mathematicians, those who would just as soon see Newton's second law of motion stated as $\mathbf{v} = (d/d\sigma)(\mathcal{R}\mathbf{q})$, but they do bother many students, besides irritating physical scientists.

Proofs

Only professional mathematicians learn anything from proofs. Other people learn from explanations. I'm not sure that even mathematicians learn much from proofs in fields with which they are not familiar. A great deal can be accomplished with arguments that fall short of being formal proofs. I have known a professor (I hesitate to say "teacher") to spend an entire semester on a proof of Cauchy's integral theorem under very general hypotheses. A collection of special cases and examples would have carried more conviction and left time for more varied and interesting material, besides leaving the audience better equipped to understand, apply, generalize, and teach Cauchy's theorem.

I cannot remember who first remarked that a sweater is what a child puts on when its parent feels cold; but a proof is what students have to listen to when the teacher feels shaky about a theorem. It has been claimed[7] that "some of the most important results . . . are so surprising at first sight that nothing short of a proof can make them credible." There are fewer of these than you think.

Experienced parents realize that when a child says "Why?" it doesn't necessarily want to hear a reason; it just wants more conversation. The same principle applies when a class asks for a proof.

Rigor

This is often confused with generality or completeness. In spite of what reviewers are likely to say, there is nothing unrigorous in stating a special case of a theorem instead of the most general case you know, or a simple sufficient condition rather than a complicated one. For example, I prefer to give beginners Dirichlet's test for the convergence of a Fourier series: "piecewise monotonic and bounded" is more comprehensible than "bounded variation"; and, in fact, equally useful after one more theorem (learned later).

The compulsion to tell everything you know is one of the worst enemies of effective communication. We mathematicians would get along better with the Physics Department if, for example, we could bring ourselves to admit that, although their students need some Fourier analysis for quantum mechanics, they don't need a whole semester's worth—two weeks is nearer the mark.

Being more thorough than necessary is closely allied to **pedantry,** which (my dictionary says) is "excessive emphasis of trivial details."

Here's an example. Suppose students are looking for a local minimum of a differentiable function f, and they find critical points at $x = 2$, $x = 5$, and nowhere else. Suppose also that they do not want to use (or are told not to use) the second derivative. Some textbooks will tell them to check $f(2 + h)$ and $f(2 - h)$ for all small h. Students naturally prefer to check $f(3)$ and $f(1)$. The pedantic teacher says, "No"; the honest teacher admits that any point up to the next critical point will do.

Enthusiasm

Teachers are often urged to show enthusiasm for their subjects. Did you ever have to listen to a really enthusiastic specialist holding forth on something that you did not know and did not want to know anything about, say the bronze coinage of Poldavia in the twelfth century or "the doctrine of the enclitic *De*"?[8] Well, then.

Skills

A great deal of the mathematics that many mathematicians support themselves by teaching consists of subjects like elementary algebra or calculus or numerical analysis—skills, in short. It is not always easy to tell whether a student has acquired a skill or, as we like to put it, "really" learned a subject. The difficulty is much like that of deciding whether apes can use language in a linguistically interesting way or whether they have just become very clever at pushing buttons and waving their hands.[9] Mathematical skills are like any other kind. If you are learning to play the piano, you usually start by practicing under supervision; you don't begin with theoretical lectures on acoustical vibrations and the internal structure of the instrument. Similarly for mathematical skills. We often read or hear arguments about the relative merits of lectures and discus-

sions, as if these were the only two ways to conduct a class. Having students practice under supervision is another and very effective way. Unfortunately it is both untraditional and expensive.

Even research in mathematics is, to a considerable extent, a teachable skill. A student of G. H. Hardy's once described to me how it was done. If you were a student of Hardy's, he gave you a problem that he was sure you could solve. You solved it. Then he asked you to generalize it in a specific way. You did that. Then he suggested another generalization, and so on. After a certain number of iterations, you were finding (and solving) your own problems. You didn't necessarily learn to be a second Gauss that way, but you could learn to do useful work.

Lectures

These are great for arousing the emotions. As a means of instruction, they ought to have become obsolete when the printing press was invented. We had a second chance when the Xerox machine was invented, but we seem to have muffed it. If you *have* to lecture, you can at least hand out copies of what you said (or wish you had said). I know mathematicians who contend that only through their lectures can they communicate their personal attitudes toward their subjects. This may be true at an advanced level, for pre-professional students. Otherwise I wonder whether these mathematicians' personalities are really worth learning about, and (if so) whether the students couldn't learn them better some other way (over coffee in the cafeteria, for example).

One of the great mysteries is: How can people manage to extract useful information from incomprehensible nonsense? In fact, we can and do. Read, for example, in Morris Kline's book[10] about the history of the teaching of calculus. Perhaps this talent that we have can explain the popularity of lectures. One incomprehensible lecture is not enough, but a whole course may be effective in a way that one incomprehensible book never can. I still contend that a comprehensible book is even better.

Conclusion

I used to advise neophyte teachers: "Think of what your teachers did that you particularly disliked—and don't do it." This was good advice as far as it went, but it didn't go far enough. My tentative answer to the question in my title is, "Yes; but don't be guided by introspection." You cannot expect to communicate effectively (whether in the classroom or in writing) unless and until you understand your audience. This is not an easy lesson to learn.

Notes

1. See, for example, Sydney J. Harris, column for February 9, 1980, *Chicago Sun-Times* and elsewhere.
2. L. R. Ford, Retrospect, *American Mathematical Monthly,* 53 (1946) 582–585.
3. *College Mathematics: Suggestions on How to Teach It,* Mathematical Association of America, 1972.
4. D. R. Stoutmeyer, Symbolic computation comes of age, *SIAM News,* 12, no. 6 (December 1979) 1, 2, 9.
5. The same point has been made by P. R. Halmos in How to Write Mathematics, *L'Enseignement mathématique,* (2) 16 (1970) 123–152.
6. H. Poincaré, *Science et méthode,* 1909, Book II, Chapter 2.
7. H. and B. S. Jeffreys, *Methods of Mathematical Physics,* 2nd ed., Cambridge University Press, 1950, p. v.
8. Robert Browning, "A Grammarian's Funeral," in *The Complete Poetic and Dramatic Works of Robert Browning,* Houghton Mifflin, Boston and New York, 1895, pp. 279–280.
9. For example, E. S. Savage-Rumbaugh, D. M. Rumbaugh, and S. Boysen, Do apes use language? *Amer. Scientist,* 68 (1980) 49–61.
10. Morris Kline, *Mathematics: The Loss of Certainty,* Oxford University Press, New York, 1980.

The Nature of Current Mathematical Research

Morris Kline

Morris Kline was born in New York City and did his undergraduate and graduate work in New York City at N.Y.U. He has been associated with N.Y.U. almost continuously from 1930 and was appointed emeritus professor in 1976. He has been a Fulbright and a Guggenheim fellow.

This essay is an excerpt from a book entitled Why the Professor Can't Teach. *Any volume bearing such a title is hardly going to be a paradigm of quiet understatement and elliptic communication. What it is, and quite openly declares itself to be, is a polemic. Morris Kline is no shrinking violet; he is a man of strong opinions, honestly held and buttressed by years of experience and scholarly achievements. But make no mistake—his is not the consensus view of the mathematical community. Indeed, this essay appears as a counterpoint to the predominant theme of the other essays in these volumes, which is that any mathematical activity is better than none at all and that mathematics research and its public support should be expanded.*

While this excerpt focuses on the abuses of research, the main message of Kline's book is that mathematics in colleges and universities is taught rather poorly. The constraints of available space do not allow the inclusion of all the arguments that the author gives. He suggests, however, that mathematics is communicated poorly because mathematicians are too narrowly educated, view themselves as creators of mathematics exclusively, eschew many vital professorial functions, delude themselves with the vision of mathematics as ultimate abstract reality, and avoid applications to and interaction with the physical world. There are those who strongly disagree with Kline's conclusions, but even they must, if they are fair, admit that there are some elements of truth in all of his accusations. And that is why his opinions have been included in this work.

> *Even victors are by victory undone.*
>
> *John Dryden*

WE HAVE TRACED the widespread rise of vigorous mathematical research in this country. We have also observed that the flourishing of research promises not only direct benefits but also indirect beneficial influence on all levels of education. However, the values that might accrue from research depend on the quality of research being done. Let us therefore look into the nature of current mathematical research.*

In mathematics, research has a very special meaning. Specifically, it calls for the creation of new results, that is, either new theorems or radically different and improved proofs of older re-

---

*Though we shall discuss mathematical research, many of its features . . . apply to other academic disciplines as well.

Source: Morris Kline, "The Nature of Current Mathematical Research," in *Why the Professor Can't Teach*, pp. 41–69. Copyright © 1978 by Morris Kline, St. Martin's Press, Inc., New York.

sults. Expository articles, critiques of trends in research, historical articles or books, good texts at any level, and pedagogical studies do not count. Thus, the criterion of research in mathematics differs considerably from what is accepted in, for example, a subject such as English. In this area, in addition to the creation of fiction, essays, poetry, or other literature, criticism, biographies that shed fresh light on important or even unimportant literary figures, histories of literature, and texts that may be primarily anthologies are considered original work. Perhaps this distinction between what should be accepted in the respective fields is wise, but let us see what it has led to in mathematics.

Because the United States entered the world of mathematical research several hundred years after the leading Western European countries had been devoting themselves to it, our mathematicians, in an endeavor to compete, undertook special directions and types of investigations.

One move was to enter the newer fields, such as the branch of geometry now called topology. The advantage of a new field for tyros in research is that very little background is needed and the best concepts and methodologies are only dimly perceived. Hence, because criteria for value are lacking, almost any contribution has potential significance. Publication is almost assured.

Of course, the ease with which one can proceed in a new field is somewhat deceptive. New fields generally arise out of deep and serious problems in older fields, and anyone who wants to do useful work must know much about these problems and grapple with them at length in order to secure significant leads. On the other hand, if all one is trying to do is prove theorems, then it is sufficient to start with almost any potentially relevant concept and see what can be proved about it. And if one gets a result that the other fellow didn't get, one may proceed to publish it.

The United States was not the only country that took such a course. After World War I, Poland was reconstituted as a nation and the Polish mathematicians undertook a concerted effort to build up mathematics in their country. They decided to concentrate on a narrow field, the branch of topology called point set theory. Why point set theory? Because at that time the subject was still new. One could therefore start from scratch, introduce some concepts, lay down some axioms, and then proceed to prove theorems. This example is offered not to malign Polish mathematicians. There were and are some very good men among them, and good men, even starting from very shallow beginnings, will make progress and produce fine work. What is significant is the deliberate and openly stated decision to start with point set theory because one did not have to know much mathematics to work in it.

Generalization is another direction of research that promises easy victories. Whereas the earlier Greek and European mathematicians were inclined to pursue specific problems in depth, in recent years many researchers have turned to generalizing previous results. Thus, while the earlier mathematicians studied individual curves and surfaces, many twentieth-century mathematicians prefer to study classes of curves—and the more general the class, the more prized any theorem about it. Beyond generalizing the study of curves, mathematicians have also carried most geometric studies to n-dimensions in place of two or three.

Some generalizations are useful. To learn how to solve the general second degree equation $ax^2 + bx + c = 0$, where a, b, and c can be any real numbers, immediately disposes of the problem of solving the millions of cases wherein a, b, and c are specific numbers.

But generalization for the sake of generalization can be a waste of time. A lover of generalization will too often lose sight of desirable goals and indulge in endless churning out of more and more useless theorems. However, those for whom publication is the chief concern are wise to generalize.

Hermann Weyl, one of the foremost mathematicians of this century, expressed in 1951 his contempt for pointless generalizations, asserting: "Our mathematics of the last few decades has wallowed in generalities and formalizations." Another authority, George Polya, in his *Mathematics and Plausible Reasoning,* supported this condemnation with the remark that shallow, cheap generalizations are more fashionable nowadays.

Mathematicians of recent years have also favored abstraction, which, though related to generalization, is a somewhat different tack. In the latter part of the nineteenth century mathematicians observed that many classes of objects—the positive and negative integers and zero; transformations, such as rotations of axes; hypernumbers, such as quaternions (which are extensions of complex numbers); and matrices—possess the same basic properties.

Let us use the integers to understand what these properties are. There is an operation, which in the case of the integers is ordinary addition. Under this operation the sum of two integers is an integer. For any three integers, $a + (b+c) = (a + b) + c$. There is an integer, 0, such that $a + 0 = 0 + a = a$. Finally, for each integer, a, for example, there is another integer, $-a$, such that $a + (-a) = -a + a = 0$. These properties are more or less obvious in the case of the positive and negative integers.

But if in place of the integers we now speak of a set of objects, which might be transformations, quaternions, or matrices, though the particular set is not specified; and of an operation, whose nature depends on the particular set of objects but is also not specified, we can state in abstract language that the elements of the set and operation possess the same four properties as those of the integers. The abstract formulation defines what is called technically a group. A group, then, is a concept that describes or subsumes the basic properties of many concrete mathematical collections and their respective operations under one abstract formulation. If one can prove, on the basis of the four properties of the abstract group, that additional properties necessarily hold, then these additional properties must hold for each of the concrete interpretations or representations of the group.

The concept of a group, very important for both mathematics and physics, is only one of dozens of abstract systems or structures—the latter is the fashionable word—and many mathematicians devote themselves to studying the properties of these structures. In fact, the study of structures is flourishing; the work done on groups alone fills many volumes.

Abstraction does have its values. One virtue, as already noted, is precisely that one can prove theorems about the abstract system and know at once that they apply to many concrete interpretations instead of having to prove them separately

for each interpretation. Further, to abstract is to come down to essentials. Abstracting frees the mind from incidental features and forces it to concentrate on crucial ones. The selection of these truly fundamental ones is not a simple matter and calls for insight. Nevertheless, there can be shallow and useless abstractions as well as deep and powerful ones. The former are relatively easy to make, and one must distinguish this type of creation from that involved in solving a new and difficult problem—such as proving, as Newton did, that the path of each planet, moving under the gravitational attraction of the sun, is an ellipse or the far more difficult problem, which has still not been solved, of finding the paths of three bodies when each attracts the others under the force of gravitation. Unfortunately, many recent abstractions have been shallow.

Beyond the shallowness of some abstractions, there are other negative features of all abstractions. Although unification through abstraction may be advantageous, mathematics pays in loss of resolution for the broadened abstract viewpoint. An abstraction omits concrete details that may be vital in the solution of specific problems. Thus, the manner of executing the processes of adding whole numbers, fractions, and irrational numbers is not contained in the group concept. The more abstract a concept is, the emptier it is. Put another way, the greater the extension, the less the intension.

Abstraction introduces other objectionable features. As a theory grows abstract it usually becomes more difficult to grasp because it uses a more specialized terminology, and it requires more abstruse and recondite concepts. Moreover, unrestrained and unbridled abstraction diverts attention from whole areas of application whose very investigation depends upon features that the abstract point of view rules out. Concentration on proofs about the abstraction becomes a full-time occupation, and contact with one or more of its interpretations can be lost. The abstraction can become an end in itself, with no attempt made to apply it to significant concrete situations. Thus, the abstraction becomes a new fragment of mathematics, and those fields that were to receive the benefits of unification and insight are no longer attended to by the unifiers.

Weyl spoke out against unrestrained abstraction, maintaining that "in the meantime our advance in this direction [abstraction] has been so uninhibited with so little concern for the growth of problematics in depth that many of us have begun to fear for the mathematical substance."

The inordinate attention given to the study of abstract structures caused another mathematician to warn, "Too many mathematicians are making frames and not enough are making pictures."

Another popular direction of research may be described roughly as axiomatics. To secure the foundations of their subject the late-nineteenth-century mathematicians turned to supplying axiomatic bases for various mathematical developments, such as the real number system, and to improving those systems of axioms where deficiencies had been discovered, notably in Euclidean geometry. Since there are dozens of branches of mathematics, there are dozens of systems of axioms. Quite a few of these contain ten, fifteen, or twenty axioms. The existence of such systems suggests many new problems. For instance, if a system contains fifteen axioms, is it possible to reduce the number and still deduce the same body of theorems? Given a system of axioms, what would be the effect of changing one or more of them? The classic and notable instance of this last-mentioned type of investigation is, of course, the change in the Euclidean parallel axiom and the resulting creation of hyperbolic non-Euclidean geometry. Changes in several of the axioms led to elliptic non-Euclidean geometry. Clearly, if a system contains as many as fifteen axioms, the changes that can be considered are numerous.

The investigation of the consequences of changing the Euclidean parallel axiom was indeed sagacious. By contrast present-day mathematicians, with little reason to do so, pursue all sorts of axiomatic investigations so that in the eyes of many practitioners, mathematics has become the science of axiomatics. The current activity in this area is enormous and overstressed. When axioms were believed to be self-evident truths about the constitution of the physical world, it was laudable to simplify them as much as possible so that their truth could be more apparent. But now that axioms are known to be rather arbitrary assumptions, the emphasis on deducing as much as pos-

sible from, say, a minimum number of axioms, which are often flagrantly artificial and chosen merely to reduce the number, is not warranted. The objective seems to be to produce more theorems per axiom, no matter how distorted and unnatural the axioms may be. Consequently, one finds long papers with tedious, boring, and ingenious but sterile material. Nevertheless, the popularity of axiomatics is readily understood. It does not call for the imaginative creation of new ideas. It is essentially a reordering of known results and offers many minor problems.

In his 1951 critique of current features of mathematical research, Weyl included axiomatics:

One very conspicuous aspect of twentieth century mathematics is the enormously increased role which the axiomatic approach plays. Whereas the axiomatic method was formerly used merely for the purpose of elucidating the foundations on which we build, it has now become a tool for concrete mathematical research. . . . [However] without inventing new constructive processes no mathematician will get very far. It is perhaps proper to say that the strength of modern mathematics lies in the interaction between axiomatics and construction.

Still another questionable activity in modern axiomatics, derogatively termed "postulate piddling," involves the adoption of axioms merely to see what consequences can be derived. A prominent mathematician of our time, Rolf Nevanlinna, has cautioned: "The setting up of entirely *arbitrary* axiom systems as a starting point for logical research has never led to significant results. . . . The awareness of this truth seems to have been dulled in the last few decades, particularly among younger mathematicians."

Felix Klein, a leading German mathematician who was active from about 1870 to 1925, remarked that if a mathematician has no more ideas, he then pursues axiomatics. Another distinguished professor once remarked that when a mathematical subject is ready for axiomatization it is ready for burial and the axioms are its obituary.

The several directions research has taken point up the fact that there are soft and hard problems—or soft and hard research. In the days when the density of good mathematicians was high, soft problems were not often tackled. Moreover, nineteenth-century mathematicians, who were the first to grasp the advantage of abstract structures, faced a higher order of difficulty than present-day mathematicians face in that type of research. In recent times soft problems have been the ones most often tackled, and even if the proofs are complicated, the results may still be merely difficult trifles.

There is still another feature of mathematical research that affects seriously the interaction of research and teaching—the chief concern of this book. Whether it involves generalization, abstraction, or axiomatics or pursues some other direction, modern research is commonly acknowledged to be almost entirely pure—as opposed to applied. Pure research may be characterized as mathematics for mathematics' sake. That is, however the theme or problem is obtained, the reasons for undertaking it may be aesthetic interest, intellectual challenge, or sheer curiosity: "Let's see what we can prove." This is the motivation in axiomatics when a researcher rather arbitrarily decides to change an axiom just to find out what changes this entails in the resulting theorems. Applied mathematics, on the other hand, is concerned with problems raised by scientists, or with a theme that a researcher believes is potentially applicable.

There is no doubt that the problems of applied mathematics are more difficult. The branches of mathematics customarily associated with applied mathematics are now several hundred years old, and the giants of mathematics have worked in them. Anyone who wants to do something significant today in partial differential equations, for example, must have quite a background. And for the processes of idealization and model building in applied mathematics one must have intimate knowledge of the relevant physical field in order not to miss the essence of the phenomenon under study.

Pure mathematics is more accessible for another reason. Whereas in applied work the problem is set by scientific needs and cannot be altered, the pure mathematician tackling problem A may, if unable to solve it, convert it to problem B, which could be A with more hypotheses or a related but actually different problem suggested by the work on A. He may end up solving problem B, or while working on it he may find unexpectedly that he can solve problem C. In any case he has a result and can publish it. In other words, the applied mathematician is required to climb a rugged, steep mountain, whereas the pure mathematician may attempt such a climb, but if he finds the going tough he can abandon it and settle for a walk up some nearby gentle hill.

Traditionally mathematics had been concerned with problems of science. But these, as we have noted, are far more difficult to solve. Only relatively few men today pursue them. The abandonment of tradition and of the rich source of problems has been justified by a new doctrine: Mathematics is independent of science, and mathematicians are free to investigate any problems that appeal to them. The research done today, so it is claimed, will be useful ten, fifty, and one hundred years from now. To support this contention the purists distort history and point to alleged examples of such happenings. But a correct reading of history belies the contention. Practically all of the major branches of mathematics were developed to solve scientific problems, and the few that today are pursued for aesthetic satisfaction were originally motivated by real problems. For example, the theory of numbers, if one dates its beginning with the Pythagoreans, was undertaken for the study of nature. Nevertheless, the break from science has widened sharply since about 1900, and today most mathematicians no longer know any science or even care whether their work will ever have any bearing on real problems.

Marshall Stone, formerly a professor at Yale, Harvard and Chicago, in an article "Mathematics and the Future of Science" (1957) admits that generality and abstraction—pure mathematics generally—are the chief features of modern mathematics in our country. The best applied mathematics, he concedes, is done by physicists, chemists, and biologists. He might well have added that mathematics developed in a vacuum proves to be vacuous.

Quite a different feature of modern research is specialization. The worldwide spread of scientific and technological pursuits has made it impossible for any individual to keep pace with a broad spectrum, and the desire to avoid being beaten to results by an ever-increasing number of competitors, and thus lose the fruit of months of activity, has almost forced mathematicians to seek out corners of their own. Mathematics is now fragmented into over a thousand specialties, and the specialties multiply faster than amoebas. The many disciplines have become autonomous, each featuring its own terminology and methodology. A general meeting of mathematicians resembles the populace of Babel after God had confounded their efforts. Pure mathematicians are unable to communicate with applied mathematicians, specialists with other specialists, mathematicians with teachers, and mathematicians with scientists. It is almost a certainty that if any two mathematicians were chosen at random and shut up in a room they would be so unintelligible to one another as to be reduced to talking about the weather. Consequently, general meetings are now far less numerous than colloquia and conferences on particular topics.

Illustrations of the narrowness of modern research are so abundant that almost any article in any journal can serve as an example. Let us note one or two simple ones. One article treats powerful integers. An integer is powerful if whenever it is divisible by a prime p it is divisible by p^2. Several papers on this less-than-enthralling theme have already appeared and more are sure to follow. Would that the papers be more powerful than the concept. Still another theme deals with admirable numbers. The Pythagoreans of the sixth century B.C. had introduced the concept of a perfect number. A number is perfect if it equals the sum of its divisors (other than the number itself). Thus $6 = 1 + 2 + 3$. If the sum of the divisors exceeds the number, the number is called abundant. Thus, 12 is abundant because the sum $1+2+3+4+6$ is 16. One can, however, ask about the *algebraic* sum of the divisors; that is, one can consider adding and subtracting divisors. Thus $12 = 1+3+4+6-2$. Numbers that are the algebraic sum of their divisors are called admirable. One can now seek admirable numbers and establish properties about them, which no doubt

are equally admirable. In this same vein are a superabundance of theorems on superabundant numbers.

These very trivial examples are, of course, chosen merely because they can be presented quickly to illustrate the narrowness and pointlessness of much modern-day research. Just as everyone who daubs paint on canvas does not necessarily create art, so words and symbols are not necessarily mathematics.

Specialization began to be common in the late nineteenth century. Now most mathematicians work only in small corners of mathematics, and quite naturally each rates the importance of his area above all others. His publications are no longer for a large public but for a few colleagues. The articles no longer contain any indication of a connection with the larger problems of mathematics, are hardly accessible to many mathematicians, and are certainly not palatable to a large circle. Mathematical research today is spread over so many specialties that what was once incorrectly said of the theory of relativity does apply to [most] research: Any one topic is understood by no more than a dozen people in the world.

Each mathematician today seeks to isolate himself in a domain that he can work for himself and resents others who might infringe on his domain and secure results that might rob him of the fruits of his work. Even Norbert Wiener, one of the great mathematicians of recent times, admitted that he "did not like to watch the literature day by day in order to be sure that neither Banach nor one of his Polish followers had published some important result before me." And the late Jacques Hadamard, the dean of French mathematicians until his death at the age of ninety-eight in 1963, said, "After having undertaken a certain set of problems and seeing that several other authors had begun to follow the same line, I would drop it and investigate something else."

There is a way of joining the crowd and yet keeping aloof from the hurly-burly. A favorite device is to introduce some new concept and develop endless theorems whose significance is, to say the least, questionable. The creator of such contrived material may even train doctoral students who, young in the ways and judgment of mathematics, may really believe in the worth of the material and so spread the name of the master.

Most of those working in specialties no longer know why the class of problems they are working on was originally proposed and what larger goals their work is supposed to aim at. The modern topologist may not know Riemann's and Poincaré's work. The modern worker in Lie algebras is not likely to know what purpose Lie algebras serve. Of course, these specialists are putting the cart before the horse. The limited problems should contribute to and illuminate the area in which they lie. But the specialists would seem to be taking the position that the major areas exist in order to provide problems on which to exercise their ingenuity. Nor do they recognize that specialization promotes one's degeneration into a narrow, uncultured person, a craftsman but nothing more. The specialist becomes what José Ortega y Gasset called a "learned ignoramus."

As the process of subdivision progresses, specialized research makes less and less provision for synthesis, for pulling strands together, for asking the basic, overriding questions, for stepping back from the easel and looking at the whole picture. Indeed, specialized research does not concern itself with synthesis. Though it may foster localized competence, it may simultaneously rationalize, and even glorify, general ignorance and deliberate unconcern for those questions that transcend the narrow bounds of specialism. Yet these questions are the ones that make sense of the whole enterprise.

Rampant specialization turns out to be a misfortune for the specialized pursuits themselves, although it seems to arise through concern for their exclusive needs. One obvious reason is that specialization encourages uninhibited intellectual inbreeding and it is a law, not only of human genetics, that inbreeding increases the incidence of undesirable characteristics. Furthermore, the process of unlimited specialization tends to bar a subject from the interest and participation of anyone outside, even when the outsider could make an essential contribution toward maintaining relevance in the questions asked and the methods used to pursue them. It also dims awareness of the fact that the pursuit of truth is indivisible, that all creative scholars, writers, and artists are ultimately engaged in one great common enterprise—the search for truth. In other words, specialization curtails the basic commitment of the scholar.

The evils of specialization have been noted by many wise men. In his history of nineteenth-century mathematics (1925), Felix Klein said that academic mathematicians grow up in company with others like trees in a woods, which must remain narrow and grow straight up in order even to exist and reach some of the light and air.

Weyl said in 1951, "Whereas physics in its development since the turn of the century resembles a mighty stream rushing in one direction, mathematics is more like the Nile delta, its waters fanning out in all directions." In the preface to his book, *The Classical Groups* (2nd ed., 1946), he expressed concern about too much specialization in mathematics: "My experience has seemed to indicate that to meet the danger of a too thorough specialization and technicalization of mathematical research is of particular importance for mathematics in America."

David Hilbert, the greatest mathematician of this century, was also concerned about specialization. He wrote:

The question is forced upon us whether mathematics is once to face what other sciences have long ago experienced, namely, to fall apart into subdivisions whose representatives are hardly able to understand each other and whose connections for this reason will become ever looser. I neither believe nor wish this to happen; the science of mathematics as I see it is an indivisible whole, an organism whose ability to survive rests on the connection between its parts.

The trend to specialization has already caused mathematics departments to split into four or more departments—pure mathematics, applied mathematics, statistics and probability (with antagonism between the two groups in this area portending a future split), and computer science. Communication among these departments is, of course, almost nonexistent, and competition for money, faculty, and students is keen.

Clearly, the evils of specialization lead to inferior work. Specialists define their own area of interest and, as we have already noted, choose areas in which they can avoid competition and the larger, more vital problems. Publication is the goal, and whatever results can be published are published. Ortega y Gasset remarked in his *The Revolt of the Masses* that specialization provides what the biologist would call ecological niches for mediocre minds.

Since specialization is the order of the day, why not journals for specialists? These are now by far the most numerous, and specialists read only the journals in their own areas, thus precluding even their awareness of anything outside their specialty. There are few journals that cover—and none that unify—developments in several fields, to say nothing about all fields of mathematics.

Mathematical research has always suffered from another evil: faddism. Like all human beings mathematicians yield to their personal enthusiasms or are ensnared by the fashions of their times. The directions of research are often determined by mathematicians with prestige and power who themselves are subject to whims or the search for novelty. In the nineteenth century, for example, the study of subjects such as elliptic functions, projective geometry, algebraic invariants, and special properties of higher-degree curves was carried to extremes. Most of this work, considered remarkable in its time, would be considered insignificant today and has left almost no trace in the body of mathematics.

It is no criticism of mathematicians that an area of research pursued vigorously for a time should prove unimportant in the long run. Mathematicians must use judgment as to what may be worthwhile, and even the wisest can make mistakes. Research is a gamble and one can't be sure that the work will pay off. However, faddism tends to carry a subject beyond any promise of significance.

Fads flourish today because usefulness to science is no longer a standard, and the standard of beauty is purely subjective. The most pointed criticism of faddism was made by Oscar Wilde: A fad is the fantastic which for the moment has become universal.

Another evil of faddism is that possibly valuable but nonfashionable ideas are disparaged. Hence, brilliant work is often neglected, though it is sometimes belatedly and often posthumously recognized. The classic example is found in the work of Gauss. Gauss, though already acknowledged as great when still a young man, feared to publish his work on non-Euclidean geometry because he would have been condemned by his fellow mathematicians or, as he put it, because he feared the clamor of the Boeotians, a reference to a dull-witted ancient Greek tribe. Fortunately, Gauss's work on non-Euclidean geometry was found among his papers after his death. By that time his reputation was so great that his ideas were accorded the utmost respect.

Researchers who place high value on their work should be obliged to read a somewhat detailed history of mathematics, a subject most mathematicians do not know. They would be amazed to find how much that was regarded as vital and central in the past has been dropped so completely that even the names of those activities or branches are no longer known. Though the lesson of history is rarely learned, fads do not, fortunately, dominate the directions of research for long. What individuals create is destined to live only insofar as it is related to the evolutionary development of mathematics and proves fruitful in its consequences.

One additional source of research papers of dubious value should be mentioned—Ph.D. theses and their offspring. The students, beginners in research, cannot tackle a major problem; what they do tackle is not only suggested by a professor but is performed with his help. The results are generally minor and, in fact, usually the professor can see in advance how to solve the problem. If he could not, he might worry about whether he is assigning too difficult a problem to a beginner.

The new Ph.D. is, in today's world, forced to produce low quality research. If he enters or seeks to enter the university field, where researchers are now more sought after, he is under pressure to publish. Under these conditions what will he publish? He is at a stage in life where he is really not prepared to publish a paper of quality. Typically, his one experience in research was his doctoral thesis, in which he was guided by a professor and gained only enough knowledge to produce an acceptable thesis. Hence, all he actually is prepared to do is add tidbits to his thesis. But he cannot afford to be deterred by the knowledge that his publications may be insignificant. Some publication is better than none. Were he to try to solve a deep problem requiring extensive background and several years to complete, with the danger of failure all the greater, he would have nothing to show for quite some time, if ever. Hence, he must tackle and publish what can be done readily, even if the solution is labored and the result pointless.

The results of pressure on faculty and young scholars to publish, the natural expansion of research in our scientifically oriented culture, the entry of the Soviet Union, China, and Japan during this century into the group of countries leading in research, and the expansion of Ph.D. training to meet the needs of universities and colleges (which in recent years has meant 750 to 1,000 mathematics Ph.D.'s per year in the United States alone) are reflected in the volume of publication. There are now over a thousand journals devoted wholly or partially to mathematical research. About five hundred are devoted solely to mathematics, and new ones are appearing almost weekly. Summaries of the articles are published in *Mathematical Reviews*, which does not cover all articles and in fact neglects pedagogy and much applied mathematics. In 1970 there were 16,570 reviews; in 1973, about 20,000. If all applied mathematics had been covered there would have been about 40,000 reviews in 1973. The expansion of publications has been going on at the rate of 5 percent annually. In the period 1955 to 1970 the volume of publication equaled the volume in all of the rest of recorded history. The published papers are about one-fourth of those submitted to journals. Hence, one can see how much effort is put forth by faculty to climb the ladder of research.

To help mathematicians keep track of what has been published, secondary and even tertiary aids, such as indices and lists of titles, have been developed. There is an *Author Index of Mathematical Reviews*, which lists by author and subject the summaries published in *Mathematical Reviews*. For the years 1940 to 1959 the *Index* has 2,207 pages. For 1965 to 1972 it has 3,032 pages and 127,000 items, whereas the *Indexes* of the previous twenty-five years, 1940-1964, covered 156,000 items in all. There is also a journal, *Contents of Contemporary Mathematical Journals* (bi-weekly), that offers an index classified by subject of all current papers and books in mathematics. About 1,200 journals are covered and these do not include some in applied mathematics. We may await momentarily an index of the *Contents* and an index of all indices.

The volume of publication has evoked critical comments from prominent mathematicians. One of them, Peter Hilton, has written, ". . . we are all agreed that far too many papers are being written and published. We are turning into a community of writers who do not read simply because we have no time to do so. It is a terrifying thought that if we were to spend eighteen hours a day reading new mathematics we would have substantially more to read at the end than at the beginning." In addition to zero population growth this country should aim for zero publication growth.

It was generally agreed in the 1930s, when the pace of research was much slower, that nine out of ten papers had little to say and had no impact on mathematics. Some significant quantitative information was supplied by Kenneth O. May, a professor at the University of Toronto, who studied the nearly two thousand publications from the seventeenth century to 1920 on the limited topic of determinants. He presents the following data:

New ideas and results	234	14%
Duplication (beyond independent simultaneous publication)	350	21%
Texts and education	266	15%
Applications of results	208	12%
Systematization and history	199	12%
Trivia	737	43%
Totals including overlap	1994	117%

The explanation of the 117 percent is that some papers fell into two or more categories; actually there were 1,707 separate papers. Professor May estimated that the significant information about determinants, including the main historical accounts, is contained in less than 10 percent of the papers. He also mentions that in 1851 there were ten duplications of a paper published in a leading journal.

Today, with far more papers published and far less concern for the significance of the research, one might estimate that no more than 5 percent of the publications offer new material. The duplication is endless. Some of it is noted in *Mathematical Reviews*. *The American Mathematical Monthly* occasionally reports duplications and errors and even cites instances of purportedly new research material that has already appeared in texts.* This is not to say that all of the other 95 percent are wasted. A few have educational value. Nevertheless, the journals are filled with papers of flea-sized significance, and these pollute the intellectual world as noxiously as the automobile pollutes the air we breathe.

Authors deliberately publish minor variants of older research or repeat older results in new terminology. Unfortunately, the introduction of new terminology is a never-ending game, and a translation of old material can pass undetected, just as a French paper must be accepted as new by one who can't determine whether it has appeared in German. One famous nineteenth-century German mathematician did simply translate English papers into German and publish them as his own. Some researchers take one reasonably coherent paper and break it up into three or four smaller ones. This stratagem permits much repetition, thus resulting in more published pages and giving the impression of a teeming mind.

The profusion of articles and the ever-increasing number of journals make it impossible for even the specialist to read what is published in his own area. Hence, though he may pretend to know what has been done, he actually ignores the literature except for the few papers that he happens to know bear directly on his immediate goal—

*See, for example, the issue of December 1976, pp. 798–801.

publication of his own paper. Months or years later some observer may note a duplication and call attention to it.

Apart from the expense involved, the flood of papers seriously hampers research. A conscientious researcher will try to keep abreast of what is being done in his area, partly to utilize the results already obtained and partly to avoid duplication. He must then wade through a vast number of papers at the expense of considerable time and effort, and at that he will not cover all the relevant literature.

The problem of keeping abreast of the literature had already begun to bother Christian Huygens in the late seventeenth century. In 1670 he complained, ". . . it is necessary to bear in mind that mathematicians will never have enough time to read all the discoveries in geometry (a quantity that is increasing from day to day and seems likely in this scientific age to develop to enormous proportions) if they continue to be presented in a rigorous form according to the manner of the ancients." Leibniz at the end of the seventeenth century deplored "this horrible mass of writing which continually increases" and which can only "drive away from the science those who might be tempted to indulge in it."

In mathematics, where the newness of a result should be readily recognized and the difficulties overcome in proof readily apparent, it would seem that papers would be easily and accurately evaluated. Most journals do send manuscripts to referees before accepting them. But the good mathematicians who might serve as referees are so busy doing their own research, and the volume of publication they must follow is so enormous, that most do nothing about judging work in their own specialty, to say nothing of other areas of mathematics. Moreover, most papers are so sparse in explanation that their correctness is hard to judge.

The narrowness of mathematicians also renders them unfit to discriminate between what is fundamental and what is trivial, between basic insight and mere technical byplay. For interdisciplinary papers it is almost impossible to find competent referees. Personal factors also intervene. Individuals favor friends and discriminate against rivals.

The state of refereeing is revealed by the reactions to a recent decision of the American Mathematical Society. Up to 1975 all papers submitted for publication in the several journals supported by the Society were sent to referees with the names and affiliations of the authors recorded on the papers. The Society decided to try, for one of its journals, blind refereeing, that is, submitting the paper to the referee without the name and affiliation of the author. The protests of referees and even of two of the associate editors of that journal were vehement. They pointed to the thanklessness of the work, the difficulty in finding competent referees, and the problem of judging the correctness and worth of a paper. In the ensuing debate, partly through published letters, the opponents of blind refereeing admitted that the name and affiliation of the author helped immensely in the refereeing process. What these opponents were really saying is that they were not judging papers on their merits but were relying on the reputation of the author and his institutional affiliation to aid in determining the correctness and value of his work. If one may judge by the protests, many referees used no more than this information to make their decisions. This debate brought into the open all the weaknesses of the refereeing process.

Moreover, today many papers are published without judgment by referees. There are countless symposia each year, and the papers read there are published automatically in the proceedings. Some universities produce their own journals, in which faculty members can publish at will. Publication in the *Proceedings of the National Academy of Sciences* is automatic not only for members but also for nonmembers whose papers are submitted through a member. The extent of the Academy's publications may be judged by the fact that in 1970 the editors decided to restrict each member to no more than ten papers per year.

The present situation contrasts sharply with what prevailed in the seventeenth, eighteenth, and nineteenth centuries. Of course, there were fewer publications. But papers were sent to referees who were not only distinguished mathematicians but also broad scholars. Even then there were slips in both acceptance and rejection. R. J. Strutt, the son of one of the greatest mathematical physicists, Lord Rayleigh, relates in his life of his father that a paper by Lord Rayleigh that did not have his name on it was submitted to the British Association for the Advancement of Science and was rejected as the work of one of those curious persons called paradoxers. However, when the authorship was discovered, the paper was judged to have merit. Nevertheless, on the whole the refereeing of earlier times was competent and critical. Moreover, the editors took pride in the quality of the work published in their journals and were anxious to maintain excellent reputations. They therefore took pains to secure competent criticism of articles submitted. It is also relevant that usefulness to science served as the major standard by which most papers were judged.

Actually, what is major or minor in research can be very difficult to determine. François Vieta, who first taught us to use letters to stand for a class of numbers, as in $ax^2 + bx + c = 0$, an idea that now seems trivial but was not advanced until after two thousand years of first-class mathematics had been created, gave mathematics the basis for all proof in algebra and analysis. Surely this idea was as valuable as any major result of Newton.

The assertion that quality of research is difficult to judge may seem to contradict our earlier assertion that most papers have little, if any, value. The worth of a few papers—for example, those that solve a long-standing problem that had baffled great minds—is certainly great. In other cases the authors state why the results they have obtained are important, so that the work can be more readily judged. When Vieta introduced letters for classes of numbers he stated that he could now make the distinction between numerical algebra and a science of algebra (to use modern terminology). Perhaps many a seemingly worthless paper has merit, but if that merit is not apparent to knowledgeable mathematicians, only an adverse judgment is in order.

Some sociologists of science are trying to measure the quality of research papers by the number of times a given paper is cited by later papers. Toward this end they invented and use the *Science Citation Index*. But this measure is almost childish. Very good papers are often soon superseded by ones that advance the subject still further. Even when the advances are minor, the later papers will surely be the ones cited. A fad will be cited many times over a period of years. Many young researchers cite their professors, even at the expense of the true creator, in order to curry favor. Accepting citations, then, would seem to require first measuring the honesty of scientists.

Modern mathematical research seems impressive. There is a vast and growing structure. Recent work has delineated more sharply the nature of the older subjects and has pointed the way to almost endless paths of new developments. Abstractions and generalizations have linked apparently unrelated subjects, giving mathematics some measure of unity, and have put some difficult classical theorems in a new setting where they become more natural and meaningful, at least to a trained mathematician. Mathematics now has a more qualitative character, in contrast to the manipulative and quantitative character of much of classical mathematics. Many new subjects have been created; and areas of older subjects that no longer seem significant have been discarded. We no longer learn all 467 theorems in Euclid's *Elements* or all 487 theorems in Apollonius' *Conic Sections*.

But a critical look produces dismay. The proliferation of new themes, generalization, abstraction, axiomatics, and specialization may yield easy successes, but they divert attention from more concrete and difficult problems concerned with ideas of substance. Abstractions and specialties abandon reality to enter clouds of thin and diffused themes. An overweeningly arrogant antipathy to papers that do not follow the modern fashions also encourages less valuable activity.

Mathematicians today care less and less about why mathematics should be created and pursued. They pay far less attention to what is worth knowing or what benefits society; nor do they question why society should support them. One of the most disturbing facts about current research is that graduate students, young Ph.D.'s, and even many established mathematicians no longer ask, Why should I undertake this particular investigation? Any inquiry that promises to produce answers and publication is regarded as worthwhile. No commendable purpose need be served except, perhaps, to advance the career of

the researcher. A problem is a problem is a problem, and that suffices. Though criticism is rarely voiced, one past president of the American Mathematical Society and the Mathematical Association of America did have the courage to deprecate much modern research.

No doubt much worthless research is done in all academic fields. But remoteness and pointlessness are far more prevalent in mathematics. The reason stems from the nature of the subject, especially as it is currently pursued. Mathematics deals not with reality but with limited abstractions. In past centuries these did come largely from real situations, and the prime motivation for the mathematics was to learn more about physical reality. It was recognized that the pursuit of well-chosen problems in mathematics proper must directly or indirectly pay dividends in scientific work, and mathematicians were obliged to keep at least one eye on the real world. But today mathematicians know better what to do than why to do it. The pointlessness of much current research is evident in the very introductions to papers. Students and professors seeking themes for investigation scan the publications and tag onto them. Many a paper begins with the statement, "Mr. X has given the following result. . . . We shall generalize it," or, "Mr. X has considered the following question. . . . A related question is. . . ." There may be no point to either the generalization or the related question. Another common introduction states, "It is natural to ask . . ."; a most unnatural and far-fetched question follows. The consequence is a wide variety of worthless papers.

Mathematical research is also becoming highly professionalized in the worst sense of that term. Research performed voluntarily and sincerely by devoted souls, research as a relish of knowledge, is to be welcomed even if the results are minor. But hothouse-grown research, which crowds the journals and promotes only promotion, is a drag on science. Intellectual curiosity and the challenge of problems may still provide some motivation, but publication, status, prizes, and awards such as election to the National Academy of Sciences are the goals, no matter how attained. Deep problems that call for the acquisition of considerable background, years of effort, and the risk of failure are shunted aside in favor of artificial ones that can be readily tackled and almost as readily solved.

This indictment of current research may surprise many people. Surely mathematicians are men of intellect and would not write poor or worthless papers. But the quality of the intellects engaged in research runs the gamut from poor to excellent. Francis Bacon in his *Novum organum* (1620) sought to mechanize research and was rightly and severely criticized. His own contemporary Galileo demonstrated through his work the extent to which originality and serendipity must enter. Bacon may indeed have oversimplified the task of research, but his expectation that anyone can do it, even "men of little wit," is not far from what happens today in mathematical research.

Professor Clifford E. Truesdell, an authority in several applied fields and a man of vast knowledge, has had the courage to speak caustically. In his *Six Lectures on Natural Philosophy* he says:

Just as the university has changed from a center of learning to a social experience for the masses, so research, which began as a vocation and became a profession, has sunk to a trade if not a racket. We cannot fight the social university and mass-produced research. Both are useful—useful by definition, since they are paid, if badly. . . . The politician, the lawyer, the physician, the general, the university official are all modest men, more modest than most mathematicians. . . . Research has been overdone. By social command turning every science teacher into a science-making machine,

we forget the reason why research is done in the first place. Research is not, in itself, a state of beatitude; research aims to discover something worth knowing. With admirable liberalism, the social university has declared that every question any employee might ask is by definition a fit object of academic research; valorously defending its members against attacks from the unsympathetic outside, it frees them from any obligation to intellectual discipline. . . .

Though each mathematician must be free to pursue the research he prefers, he does have the responsibility to produce potentially applicable papers or papers that offer high aesthetic quality, novelty of method, freshness of outlook, or at least the suggestion of a fruitful direction of research. But far too many mathematicians take advantage of the facts that potential use is difficult to judge and aesthetic quality is a matter of taste. Hence, the good is swamped by the bad. Of course, as in the past, history will decide what is of lasting value. It is the deserved fate of inferiors to fall into oblivion. But the temporary profusion of ideas they introduce constitute today a hampering and almost insuperable obstacle to real progress.

Whether or not current research will prove more hindrance than help to the advancement of mathematics is, however, not our primary concern. We undertook to survey the nature of this research because its maturation seemed to promise improvements at all levels of our educational system. . . .

Two Reviews of *Why the Professor Can't Teach*

Harry Pollard and Peter Hilton

Harry Pollard received his undergraduate and graduate degrees in mathematics from Harvard. After appointments at Kenyon College, Columbia, Yale, and Cornell, he has been a professor at Purdue since 1961.

Peter John Hilton was born in London and received his Ph.D. from Cambridge in 1952. He held academic appointments at Cornell and the University of Washington and has been professor of mathematics at Case Western Reserve University since 1973. He has been co-chairman of the Cambridge Conference on School Mathematics, chairman of the U.S. Commission on Mathematics Instruction, chairman of the committee on applied mathematics training for the National Research Council, and vice president of the Mathematical Association of America.

Morris Kline's treatise on the sins of mathematicians as educators did not pass entirely unobserved through that community. While the Gallup organization did not survey the mathematical community to quantify its reaction, a major journal provided not one but three reviews of Kline's book in the same edition. The reviews were divided.

The reasons for including two of the reviews in this volume are twofold. First, and most obvious, they provide a useful counterbalance to Kline's assertions. Kline has made some serious accusations and fairness demands some space for rebuttal. The second reason is more obscure. Both Kline's attack and Pollard's and Hilton's defenses are discussions much involved with values. As has been observed elsewhere in these volumes, a widely accepted myth holds that science is a dignified, rational, detached, and analytic devotion to knowing things as they really are. The myth suggests that somehow science and its consort, mathematics, have freed themselves from irrational acceptance and rejection of ideas based on value-laden impulses. It has been suggested that this myth is just that, myth. Myths are useful in crystalizing ideals and providing models for ultimate behavior. There is nothing wrong with myths as long as the believers recognize the difference between the reality of the fallen world in which we all continue to struggle and that mystical, mythical vision of the heavenly city that motivates us. When mathematicians quarrel over values, the reader may hope to see reasoned and elliptic discourse but shouldn't be surprised when it doesn't appear.

DR. KLINE IS distinguished both as a scholar and as a historian of mathematics. But he is also an angry man. So it is important to read his book with enough care to separate truth from conjecture, and to disinter both from a deliberately vituperative language which will not win him many allies where he needs them most—among professional mathematicians. The title alone is disastrous to its main purpose. (On January 3, 1978, long before I was invited to review the book, Dr. Kline informed me that the subtitle was his original choice; the title used was insisted upon by the

Source: Harry Pollard, Book Review of *Why the Professor Can't Teach, American Mathematical Monthly* 86 (1979): 404–407. Peter Hilton, Book Review of *Why the Professor Can't Teach, American Mathematical Monthly* 86 (1979): 407–412.

publisher.) If the reader happens to be a mathematician who loves to teach, like me, he is on the defensive as soon as he opens the book and launches his counterattack before he has read it all.

1. Kline's Indictment; the Main Charge

Our undergraduate and high-school teaching of mathematics is a shambles. (Kline suggests that this generalizes to other fields, though the details are left to the reader.) The principal cause is the selfishness of university administrators who need lots of money. Money is best obtained through prestige. Prestige, in turn, comes from distinction in research [football and basketball also help], which administrators know to be "in direct conflict with teaching." Co-defendants are the professors who prosper by committing the offense of research to the neglect of teaching. They achieve higher salaries, promotion, and recognition if they concentrate on publication rather than on the classroom.

2. Defense Against the Main Charge

Let me begin by agreeing with Kline that our teaching is deplorable, at least in the universities and high schools. But I quarrel with his simplistic analysis of the causes (and therefore with the futile remedies he proposes; see section 5).

I believe the problem to be a social one. The prosecutor overlooks the fact that good teaching requires willing students, or at least nonresistant ones. The current mass production of vocation-oriented graduates who want degrees and not learning cannot be put at the doorstep of provosts, deans, and researchers. This is especially true in our state universities, which rely largely on public funds and which teach most of the students. It is *this* demand that creates calculus classes of 500 students, which *no one* can teach effectively. Doubling or even tripling teaching loads cannot solve the problem, because time, space, and money are not available.

And it is this demand that means his achieving

a degree in a field no longer guarantees that the graduate has a thorough basic knowledge of that field; it only guarantees that he doesn't know anything else.

The society in which learning is admired and pursued for its own sake has disappeared. Industry has become a sport, and sport an industry. What is expected now is technological "progress" so that we can live longer to enjoy improved TV and to bolster up our defenses against communism. By some quirk which only mathematicians understand—and they are not about to "squeal"—it is generally supposed that research mathematics contributes to this progress. In fact 99.44 percent of it is as pure as Ivory soap and as useful to technology as a Cyrillic New Testament is to Billy Graham. (This includes so-called "applied" mathematics. Statisticians and computer scientists have long since declared their independence.)

But mathematicians are as human as politicians, and so have profited in salaries, in esteem, in travel grants, and in clinics for the microscopic examination of sets of measure zero. Given his choice, what sane young man would not choose to pursue "research," however inept he may be, rather than to explain the meaning of dy/dx, which, unlike Leibniz, he doesn't really understand, to students who don't want to. Even Ph.D.'s in Education are less concerned with teaching teachers than in statistical "research" in educational psychology, whatever that is.

These things are consequences of our technological bias, which has even forced some of the old-fashioned "ologies" to disguise themselves as social "science." In this form they find recognition and access to public research funds. So to blame administrators and professors for the sad state of teaching is like blaming the police for the rise of crime. If Kline had accused us of profiteering from the public misunderstanding of what we do I'd go along, but he doesn't.

3. The Case Against Research

Since Kline claims that research interferes with teaching, the quality of that research seems irrelevant. Possibly his charge against the professors could be reduced from the first to the second degree if he could be convinced that their research is worthwhile; he doesn't say. In any case we are told that most current research is meaningless; it is largely abstract and has little contact with the real world, which gives rise to *genuine* problems. For him Marshall Stone represents the enemy, who is quoted as follows:

> Nevertheless the fact is that mathematics can equally well be treated as a game which has to be played with meaningless pieces according to purely formal and essentially arbitrary rules, but which become intrinsically interesting because there is such a great fascination in discovering and exploiting the complex patterns of play permitted by the rules. Mathematicians increasingly tend to approach their subject in a spirit which reflects this point of view concerning it. . . . I wish to emphasize especially that it has become necessary to teach mathematics in a new spirit consonant with the spirit which inspires and infuses the work of the modern mathematician, whether he be concerned with mathematics in and for itself, or with mathematics as an instrument for understanding the world in which we live. . . . In fact, the construction of mathematical models for various fragments of the real world, which is the most essential business of the applied mathematician, is nothing but an exercise in axiomatics. . . . When an acceptable modern curriculum has been shaped in terms of its mathematical content, one must still be concerned with the spirit which animates the subject and the manner in which it is taught. It is here that it is highly appropriate to demand that, even in the earliest stages, an effort should be made to bring out both the unity and abstractness of mathematics.

This he counters by a quotation from Courant:

> A serious threat to the very life of science is implied in the assertion that mathematics is nothing but a system of conclusions drawn from the definitions and postulates that must be consistent but otherwise created by the free will of the mathematician. If this description were accurate, mathematics would not attract

any intelligent person. It would be a game with definitions, rules and syllogisms without motive or goal. The notion that the intellect can create meaningful postulational systems at its whim is a deceptive half-truth. Only under the discipline of responsibility to the organic whole, only guided by intrinsic necessity, can the free mind achieve results of scientific value.

A plague on both their houses. On the one hand, to dismiss a large part of mathematics as "nothing but an exercise in axiomatics" is silly. For example, the restatement of mechanics in the language of modern differential geometry and topology clarifies concepts such as stability, which have classically been somewhat vague; but it still requires hard concrete analysis to establish the stability of even the simplest nontrivial system. As to Courant on the scientific value of mathematics, let me remind the reader that much of the brilliant work of Poincaré, Birkhoff, and Wintner was suggested by problems of celestial mechanics, but what astronomer cares? And neither view mentions the ultimate test of great mathematics: great theorems, irrespective of the source. Gauss could find them everywhere, in number theory as well as in the theory of magnetism. (I urge that all participants in this debate read J. T. Schwartz's *The Pernicious Influence of Mathematics on Science,* Proc. Int. Conf. for Logic, Methodology and Philosophy, Berkeley, 1960.)

Just as in art and literature the question of what mathematics is important can be settled only by history, and not by pontification. And until history speaks I agree with Hilton that referees will have to make the judgments.

4. Further Charges

The current textbooks, written by professors to make money, are pretty much of a kind, the parts are interchangeable, and students generally find the writing unreadable. Many of the writers pay lip service to applications, but don't really know enough to do them justice. Agreed. In fact, I fail to see why old Granville or Osgood went out of print, or why students of the current calculus books need training in weight-lifting to find them usable. (A publisher's representative recently asked in what way my proposed calculus book is "different." He busily recorded my claim that it would be shaped like a cube and give the answers only to the Fibonacci numbered problems.)

The training of high-school students gives them no idea why mathematics is either interesting or important. Again, I agree. My own experience in the training of high-school teachers convinces me that they can't teach what they don't know. But whose fault it is is hard to track down; I'm tempted to blame professional "educators," but I can't prove my case.

Dr. Kline deplores the indisputable fact that in the universities promotion depends mostly on publication; good teaching is seldom taken into account in judging. This coincides with my own experience on promotions committees where generally good teaching = no complaints in the dean's office. On the other hand, it is also my experience, and that of most of my colleagues, that with very rare exceptions the good teachers and the exciting lecturers who communicate their enthusiasm to students are also devoted to research and scholarship. But my experience is confined to universities; I cannot speak for the four-year colleges.

5. Remedies

Let me begin with a passage (pp. 235–6) from Kline's final chapter:

> The defects in our educational system cannot be eliminated by one measure. There is no one cure for all diseases. Yet, little by little, medicine has conquered some and alleviated the gravity of others. In the educational field the universities' insistence on research as the qualification for appointment and tenure of professors (despite the low quality of much of the research and its irrelevance to teaching), large lecture classes, the use of teaching assistants on a wide scale, and inadequate textbooks are all highly detrimental to the progress of mathematics and to the effectiveness of education.

Some helpful steps are apparent, and we have to be willing to take them.

The first remedy lies in recognizing scholarship as well as research. Research in mathematics means the creation of new results or, at least, new methods of proof. Scholarship—which fundamentally implies breadth, knowledge in depth, and a critical attitude toward that knowledge—is currently deprecated. This distinction is not made in the social sciences, the arts, and the humanities. The person who digs up facts about an older civilization, who writes a detailed and perhaps critical biography of some major or minor historical or literary figure, or who puts together various theories of economics or government is considered creative, though there may be no single new fact in a given work. Of course, there are seminal thinkers in the nonmathematical fields. Some of their work is as novel, as creative, as anything produced in mathematics. But the distinction between old and new cannot be made as readily. In any case, in these fields new work is only a small part of what is accepted and even honored as research. The re-search of what has been done is accorded as much distinction as new work. In fact, a critical biography or evaluation of a man or an era is often lauded far more than the man or men whose work is being assessed. A lucid explanation or interpretation of mathematical research is worth far more than most research papers. Unfortunately, such presentations, even if of high quality, are held in low esteem. But it is scholars—people with a deep and broad knowledge of mathematics and an ability to communicate, whether or not they contribute new results—who can correct many evils and perform many vital tasks.

No one will quarrel with the importance of scholarship, but I think Kline makes two errors. First, scholarship in mathematics exists and *is* admired. There has been an abundance of good books, expository articles, and monographs, for example by Pólya, by Titchmarsh, by E. Artin, by J. Moser, by the writers of several volumes of Rota's new *Encyclopedia*. But is it only a coincidence that all of these scholars are also leaders in research? Second, it is not clear that the recognition of scholarship in the humanities and in the social sciences has done much for *their* teaching. For example, what do most history teachers know about the history of science, the major influence on mankind since the middle ages?

To support his ideas about scholarship Kline proposes a D.A. (Doctor of Arts) to replace the present Ph.D. for nonresearch scholars. In view of the shortage of jobs for almost any kind of degree during the next few years, judgment ought to be postponed.

As to Kline's proposal that graduate and undergraduate become independent institutions I have nothing to add to Hilton's commentary which appears in the *Mathematical Intelligencer*, Vol. 1, no. 2 (1978), pp. 78–80.

There is more, but room permits only a final quotation (p. 270):

> Reforms are needed not only to improve mathematics education. Both the survival of mathematics in the curriculum and of research itself are at stake. The concentration on pure, esoteric studies will ultimately mean less support from society and, as Richard Courant once predicted, all significant mathematics will be created by physicists, engineers, social scientists, and schools of business administration.

I believe the first statement, but none of the rest. Although I am an "applied" mathematician the Prime Number Theorem represents to me the ultimate in mathematical achievement. Like art and poetry such theorems will be created whatever support society chooses to grant.

HARRY POLLARD

EXCERPTS FROM THIS book were published in the *Mathematical Intelligencer*, Vol. 1, No. 1 (1978), 5–14. In Vol. 1, no. 2 (1978), 76–80, of the same journal I wrote a response to Kline's argument, at the invitation of the editors. In reviewing the book now it would be gratuitous for me to repeat what I said there. The question I asked myself, in reading the book in its entirety, was whether, in my response, I had been fair to the argument of the book, taking into account the

fact that I had based myself merely on a small part of the text (though a part selected by Kline himself). The conclusion I have reached is that I had been entirely fair, and that the strictures which I made against the book are even more valid when one reads the entire text. Moreover there is a further serious demerit of the book which comes to light on a more comprehensive and detailed reading, and this is that it is full of internal contradiction. I will develop this point later.

On the positive side, it should be admitted, the book does have certain distinct merits. It contains a valuable mini-history of mathematics in the United States; it draws attention—if attention is still required—to the fact that too much original work is published, and to many unfortunate consequences of that plethora of new mathematics; it advocates relating mathematics education to science and to science education, an admirable prescription and one to which a recent conference in Bielefeld devoted itself; and it provides an excellent recipe for good teaching. I say all this not in order to ingratiate myself with those who are sympathetic to Kline's point of view, but in order to insist that it is such a great pity that these valuable services are embedded in a text which is, in its essence, a farrago of prejudice. Almost every page contains some vituperative attack on Kline's fellow mathematicians; a detailed list of the unfairnesses and injustices which he perpetrates on his colleagues would require a review even longer than the book itself. Let me therefore try to give something of the flavor of the book, giving quotations where necessary.

Kline's own attitude toward the role he is playing is well illustrated by the quotation from *Hamlet* which appears before the Preface.

> Whether 'tis nobler in the mind to suffer
> The slings and arrows of outrageous fortune;
> Or to take arms against a sea of troubles;
> And by opposing end them.

Kline sees himself as battling against the forces of evil in education. But it is not plain in what respect Kline himself may be suffering or may have suffered, nor in what respect his own fortune has been outrageous. What risk is Kline now running by making this attack? Hamlet's choice was of the stuff of tragedy; Kline's choice, to publish this tirade or not, was made in a far less spiritual context.

Kline's method is that of vast generalization and oversimplification. Indeed it is an irony that, whereas he attacks research mathematicians for what he perceives to be their myopic passion for generalization in mathematics, he indulges in such immoderate generalization himself about the *entire* community of research mathematics. Indeed, generalization does not even stop there; for the blurb on the cover of Kline's book invites the reader to generalize further, from mathematics to the entire academic community. Such further generalization is often self-evidently absurd, since the generalized statement would not be simply wrong but actually meaningless. How do we generalize to the whole of academic research the statement that all good mathematical research has taken place in response to the attempt to solve nonmathematical problems? Amusingly, Kline is most ambivalent on this generalization beyond mathematics. On page 41 he states, "In mathematics, research has a very special meaning." However the previous sentence to the one quoted carries an asterisk referring to a footnote which says, "Though we shall discuss mathematical research, many of its features, as earlier noted, apply to other academic disciplines as well." Let us leave to Kline the reconciliation of those two statements!

The flavor of the book is conveyed by Chapter 1 in which a mythical Peter Landers takes a position at "Admirable University" (having gained his Ph.D. from Prestidigious (*sic*) University) and endeavors to do a good job of teaching in the face of insuperable odds. The chapter makes lively reading, as one would expect in view of the author's fluent style. This style, employed, as in his earlier works, to spread knowledge, may be characterized as limpid and felicitous; but here Kline uses his artistry to paint a picture that is the purest travesty.

And as the book begins, so it continues. We are treated to immoderate attacks on mathematical research, on the quality of the teaching done by young Ph.D.'s, on the publication and refereeing policies of the mathematical research community, and on present-day mathematics itself. In order not to make this review unduly long let me concentrate here on Kline's attack on the policies of mathematics journals publishing research. We learn on page 62 that most good mathematicians do not serve as referees. We are also told: "The narrowness of mathematicians also renders them unfit to discriminate between what is fundamental and what is trivial, between basic insights and mere technical byplay. . . . Personal factors also intervene. Individuals favor friends and discriminate against rivals." On page 83 we find a further rich vein of calumnies: "Evaluation of research boils down to quantity of publication; the contents are irrelevant. As long as his peers accept it, a researcher can publish almost anything—and his peers do accept it, because they wish the same treatment." Kline returns to the same theme on page 248, where he writes: "The criterion of publication in a respectable journal also ensures nothing, because almost anything can be published these days." There are many other statements in the book of a similar tone; but let me complete this lugubrious list of quotations by citing finally a very explicit and particularly scurrilous attack. Kline writes, on page 268: "Most editors of the *American Mathematical Monthly* . . . also reject articles critical of the existing conduct of education."

I believe that everybody reading this review will know that Kline's charges against the editorial policy of mathematics journals are absolutely ridiculous and unfair. The distressing fact is, however, that most readers of Kline's book will not be able so surely to dismiss Kline's canards; and indeed many may well find that his ill-tempered remarks strike a sympathetic chord within their own thinking. For Kline is feeding a very popular prejudice—the self-serving and dishonest modus operandi of the scientist and the academic. Kline is betraying his profession to the general public.

For what impression is Kline giving of the community of research mathematicians? The picture he paints is one of total lack of standards; total philistinism; total ignorance; total unconcern for teaching (typical here is Kline's remark on page 146, ". . . all of teaching is a chore to be disposed of as quickly as possible"); and, to top it all, a narrow and venal self-interest. I was particularly offended, in this last matter, by Kline's remarks on page 225, where he writes, "Professors do learn remarkably fast—what the market wants." I feel bound to add that Morris Kline is in a peculiarly weak position to make this particular charge against his colleagues.

If we are to attempt to view objectively the validity of Kline's argument—and I readily confess that this is a very difficult undertaking—then we should be concerned with its internal consistency. I therefore regard it as highly relevant to point out that the argument contains many explicit contradictions. I have referred already to Kline's ambivalence, to call it nothing worse, as to the special nature of mathematical research. Let me give a few further examples. On page 152 we read: "However, the lack of clear standards of teaching, the professor's ignorance of pedagogy, and the obligation . . . to cover ground prescribed in syllabi produce the same effect as incompetence and dishonesty." Yet, on page 153, we read, "Nevertheless, myopic professors impose their own interests on the students, with the result that their courses are largely useless to most students and to society."

On page 166 we are told (in my view, utterly erroneously), "Even the fact that the sum of the angles of a triangle is 180° is hardly attractive." This is immediately followed by "Moreover, beauty is a matter of taste . . ."! Again, on page 200 Kline quotes approvingly from A. N. Whitehead: "It is a profoundly erroneous truism . . . that we should cultivate the habit of thinking of what we are doing. The precise opposite is the case." Yet, on page 217, Kline is capable of writing: "But the symbolism is invented by human beings to express their thoughts. The symbols cannot transcend the thoughts."

A final example must suffice. In advocating the role of the scholar within the academic community (I dealt at length with this question in my article in the *Mathematical Intelligencer*), Kline remarks (page 237), "Scholars can elucidate the inscrutable results contained in research papers." Yet on the very next page he can write, "Without scholarship the currently vast number of proliferating disciplines steadily gain in quantity as they lose in quality, vision, and effective use of the little in them that is worthwhile." Kline

seems able to dispense himself with the services of the scholar in forming his own judgments! Indeed he expresses himself even more strongly on page 251, where he writes, "The research has sunk to fruitless specialization and our classrooms on all levels are staffed with poorly trained or mistrained teachers." Evidently Kline does not find modern mathematical research inscrutable!

There is also much special pleading in Kline's argument. Again we must allow a few examples to illustrate the point of our charge.

As a first example consider the statement on page 84: "This recourse to peers is hardly likely to produce a fair judgment. We have already noted (Chapter 3) the defects of the refereeing process, and all of these apply as well to the judgment of published research by peers." The attack on the refereeing process in Chapter 3 begins, as we have remarked earlier, on page 62. It consists first of the statement, already quoted, that most good mathematicians do not serve as referees. It continues with a comment on blind refereeing, which is plainly irrelevant to peer evaluation. There follows a complaint about the number of papers published and not refereed. There is then an anecdote about Lord Rayleigh and the comment, "On the whole the refereeing of earlier times was competent and critical." This Kline explains by the fact that in those days the editors took a pride in the quality of the work published in their journals—with a very plain implication about the standards of contemporary editors. Thus I find nothing in Chapter 3 that refers in any way whatsoever to the case for or against the efficacy of peer evaluation.

As a second example of special pleading consider the content of page 201. Kline, arguing for the maintenance of certain topics in the high school curriculum, observes that students in college "will be asked to perform calculations such as $1/a + 1/b$, $a^5 \cdot a^3$, $(a + b)^2$." Devoting his argument to the first of these calculations, and concerned to justify the continued prominence of the addition of fractions in the high school curriculum, Kline argues that the addition $1/a + 1/b$ is carried out in precisely the same manner as $1/2 + 1/3$. He concludes, "Hence, one must learn the skills of arithmetic to do algebra." Here Kline is advocating the presence in the pre-college curriculum of a topic whose only justification will come at a later stage of the mathematical education of the student, a stage which many students will not, in fact, reach. This runs counter to the very sensible principles he has himself enunciated for justifying the presence of some given material in the curriculum. Further, we do not add $1/a + 1/b$ as for example we add $1/2 + 1/2$—surely about the most important example of the addition of fractions! Thus the connection between the adding of fractions and the adding of rational functions is by no means as simple as Kline makes out. Moreover, had he taken the example $(a + b)^2$, then the argument would have gone entirely the other way. For it is surely common ground that if called upon to compute $(6 + 4)^2$ we would be ill-advised to first expand the expression to $36 + 48 + 16$. The entire argument here appears specious but it is presented to the lay reader as being incontrovertible and obvious.

As a final example of false reasoning consider the extraordinary statement on page 126, "But number and geometric description are insignificant properties of real objects." The mind boggles at such an assertion. Offer one child one apple and another child two apples and see which feature of the difference between the two offerings is most readily apprehended by the child. If a footballer were asked to describe a football field would he be expected to omit the fact that it is rectangular? Kline bolsters his absurd statement by asking the question, "The rectangle may indeed be the shape of a piece of land or the frame of a painting, but who would accept the rectangle for the land or the painting?" Kline appears not to understand the nature of abstraction and thus not to be aware that the question is total nonsense.

It is surprising, in a great expositor and a great teacher, to find evidence of strange attitudes to teaching itself. Let us leave on one side Kline's naive faith in the efficacy of formal instruction in pedagogy; this at least is a point of view which many others adopt and a legitimate topic for argument. However I find myself appalled by the extreme vocationalism that Kline appears to be recommending in the design of the curriculum. On page 71 Kline, arguing that the typical researcher's knowledge is useless to 95 percent of the students who take mathematics, concludes that that knowledge should not have a place in what the student is taught. A little later he repeats that training students in the professor's speciality "is useless to almost all of his students."

I must simply set on record that I do not believe that one should determine the details of a curriculum on the basis of the techniques which one believes a student is likely to be using in the first few years of his subsequent employment. Our function is to educate; and we are at our best as educators when we are vitally interested in the subject matter of what we are teaching. This is, of course, not to say that syllabi should be *determined* by the tastes of the instructors. It is to say, however, that applications and illustrative problems and examples may be expected to arouse the enthusiasm of students if presented by enthusiastic (and, of course, skillful) teachers. Kline appears to reject this proposition. Indeed, he indulges in a peculiarly unappetizing sarcasm in stigmatizing the presentation of the Königsberg bridge problem, and Euler's solution, in a liberal arts course, asserting (page 123), "But mathematicians will not let the dead rest in peace, and they revive the problem as though it were the most momentous one facing our civilization." Of course, it is not revived in those absurd colors; it is revived as a beautiful, though elementary, example of combinatorial reasoning.

But even here there may be scope for argument. However, Kline appears to be bordering on the irresponsible when he advocates (page 189) that "positional notation in bases other than ten . . . should be taught to prospective teachers," though not to elementary school students, on the grounds that "a teacher must know more than he teaches." Where are Kline's principles now if he recommends something for the prospective teacher simply on the grounds that it will be something that his students will never have to know? On page 201 (a page from which we have already quoted liberally!) in this same chapter on elementary education, one finds Kline arguing against the proposition that the prospect of the availability of hand calculators should influence the choice of curriculum. He says that "estimation as to the reasonableness of an answer calls for knowing a good many arithmetical skills." I might venture the criticism that one does not "know" a skill; my principal point here, however, is that the arithmetical skills required in estimation are not the ones which figure traditionally in the curriculum.

As Kline continues his prescription for elementary education—and let me repeat that he says many very valuable things here—he appears again to go off the rails in a remarkable sequence on page 203. A salesman selling a customer three pairs of shoes at twenty dollars a pair asks the customer for sixty dollars. Kline continues, "But the customer instead replies that three pairs of shoes at twenty dollars a pair is not sixty dollars, but sixty pairs of shoes, and he asks the salesman for the sixty pairs. Is the customer right? As right as the salesman." Once again the mind boggles. The salesman said correctly that the three pairs of shoes would *cost* sixty dollars. He never said that three pairs at twenty dollars a pair *is* sixty dollars. But what is all this extraordinary confusion in aid of? We find to our astonishment that Kline is describing a simple situation which "can be used to make the point . . . that numbers are abstractions"!

In this last excerpt from Kline's fantasy world we seem to come close to one of his real difficulties. He is not happy with the concept of abstraction, and this affects his attitude toward mathematics. We were already troubled on page 133, where Kline wrote: "But the creation of non-Euclidean geometry shattered centuries of confidence in man's intellectual potential. Mathematics was revealed to be not a body of truths but a manmade approximate account of natural phenomena. . . ." Surely we all know that what was shattered was man's belief in the categorical nature of Euclidean geometry, not his confidence in his intellectual potential. Moreover it is precisely science and not mathematics which is an approximate account of natural phenomena. Mathematics certainly is a body of truths in the sense of being a body of deductive truths.

Kline's uncertainty in the presence of abstraction is nowhere more clearly revealed than on page 174, where he writes, "Negative numbers are not just inverses to positive integers under addition; they are the number of degrees below zero on a thermometer." This is plain nonsense. Negative numbers may be used to measure temperature, but they are not necessary for this purpose. Moreover, the number of degrees below zero in a temperature of minus sixteen degrees is sixteen degrees! When I first read Kline's remarkable statement I mentally added "and fractions are not parts of pies." To my astonishment I found on page 191 that Kline actually asserts that they are!

As I argued in the *Mathematical Intelligencer*, and as I have hinted more than once in what I have already written, Kline's thinking is constrained and distorted by his view of the relationship of mathematics to science; and I would like to devote the remainder of this review to an attempt to elucidate that view and to indicate its erroneous nature.

To Kline there are only "alleged" examples of mathematics being developed independently of science and proving subsequently useful to science. Kline claims that all that is good and healthy in mathematics has been directly inspired by science. In asserting and exploiting this proposition he has in mind the totality of mathematical knowledge. However, it is striking that, in endeavoring to persuade the reader of the correctness of his proposition, he writes, "Practically all of the major branches of mathematics were developed to solve scientific problems. . . ." Leaving aside the uncharacteristic caution that Kline exhibits in using the word "practically," what is striking here is that Kline is talking of *branches* of mathematics. Now it is not in dispute that major branches of mathematics have arisen in response to the desire to solve scientific problems. What is in dispute is whether all the significant results in any given branch have themselves been developed to solve scientific problems and whether their ultimate validity depends on their having been so developed. I would have thought that the situation was already sufficiently clear, but it may be valuable to point to two recent and very different examples to show that mathematics may well be developed purely for its intrinsic interest and power, and may then prove to be of great value outside mathematics.

The first example is simply stated. A recent paper in the *American Mathematical Monthly* [84 (1977) 82–107] is entitled "Error-Correcting Codes and Invariant Theory: New Applications of a Nineteenth-Century Technique." The author, Dr. N. J. A. Sloane of Bell Telephone Laboratories, received the Lester Ford Award at the recent Providence meeting for this paper. Kline characterizes invariant theory (page 56) as a nineteenth-century fad. It here proves invaluable to solve a real twentieth-century problem.

A second example is taken from the field that Kline seems to hold most dear, physics. Today's theoretical physicists are writing of gauge fields. It turns out that the mathematics is that of fiber bundle theory, a part of algebraic topology which has been developed very extensively in recent years as a purely mathematical discipline. A gauge type is nothing but a principal fiber bundle. A gauge potential is a connection on that bundle. Dirac's monopole quantization is the first Chern class of a bundle for the unitary group $U(1)$. C. N. Yang has written (1977): "That non-abelian gauge fields are conceptually identical to ideas in the beautiful theory of fiber bundles, developed by mathematicians without reference to the physical world, was a great marvel to me. In 1975 I mentioned this to Chern, and said, 'This is both thrilling and puzzling, since you mathematicians dreamed up these concepts out of nowhere.' He immediately protested. 'No, no, these concepts were not dreamed up. They were natural and real.' "

Chern is here taking a view of the influence of "reality" on mathematics far more subtle and sophisticated than that which Kline advocates. In our perceptions of geometric relationships it is natural for us to formulate the notion of a fiber bundle. This proves to be of enormous importance in many parts of mathematics. It is therefore no surprise that it is now proving important in physics.

Unfortunately for Kline, it seems that topology is a branch of mathematics to which he is peculiarly averse. His view of the nature of topology is well illustrated by what he writes on page 42: "One move was to enter the newer fields, such as the branch of geometry now called topology. The advantage of a new field for tyros in research is that very little background is needed and the best concepts and methodologies are only dimly perceived. Hence, because criteria for value are lacking, almost any contribution has potential significance. Publication is almost assured." Moreover, topology is listed on page 151 as one of the mathematical disciplines "devoid of applications." What Kline notices is that advances in topology are rarely achieved in response to physical problems; what his simplified view of the relation of mathematics to science has caused him, quite fallaciously, to infer is that topology must therefore be sterile and narrow, if not actually trivial.

Is it really necessary to continue to insist that mathematics is not the same sort of pursuit as science? I owe to Professor Rheinboldt the pertinent remark that applied mathematics is not just a part of mathematics but is mathematics plus something else, the art of applying it to "real" situations. I would have expected a celebrated practitioner of this art like Kline to understand this. Yet we find him making the analogy (page 175) between the problem for the mathematics student of applying mathematics, and the problem for the French youth of translating his thoughts into English. I can find no way of making this analogy valid.

We should share with Kline the view that mathematicians should be far more sensitive to the relationship of mathematics to science than they have been in recent years. This does not mean, however, that they should devote themselves exclusively, either in their research or in their teaching, to problems coming exclusively from outside mathematics. Kline's philistinism is surely quite as sterile as the vacuous generalization which he fairly castigates (while unfairly and unjustifiably regarding it as characteristic of the whole of modern mathematics).

To sum up we must conclude that Kline's book is an intemperate emotional outburst, and that the author has not only missed an opportunity to devote his great talents to the improvement of the quality of mathematical education but has also placed in the hands of the enemies of education in general and mathematics education in particular a potent if unreliable weapon.

PETER HILTON

How to Teach a Robot

Marvin Minsky

Marvin Lee Minsky was born in New York City, received his undergraduate training at Harvard, and earned his doctorate in mathematics at Princeton in 1954. He was a junior fellow of the Society of Fellows at Harvard and has been a professor of electrical engineering at M.I.T. since 1964. He is a member of the National Academy of Science, a fellow of the Institute of Electrical and Electronics Engineers, and a fellow of the New York Academy of Science.

If one wishes to teach a robot one must first understand how the robot learns. However, a robot is not a given; a robot is not a naturally occurring object like a trainable clam or a clever rhododendron. Robots are manufactured by people. The capacities of each robot are embedded in its memory banks by the builder. Given this, its creator should design the robot in such a way that there is a predetermined strategy for teaching the creature. Thus, how to teach a robot can be reduced to the problem of what is teaching (or learning if one is the robot) and how can it be simulated by current technology—a very interesting question.

IT IS OUR goal at the Artificial Intelligence Laboratory at the Massachusetts Institute of Technology to conduct research on techniques to endow robot-like devices with human learning, viewing and manipulative capabilities.

Established under an ONR (Office of Naval Research) contract with ARPA (Advanced Research Projects Agency) funding, our laboratory is learning how to design robots that will be able to survey their environment and move about in it under control by natural English instructions. Such robots would not only see (the eye is a television camera) and hear, but would also have a sense of touch.

These devices, which would be remotely controlled by computer, are expected to be able to supplant or supplement man in performing tasks in hostile, or stressful, or very remote environments, such as deep sea exploration.

The approach at our laboratory is different from that taken at other research centers. We see the difference as fundamentally in the approach to handling apparent diversity of kinds of knowledge. The common approach at other centers is to seek ways to render it more uniform so that very general or logically clear methods can be used. Our approach is to accept diversity of knowledge as real and inevitable, and find ways to manage diversity rather than eliminate it. An exciting aspect of our novel approach is that it promises at last to break up the stereotype of the computer's slavish dullness, or the superspeed moron character.

A good example of a degree of common sense is supplied by the interactions of the programs in the "Blocks World" designed by Terry Winograd.[1] Winograd's system is a large intricate system. It is called the Blocks World because the robot interacts within a simulated world composed essentially of blocks of various colors, shapes and sizes. The Blocks World is used to serve as a subject domain for the development of a language understanding system. This system is radically more ambitious than earlier attempts to deal with natural language in several respects. It is as much or more concerned with the problem of represent-

Source: Marvin Minsky, "How to Teach a Robot," *Naval Research Review* 25 (1972): 1–13.

ing the meanings in a discourse than with the grammatical structure. Winograd asserts that meanings and syntactic structures are so intimately related that it is not practical to try to draw a definite boundary between the procedures that are to be used to draw logical inferences about the meanings carried out in the discourse.

The type of discourse currently in use is illustrated by the following sample carried out in real time with the robot's response displayed on a cathode ray tube (CRT) screen. Figures are included to show the state of the scene at various stages. The natural English discourse is the result of intensive study by Professor Winograd.

1. Pick up a big red block.
   ———OK.
   The system answers "OK" when it carries out a command. In order to pick up the red block, it had to clear it off by finding a space for the green one and moving the green one away.
2. Grasp the pyramid.
   ———I DON'T UNDERSTAND WHICH PYRAMID YOU MEAN.

There are three pyramids in the scene, so the program does nothing.

3. Find a block which is taller than the one you are holding and put it into the box.
   The system has to figure out what is meant by "one" and "it," as well as using deduction to decide which block it is holding.
   ———BY "It," I ASSUME YOU MEAN THE BLOCK WHICH IS TALLER THAN THE ONE I AM HOLDING.
   Printed out to keep us informed.
   ———OK.
   The hand has to set down the red block to pick up the taller blue one. Figure 1 shows the result of the system's manipulations so far.

4. Will you please stack up both of the red blocks and either a green cube or a pyramid?
   ———OK.
   Logical connectives such as "and" "or" "either" etc. are handled in both the grammar and semantics. A command is executed even if it looks like a question. The command is carried out by the following series

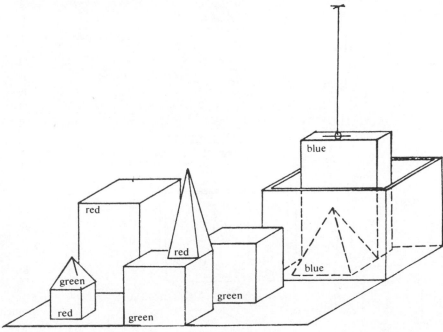

Figure 1

of steps: It puts a green cube on the large red block (note that it chooses the green cube with nothing on it), then removes the small pyramid from the little red cube, so that it can use that cube to complete the stack as specified, resulting in the situation of Figure 2.

5. Which cube is sitting on the table?

———THE LARGE GREEN ONE WHICH SUPPORTS THE RED PYRAMID.

Ordinarily the system would be satisfied with calling this "a big green cube," but since we asked "which cube" it has to be more specific in naming it. The use of substitute nouns (such as "one") and pronouns.

In answers the computer makes the discourse more natural.

6. Is there a large block behind a pyramid?

———YES, THREE OF THEM: A LARGE RED ONE, A LARGE GREEN CUBE AND THE BLUE ONE.

7. Put a small one onto the green cube which supports a pyramid.

"A small one" must contrast with the earlier phrase "a large block," so this means "a small block."

———OK.

8. Put the littlest pyramid on top of it.

Words like "littlest" are not in the dictionary but are interpreted from the root forms like "little."

———OK.

DOES A STEEPLE . . . . .

I DON'T KNOW THE WORD "STEEPLE."

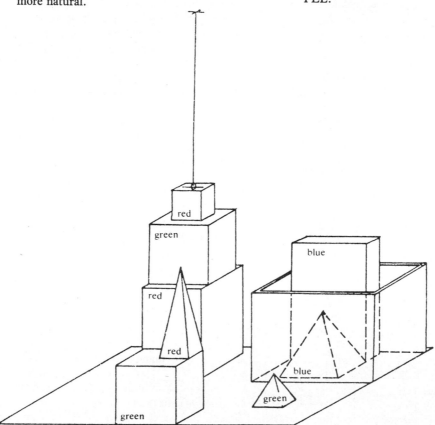

Figure 2

The system interrupts immediately when it sees a word it can't figure out.

A "steeple" is a stack which contains two green cubes and a pyramid.

The quote marks indicate that we are defining a new word.

————I UNDERSTAND.

9. Are there any steeples now?

————NO.

The new definition is used as a description to recognize steeples.

10. Build one.

————OK.

The description given in the definition is enough to deduce a plan for building new objects as well as recognizing them. The word "one" means "a steeple," and the plan is carried out. First, one of the large green cubes is cleared off by removing the red cube and two pyramids. Then the two green cubes and the tall red pyramid are stacked up to fit the description.

11. Thank you.

————YOU ARE WELCOME!

Idioms can be defined without modifying the grammar.

The syntactic and semantic systems generate construction goals, like "build a steeple." The definition of the goal given by the human operator ("a steeple is a stack which contains two cubes and a pyramid") is converted into a plan—a step-by-step specification of subgoals—that is interpreted as a program for building a steeple: find a cube; put another cube on it, put a pyramid on that. Now when a first cube is found, its top might be cluttered with other objects. We do not want the robot, like the assembly-line machine in Charlie Chaplin's movie *Modern Times,* to smash the second cube down. But we do not want to write into our plan "find a first cube and remove the things on it" because (1) it is so obvious to say it and (2) it only sweeps the problem under the rug: the program will have to find a clear surface somewhere to put down the objects it takes off the first cube.

Winograd's system faces the problem once and for all. An almost autonomous network of statements and procedures "know" that to put one

thing on another, there must be a place where it will fit. If there is no such place, one must make one or fail. To "make a place" one must move something else where *it* will fit. But one cannot put something on itself, even if there is room, because it will not be where it was at the future moment of setting it down after moving it. Instead of writing this sort of thing into each particular application program, we create once and for all a "microworld" of knowledge about how things are supported, how supports change when things are moved, and so forth. This knowledge is invoked by the occurrence of patterns either in the outer world, or in goal-statements, whenever they occur, and the same common sense processes intervene and take over the actions until their invoking patterns disappear. For example: there is in the micro-world a statement whose effect is

If A is supported by B, and A is moved, then erase from the current description of the situation any statement of the form "B supports A."

Notice the indirect character of this. It is a statement not about the physics of support but about when to forget statements concerning support. (When you paint an object, and then move it, analogous statements about the colors should *not* disappear.) One could conceivably do without this advice at the cost of recomputing, after each change in the world, all the relations between subsets of objects. This is impractical and is a common cause of examples in which a system works on "toy" problems and collapses on real ones. Or one could do without this advice, at the cost of recomputing, after each change in the world, all the logical consequences of that change; this leads in a different way to bad performances. One can make heuristic compromises: motions change geometrical relations but not (usually) other attributes of objects. The art, and science eventually, is in finding which points are so immediate that one should know them directly and which can be left to more general but more laborious deductive systems.

Common sense is not magic. If we want our computer to act as though it knows the elementary strategies about physics and geometry, we must give it the knowledge somehow. But we need not do this anew for each program! So our next goal is to learn how to refine the ideas in the Blocks World, and the ideas in pattern-matching invocations that make this knowledge engage relevant situations, so that we can keep this "data" permanently in the system. Then any program written therein will automatically behave sensibly in that sphere of activity.

Some Features of a New Programming Style

1. Use of the Language PLANNER.   Programming languages such as ALGOL are designed to make it easy to express the kind of statement that certain classes of users are likely to require: for example, elementary mathematical operations and repetitive loop structures. In programming for Artificial Intelligence we need to express very easily such instructions as

To achieve Goal A, set up sub-goal B and if this fails, try C or D.

Carl Hewitt[2] has designed a language which is expressive in talking about just this kind of device. Its expressive power is so great that a graduate student was able to write a PLANNER program, to solve high-school geometry problems, in only a few days of work. His program was comparable to one that required several man-years a decade ago. This ability to perform experiments in Artificial Intelligence rapidly and flexibly is a most decisive change in the style and fertility of work, and a limited version of the new language is already being used in several other centers. We are concerned however that a restricted form of the language may become too well established, and will endeavor to make the best possible form generally available.

2. Program-Understanding Programs.   This is an area in which rapid growth is very likely. It is closely related to the Natural Language project (Winograd) and PLANNER (Hewitt). The explicit goal is to write programs capable of understanding programs.

We hope over the next year to go further into systems that understand more about processes. There are a number of different aspects of this general goal that arise over and over again in work on Artificial Intelligence and in many branches of computer science.

Learning programs like that of Patrick Winston[3] produce descriptions of structures from a sequence of examples that have been presented. Much of learning involves the acquisition of new processes. We do not believe that there is necessarily a large difference between acquiring descriptions that represent the structures of objects and descriptions that represent the specification of procedures. But if we are to be able to do the latter, we must experiment with problem-solving systems that deal directly with the semantics of programs, and such experience is generally lacking.

More generally, in order for a learning program to be versatile, it must be able to analyze procedures that it learns, to adapt them to new situations, to debug them, *etc.* We believe that children who are not able to cope with complicated situations are that way partly because their process-understanding capability is inadequate.

3. Automatic Mechanisms for Fallible and Contingent Instructions.   The image of a classical computer program is that of sequence of actions performed one after the other and expected to succeed. In Artificial Intelligence programming, an action might be an attempt that fails. In this case it is necessary to ensure that when it gives up, the micro-world in which it works is not left cluttered. The PLANNER system contains special mechanisms that enable the system to restore a description to its former state with some relevant data about the failure.

It is slightly ironic that the most popular approaches to Artificial Intelligence programming force knowledge to be stated in a form of logic as assertive propositions such as:

"The Large Box is Red."

Now, there is no problem in such simple statements about attributes. But other kinds of knowledge are better stated as procedures (or programs) rather than as facts. Even such a simple statement as:

"If there are no cars coming, cross the road."

is misleading if translated into a logical implication such as:

For every x, if (x is a car) and (x is not coming) then (crossing is permissible).

It is more naturally transcribed as:

"Look left, look right, if you have not seen a car, cross."

The distinction between these modes of expression is not merely verbal. A deeper aspect is seen by picturing a logical theorem prover trying to prove by resolution or other logical principles that no car is coming! Deeper yet are the consequences in more complex situations. We believe that even in the size of programs we are now using they make a difference between easy programming and very difficult programming. With more complexity we believe that the difference can become one of possible *versus* impossible.

An example of procedural necessity may be seen in the concept of nearness. Everyone knows what "near" means. If we told you that the car is near the garage and the garage is near the house, then we can be sure that the car is near the house. But we cannot put this transitivity into a formal logical system by a rule like

Rule 1. If (A near B) and (B near C)

for unrestricted application for this rule would yield absurdities like "1 is near 100" because 1 is near 1.001 and 1.002, *etc.!*

It is clear what the real problem is. In any particular context, "Near" is used to represent range, and if one uses chains of longer than a few steps, one may get out of the range. To express this, one might add a rule like:

Rule 2: Do not use Rule 1 more than (say) four times unless there is some basis for believing that you are still in the same size range.

This cannot be said in any ordinary "logical system." No system of mathematical logic allows statements inside the logic to talk about the deductive process that uses the logic. This is bad for intelligent systems, because in solving a hard problem one must devote much attention to monitoring and planning the problem-solving activity. We can state Rule 2, or the equivalent, in a PLANNER-like language, quite directly.

This attitude is not shared by most other groups working on Artificial Intelligence, and there is a widespread commitment to try to represent ordinary reasoning in terms of a "consistent" mathematical logic system. There is perhaps some analogy with a generally unsuccessful earlier preoccupation with perceptrons and linear-separation clustering algorithms—another kind of attempt to find a uniform way to represent all different kinds of things. On the other hand, there is a great deal to be gained by understanding both sides of such questions.

There is an interesting sidelight on this. Many people interpret Gödel's theorem as showing a difference between man and machines. It does not. What it says is that any system which is able to discuss its own procedures, and apply these to itself, has the potentiality of deducing some falsehoods. It is perfectly possible to program computers to be able to discuss their own procedures—Winograd's program comes close to this—and we believe that this is the best path toward intelligent programs. Rule 2 is a simple instance. We do not believe that enough is known today to make worthwhile a search for an adequate and "consistent," logically intelligent system (that is, one that is inherently unable to have any self-contradictions). This has never been done even for ordinary mathematical arguments, to say nothing of everyday common sense.

What humans do is much more PLANNER-like. Suppose that one deduces a contradiction in some argument or finds that some plan that was expected to work out does not. One looks backwards and tries to localize the trouble. Then one constructs and remembers a pattern-invoked heuristic rule, to prevent that kind of deduction being made again. "Rule 2" is just such a device. A more technical example is provided by the way real mathematicians deal with "naive set theory." They do not reject it as did Bertrand Russell in his attempt to rebuild mathematics without it. Instead they now have rules like: "If your statement resembles Russell's Paradox (because it talks about itself) then be careful; find another way to do it." It is astonishing how successful a few simple warnings like this have been in keeping contradictions out of ordinary mathematics. And we believe that among the most important forms of everyday human knowledge are just such rules that indicate which lines of thinking are unsound. Another example: whenever one finds a theoretical outlook which can explain things "too easily," as do mystical concepts of "unity in everything" or the dialectical elements in Sigmund Freud's Theory (in which many causes can produce opposite effects) one says to himself that "Aha, this method is *too* good." Then one tries to build up protective knowledge structures for preserving what one can (Freud did indeed propose many valuable new ideas about how knowledge is represented and misrepresented) of the new theory.

We believe it is the only promising approach, today, to understanding intelligence. In taking this path, however, we must be very clear about the risks. We must understand that as our programs get better at analyzing their own processes, and incorporate better heuristics for preventing unsound kinds of reasoning from emerging, the possibilities of contradictions become buried more deeply, but are not eliminated. We must not be entirely diverted by good empirical results. We must not give up on trying to get a complete theory. It is certainly not inconceivable that we can some day construct a systematic theory of consistency in a logical area wide enough to cover all important areas of intelligence. Such research will be vital, some day, in protecting our interests, if and when we become able to construct extremely intelligent machines!

4. Mini-Theory Construction as a Technical Goal.   We see the problem of Artificial Intelligence as more than just programming existing knowledge. It also involves the acquisition and classification of new substantive knowledge about such areas as intentions, excuses, and goal structures. A curious feature is that, in the past, such inquiries that have been conducted have been the domain not of "scientists" but of analytical philosophers and literary critics! Because their analyses were limited by the lack of computational

models, we are able to go further. These advances depend on increasing sophistication in areas of thinking far removed from the usual computer science courses.

For example, Eugene Charniak in our laboratory is working on making programs understand narrative. This work has reached the level of an experimental program capable of answering some questions like the one in the following example. Below is a story taken from a children's reader which is "read" to the computer. Next is our question, the computer's answer and comments on the process. In its present form the program interacts with a special format; we have translated this into English for simplicity of reading, and much more needs to be done before ordinary tests could be "understood" this well.

Story

Jack and Janet are in the house. Jack is holding a box of pencils and a box of paints.

"Janet, see the paints and pencils that Daddy got for us," Jack said.

Janet went to look at them.

"Are the paints for me?" she asked.

"No, the paints are mine," said Jack. "The pencils are for you, Janet."

Janet said to herself, "I want the paints."

Jack began to paint a picture of a red airplane. Janet went to look at it.

"Those paints make your airplane look funny," she said. "You could make a good picture of a red airplane with these pencils."

Question: Why did Janet say that the paints were bad?

Answer: She wants the paints.

Comments: The program must interpret "funny" as "bad" in this context (this is not done for it in the input format). Even then Janet really said the picture was bad, and it is necessary to transfer this to the paints. Then the program must know that if you want something another person has, you might make nasty comments about it in order to get it. If we had asked, "is the picture funny," the response would have been (in essence) "No, she said so but she had an ulterior motive." To do this the program needs a lot of information about wanting, trading, giving, owning. Statements can not be taken at face value—translated into simple logical statements. They must be treated as evidence for the program to use to build a model of what really might be happening.

So far as language is concerned, there are a number of new areas that demand investigation such as the problems in handling other aspects of ordinary grammar and the need for additional new primitives. These problems are inseparable from those that arise from adding a wider range of meanings to the entire semantic system. What happens when we try to extend Winograd's system beyond those problems that it now can handle with respect to the Blocks World? There are alternative concepts of how to proceed, and let us consider two extremes:

One approach is to add to the Blocks World incrementally. It is easy to add new kinds of objects, and properties for them, to the syntactic-semantic-problem solving complex.

It is somewhat harder to add new predicates about spatial relations; for example, "Next to" might be important in some problems. But such an increment means that one must also add new procedures for taking account of such new elements, be they mentioned explicitly in a main goal derived from a natural language command, or generated internally in a description invoked by a theorem already present. The new procedures represent ways to solve problems and understand situations, but they cannot be used efficiently unless recommendations are added to the theorems of the older knowledge base so that the syntactic and semantic systems can handle the nuances associated with the wider spectrum of meanings that the system is now required to deal with.

Presumably, as this kind of incremental extension is made, some changes will be easy. Whenever the system does something that "it should know better than to do" the programmer can intervene and attempt to adjoin new "advice" as a new theorem, recommendation, or entry in the dictionary, or as a fragment of PROGRAMMER or PLANNER program. Sometimes this will be difficult because, instead of a small addition or change, the system will want a new kind of data-

structure, or a new heuristic strategy for achieving a new kind of goal.

For example, Winograd's Blocks World does not have a variety of "uses" for the mechanical structures it builds. It does not have any concept, at present, of multiple-support-upwards. It can deal with situations in which one object supports many others, as several stacks on a cube on a table; but it cannot handle such structures as bridges and arches in which one object is supported by several. When a child builds a high tower that turns out to be unstable, he has ideas about reinforcing it by providing multiple support to lower elements.

How hard is it to add such concepts? We do not really know, yet. At first it might appear very difficult to do incrementally because the data-structure in the original Blocks World assumed single support, and all the theorems about construction and interference between goals are written in terms of this single support. On further examination, by introducing a new idea of "compound object," many such problems disappear. Only time will tell how far such ideas will take us.

At the other extreme from the incremental approach would be one based on a concept of "micro-worlds" (referring to suborganization of knowledge, not to physically separate parts). The original Blocks World is an elegant "mini-theory" which, by itself, is a highly satisfactory model of certain kinds of interactions between purposes and physical relations. Is there no way to preserve its effectiveness, intact, in a larger system?

If the new area of meaning were very different, it would be much clearer what to do. If, for example, we wanted to talk about what the objects of the Blocks World were used for, (boxes are used to store things away that one does not expect to need soon, towers are used to make high structures, pyramids are not used for anything,) we would have little trouble. We could build a different micro-world about block structures, and their uses, and procedures for designing structures we needed for different purposes, and then turn to the Blocks World to find how to make the structures. Presumably, it would not be excessively hard to add to the system a collection of theorems and recommendations that would serve to tie the two separate micro-worlds into a system that could solve problems that need both kinds of knowledge.

Even this has not yet been done, however. So one of our objectives is to accumulate experience in finding ways to interconnect two comparatively separate micro-worlds. Another objective is to get experience in the kinds of problems involved in extending an existing micro-world. The interaction experience is somewhat more valuable because, if it can be done properly, the interaction advice may be able to survive the repeated extension of the micro-worlds involved.

There are other major activities in this laboratory, concerned with more immediate applications of new programming ideas. Most highly developed is our work on machine vision, which will be the subject of a subsequent article.

Notes

1. Terry Winograd, "Procedures as Representation for Data in a Computer Program for Understanding Natural Language," Massachusetts Institute of Technology, 1971.
2. Carl Hewitt, "PLANNER," Project MAC, Massachusetts Institute of Technology, 1968.
3. Patrick H. Winston, "Learning Structural Descriptions from Examples," Massachusetts Institute of Technology, 1970.